WORLD® AIR POWER
JOURNAL

Aerospace Publishing Ltd

AIRtime Publishing Inc.

Published quarterly by
Aerospace Publishing Ltd
179 Dalling Road
London W6 0ES
UK

ISSN 0959-7050
Aerospace ISBN 1 86184 015 2
                (softback)
                1 86184 007 1
                (hardback)
Airtime ISBN   1-880588-07-2
                (hardback)

Published under licence in USA and
Canada by AIRtime Publishing Inc.,
USA

Editorial Offices:
WORLD AIR POWER JOURNAL
Aerospace Publishing Ltd
3A Brackenbury Road
London   W6 0BE   UK
E-mail: info@aerospacepbl.co.uk

Publisher: Stan Morse
Managing Editor: David Donald

Editors: Robert Hewson
         E-mail: airpower@compuserve.com

         David Donald
         E-mail: dave@aerospacepbl.co.uk

Sub Editor: Karen Leverington

Editorial Assistant: Tim Senior

Origination by Universal Graphics
Printed in Italy by Officine Grafiche
        de Agostini

Correspondents:
General military: Jon Lake
USA Washington: Robert F. Dorr
USA Southwest: Randy Jolly
Europe: John Fricker
Russia/CIS: Yefim Gordon
Asia: Pushpindar Singh
Canada: Jeff Rankin-Lowe
Argentina: Jorge Núñez Padin
Chile: Patrick Laureau

The *World Air Power Journal* web site can be
found at:

http://www.airpower.co.uk

The Editors extend their thanks and appreciation
to the following individuals who made an
important contribution to this issue of
World Air Power Journal:

Thanks to Michael J. Gallo (VP and COO Kelly Space
and Technology, Inc.), Robert Keltner (Eclipse program
manager), Emily Chase (Dir. of Public Relations), all at
the NASA Dryden Flight Research Center, Gray Creech
(Public Affairs) and Tony Landis for their assistance with
the Project Eclipse Briefing.

To honour their customer confidentially obligations,
Gulfstream Aerospace was unable to provide information
on many specific aspects of the Gulfstream – Special
Missions article, but did provide valuable background
information and general briefings. Others who made an
important contribution in the US were: John Binford, Bill
Brabant, David F. Brown, Bill Crimmins, Steve Czerviski,
Jon Chuck, Norris Graser, John Gresham, Sunil Gupta,
Stephen Harding, Alex Hrapunov, Marty J. Isham,
Rosemary Kephart, Benjamin Knowles Jr, Robert J. Mills,
Al Mongeon, Matt Olafsen, Kevin Patrick, Brian C.
Rogers, Douglas E. Slowiak, and Charles Taylor.
Special thanks are also due to: Peter Liander, Jan
Charleville, Jan Jørgensen and Robert F. Dorr.

For their help with the CH-53 article: HMH-461 pilots:
Major William 'Chip' Munck, Captain Tom 'Lucky'
Pecina, Captain W.P. 'Boo Boo' Bair. CH-53 maintainers:
Captain Eric 'Smithers' Focht, Sergeant James Bruns,
Sergeant Tim Dryden. Captains Blau, T.V. Johnson,
Riggle, John Milliman. Major Margaret Kuhn, Captain
Arnoux Abraham, Corporal Butler, Sara Fullwood, SSGT
Flora, and the many others who helped.

Special thanks to Flt Lt Jim Anderson, RAF Lossiemouth
CRO, Tim Lewis and Dale Donovan at Strike Command
PR Office, and all the personnel of No. 12 Squadron,
including Wing Commander Ricci Cobelli, Sqn Ldr
Colin Dooley, Sqn Ldr Andy Box, Sqn Ldr Simon
Pearson, Flt Lt Paul Shakespeare, Flt Lt Andy Blythe and
Flt Lt Andy Glover, for all their assistance with the
Lossiemouth feature.

The Editors would like to extend their sincere thanks to
Steve Zaloga for his outstanding efforts on, and assistance
with, the Tupolev Tu-22/Tu-22M article. Thanks also are
due to our Russian Correspondent, Yefim Gordon.

World Air Power Journal is a
registered trademark in the
United States of America of
AIRtime Publishing Inc.

World Air Power Journal is
published quarterly and is
available by subscription and
from many fine book and hobby
stores.

**SUBSCRIPTION AND BACK
NUMBERS:**

**UK and World (except USA and
Canada) write to:**
Aerospace Publishing Ltd
FREEPOST
PO Box 2822
London
W6 0BR
UK

**(No stamp required if posted in
the UK)**

USA and Canada, write to:
AIRtime Publishing Inc.
Subscription Dept
10 Bay Street
Westport
CT 06880, USA
(203) 838-7979
Toll-free order number in USA:
1 800 359-3003

**Prevailing subscription rates are
as follows:**
Softbound edition for 1 year:
    $59.95
Softbound edition for 2 years:
    $112.00
**Softbound back numbers
(subject to availability) are
$16.00 each, plus shipping and
handling. All rates are for
delivery within mainland USA,
Alaska and Hawaii. Canadian
and overseas prices available
upon request. American Express,
Discover Card, MasterCard and
Visa accepted. When ordering
please include card number,
expiration date and signature.**

U.S. Publisher:
    Mel Williams
Subscriptions Director:
    Linda DeAngelis
**Charter Member Services
Manager:**
    Janie Munro
Retail Sales Director: Jill Brooks
Shipping Manager: E. Rex Anku

WORLD AIR POWER®

JOURNAL

CONTENTS

Military Aviation Review

International

NATO E-3 upgrades

Seventeen Boeing E-3A AWACS of NATO's Airborne Early Warning Force based at Geilenkirchen, Germany, are undergoing an $891 million Radar System Improvement Programme (RSIP) with Daimler-Benz Aerospace (DASA) at Manching, near Munich. In November 1997 DASA began installing RSIP kits, supplied by Boeing and its sub-contractors, which include Northrop Grumman, OGMA in Portugal and ATA in Greece. The RSIP kits will increase the sensitivity of the E-3's Westinghouse APY-1/2 radar and allow it to detect and track smaller targets over longer ranges in the pulse-Doppler mode. They also include a new radar computer and control maintenance panel, electrical and mechanical hardware, plus improved ECM systems.

Boeing is supplying eight more RSIP kits for BAe installation in the RAF's seven E-3Ds, and an initial four for 32 USAF E-3B/Cs, installed from December by service personnel at Tinker AFB, OK. An associated $450 million USAF mid-term upgrade contract was also received by Boeing in November for the mission systems of NATO's E-3 fleet, involving engineering and manufacturing of flat-panel displays, integrated multi-sensor merging, digital communications systems, broad-spectrum VHF radios, and GPS.

This is Boeing's third NATO E-3 upgrade since 1993, when the Mod 1 near-term programme added Link 16 datalink to their Joint Tactical Information Distribution Systems, new colour displays and Have Quick secure UHF radios. ESM upgrades were later included in this programme, which ended in October.

This Bulgarian An-2 is attached to the liaison flight of the Tactical Aviation Corps. It was used as a parachute jump ship during the air show at Plovdiv, in November 1997.

Below: Seen departing Hopsten AB for Holloman AFB, New Mexico (on 12 November 1997), this JG 72 F-4F was one of six making the transatlantic crossing that day to join the 12 Luftwaffe F-4Fs already stationed in the USA. Note the unusual 'Egypt One' grey scheme.

US and UK halt Iraq crisis

During deployment of British and US forces to the Persian Gulf area in November 1997, following Saddam Hussein's expulsion of the UN inspection team charged with tracking down his weapons of mass destruction, Central Command chief USMC General Anthony Zinni said that Iraq's air defences were still 'robust', if slightly below 1990-91 Gulf War standards. Many SAMs were still in service, he added, including SA-2, SA-3, SA-6 and French ROLAND systems.

The UN had previously discovered and destroyed more than 150 Iraqi 'Scud'-type SSMs and 75 chemical warheads, together with some 40,000 other chemical weapons and several research and production facilities. Iraq was suspected of concealing at least 25 more 'Scuds' and many hundreds of tons of chemical and biological materials in 20 or more new underground bunkers, and apparently in most of the many presidential palaces.

US forces deployed in the Gulf area during the November crisis included two carrier air groups aboard the USS *Nimitz*, and its sister ship, USS *George Washington*, redeployed from the Mediterranean. They were reinforced by four F-16s and a KC-135 tanker in Incirlik. Six of the 49th Fighter Wing's F-117As were flown to Kuwait, while six B-52Hs relocated to Diego Garcia.

For the first time, two B-1Bs, with newly-acquired CBU-97 delivery capability, formed part of a batch of over 30 USAF combat aircraft making up an Air Expeditionary Wing deployed to Shaikh Isa Air Base, Bahrain, from 20 November. This also

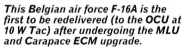

This Belgian air force F-16A is the first to be redelivered (to the OCU at 10 W Tac) after undergoing the MLU and Carapace ECM upgrade.

included 12 F-15Cs, 12 F-16Cs, plus six F-16C(J) SEAD versions equipped with HTS, four KC-135T tankers, and Patriot SAM/ABM launchers. They supplemented previous USAF A-10, F-15, F-16 and support detachments totalling some 200 aircraft in the area.

UK support in the Iraq crisis was provided by HMS *Invincible*, transferred from the Mediterranean, with its normal complement of six 801 Sqn Sea Harrier FA.Mk 2s, seven 819/820 Sqn ASW Sea King HAS.Mk 6s, and three 849 Sqn Sea King AEW.Mk 2As. They were supplemented by seven RAF BAe Harrier GR.Mk 7s from No. 1 Squadron flown down to Gibraltar from their Wittering base.

Eurofighter production approved

As the last Parliamentary hurdle for the Eurofighter programme in late November 1997, the German Bundestag's long-delayed approval (by a narrow majority) of production investment funding cleared the way on 22 December for the defence ministers of the four partner countries to sign the inter-government agreement in Bonn for the full-scale production phase.

Contracts which will eventually exceed $50 billion then followed with the Eurofighter industrial consortium for 620 aircraft, including at least 98 fully-operational two-seat versions, for delivery from 2002 onwards.

Apart from full-scale Eurofighter production, the Memoranda of Understanding signed by Volker Ruehe for Germany, Benjamino Andreatta for Italy, Eduardo Serra for Spain, and George Robertson for the UK also covered integrated in-service logistic support. With a current commitment to 232 aircraft, the UK is still the main partner in the consortium, followed by Germany (180), Italy (121, reduced in 1997 from 130), and Spain (87).

According to the UK MoD, Britain's current estimated Eurofighter procurement costs are now £15.9 billion ($26.5 billion). This compares with £12.7 billion estimated in mid-1997, when the UK had also spent £2.7 billion from an estimated £3.5 billion requirement for R&D. On these revised figures, each of the RAF's 232 Eurofighters will have a programme unit cost of $114 million, excluding R&D, or $136.3 million inclusive. The latter figure compares with current estimates of $183 million for each of the USAF's planned 339 Lockheed Martin F-22s, based on $18.7 billion for engineering, manufacturing and development costs, plus the cost-capped $43.4 billion total for production.

Initial Eurofighter production funding of DM847 million ($480 million) in allocations within the 1998 defence budget – itself finally approved on 27 November – was earlier approved in Germany for 140 air defence variants and 40 with multi-role ground attack capabilities. Production authorisations will total DM23.1 billion ($13.06 billion), including DM1.18 billion in 1999, DM1.35 billion in 2000 and DM1.58 billion in 2001, with further similar annual funding until around 2014.

Germany's DA.5 Eurofighter completed the 500th test sortie in the overall flight development programme in October, and by 21 November the overall total for the seven pre-production aircraft had reached 532, in 465 flying hours. Eurofighter had flown at speeds up to Mach 1.9, a height of over 40,000 ft (12912 m), sustained angles of attack to 25°, and turns up to 7*g*.

Europe

BELGIUM:

Army helicopter plans

In the early 2000s the Belgian army's Light Aviation Group at Bierset plans to replace 30 or so Aérospatiale SA 313/318C Alouette II helicopters and 10 Britten-Norman BN-2A Islander transports currently equipping 16 Battalion. Helicopters will supersede both types, with up to about 20 smaller rotorcraft in the Eurocopter EC 120 class replacing the Alouettes. Eight medium transport helicopters, such as the Bell 412EP or Eurocopter AS 532, will replace the Islanders.

CROATIA:

CN.235 deferred

Long-term Croatian military plans to acquire three Turkish-built Airtech CN.235M tactical transports costing some $45 million have reportedly stalled because of funding problems. Croatia's armed forces were expected to receive the equivalent of about $1.2 billion in 1997, but defence spending as a proportion of GNP is being cut from about 9 per cent to 5-7 per cent.

FRANCE:

1997/98 procurement plans

Despite cuts of FF4.6 billion ($792 million) imposed by the incoming Socialist government on 1997 procurement spending totals of FF81 billion ($14 billion), the French air force (AA) is due to take delivery of 11 Dassault Mirage 2000DAs upgraded to -5 standard (of 37 on order), plus six Mirage 2000Ds from total requirements for 86, in the current year. Delivery of the 51st Mirage 2000D took place in December, and AA receipts due in the coming year include 14 Transall C.160s upgraded with new avionics from 71 in current service, and the first of four new AS 532A2 Cougar armed helicopters on order for the RESCO combat rescue programme.

An additional CN.235M funded in the 1998 budget is presumably part of the AA's requirement for a second batch of seven to follow the eight in current service, although no deliveries are due in the current year. Three SOCATA TBM 700s ordered in FY98 increase overall French service totals to 28, with four more deliveries due in 1998.

An FY98 French navy order for two Dassault Rafale Ms supplements the initial FF7 billion May 1997 contract for the first 13 production aircraft, comprising 10 for the Aéronavale, and three for the AA. Flottille 12F will start replacing its F-8P Crusaders with its first Rafale Ms in 2002, and Parliamentary negotiations are continuing to allocate some FF17 billion ($2.93 billion) for multi-year procurement of 48 more Rafales, including some for export,

between 1998 and 2003. First AA Rafale deliveries are not due until 2005. The Aéronavale is also due to receive its two E-2C Hawkeye AEW aircraft on order in FY98.

KC-135 fleet additions

The French air force received three former AMARC inmates (62-3497, 62-3525, 62-3574) during the Summer of 1997 which have be converted to C-135FR configuration prior to delivery. All three followed a similar process of conversion and short term storage before fitting out with the new CFM56 engines and delivery. A further two, (62-3555 and 63-8009) have been identified as possible future conversions for the AA.

GERMANY:

Boeing 707s to NATO

The last of its four Boeing 707-320s was transferred late in 1997 by the German air force to the NATO Airborne Early Warning Force, following replacement by five Airbus A310s. Two A310s are now being modified as multi-role transport/tankers. NAEWF will use the ex-Luftwaffe Boeings for crew training and support roles. German army General Klaus Naumann, chairman of NATO's military committee, said that consideration was now being given to the formation of a unified tanker force for the alliance, on a similar basis to the NAEWF.

GREECE:

New aircraft procurement

Procurement funding totalling $8.7 billion by mid-1999 has been approved by the Greek government as part of its armed forces modernisation plans. They include new combat aircraft,

although Lockheed Martin started deliveries in September of the first eight from a second batch of 32 Block 50 F-16CGs and eight two-seat DG combat trainers to supplement the original 34/6 Block 30 versions. DASA and Israel's Elbit Systems are working on upgrading the HAF's original F-16s with new avionics and equipment. More orders are expected soon, however, for additional F-16s or new F-15s to replace F-4s, F-5s and T-33s, although the Mirage 2000-5 and other combat aircraft are also being evaluated.

Recent US Foreign Military Sales (FMS) have included seven armed Boeing CH-47Ds for Greek Army Aviation (EAS). With spare Allied-Signal T55-L-714 turboshafts, 28 7.62-mm M60 and eight 12.7-mm M2 machine-guns, plus defensive subsystems, the FMS contract totals around $376 million. The new CH-47Ds will supplement 10 CH-47Cs in current EAS service.

IRELAND:

Police air expansion

A Eurocopter AS 355N Twin Squirrel helicopter was added late in 1997 to the sensor-equipped Pilatus Britten-Norman Defender 4000, to start equipping the new Air Support Unit of the Garda Siochana (Irish Police) at Casement Aerodrome, Baldonnel. The Twin Squirrel was accepted from McAlpine Aviation as UK Eurocopter dealers, at Kidlington, near Oxford, by Garda and Irish Air Corps members, who man the unit.

Initially registered G-BXEV, the Twin Squirrel is equipped with a Leo 400 Spir SPTV infra-red unit in a chin-mounted ball turret, with front and rear cabin monitor screens and video recorders, light-intensification night goggles, a steerable searchlight, and a loud-hailer. It also has high-clearance skids and a three-axis autopilot.

Above and left: T-33s are still a common sight at Greek air force bases. Approximately 40 aircraft are still in service, including orange-painted target tugs.

ITALY:

Last Harrier II Plus

At a 25 November ceremony attended by the Chief of Staff of the Italian Navy, Admiral Angelo Mariani, the Italian Navy accepted the 13th and final AV-8B Harrier II Plus assembled at Alenia's Aeronautics Division. This brings to 16 the total of Harrier II Plus aircraft and two TAV-8B trainers flown by the Italian navy.

In July 1997, the Spanish navy took delivery of its eighth and last CASA-assembled Harrier II Plus. The Spanish navy also flies 10 AV-8B Harrier II day-attack aircraft and is considering remanufacturing them to the II Plus configuration.

Through the remanufacturing programme, Boeing is converting 72 day-attack Harriers into II Plus aircraft for the US Marine Corps.

Eurofighter and C-130J contracts

Recent Italian air force (AMI) contracts for Eurofighter and the Lockheed Martin C-130J Hercules II, plus a planned upgrade of Italy's 12 long-serving C-130Hs, will account for some L1,169 billion and L251 billion, respectively, in the 1998 defence budget of L22,108 billion ($13 billion). As fourth customer for the C-130J, Italy is buying 18 from a L2,000 billion ($1.18 billion) November 1997 contract, to supplement from 1999 the C-130Hs and 30-plus Alenia G222s in the AMI's 46° Air Brigade at Pisa.

Four AMI C-130Js may be modified during production for airborne early-warning roles with Northrop Grumman's E-2C dorsal radar and associated equipment, instead of Italy's planned purchase of additional AEW Hercules IIs, because of defence economies.

Italian budget priorities for 121 Eurofighters, C-130J and other new equipment programmes seem likely to defeat AMI plans to acquire up to 18 upgraded C-27J versions of the G222, to equip a fourth transport squadron.

Other AMI transport funding includes L130 billion ($76 million) for two Airbus A319CJs to replace two

Military Aviation Review

Douglas DC-9-32s in the 31° Stormo at Ciampino. This unit will also receive two Dassault Falcon 900EXs in place of its Gulfstream GIIIs for government transport. A long-standing AMI requirement to replace 25 SIAI-Marchetti S.208, 17 Piaggio P.166 and some 20 Piaggio PD.808 light transport and communications aircraft will be partly met by a L120 billion ($70.57 million) order for another 12 Piaggio P.180 Avantis. They will follow six already operating with the AMI, mainly in the 31° Stormo from Ciampino for VIP and government transport, and three now being delivered to Italian Army Aviation (ALE). Other new ALE equipment will include its long-awaited second batch of 15 upgraded Agusta A 129 light attack helicopters, to supplement the 45 delivered earlier, together with five more Agusta/Bell 212s built for Iraq but later embargoed.

POLAND:

Huzar upgrade re-examined

Controversy has continued over the former Polish government's November nomination of an Israeli team, including Elbit Systems Ltd, El-Op Electro-Optics Industries, and Rafael Israel Armament Authority, for the planned $650 million avionics/weapons system upgrade for up to 100 PZL-Swidnik S-1W Huzar armed assault helicopters. Elbit's bid was chosen over submissions by a Boeing North American (formerly Rockwell), Saab Dynamics, Finmeccanica, and GEC-Marconi Avionics team, using the Hellfire missile and fire-control system. The new Solidarity government in Warsaw has withheld endorsement of the Elbit submission while investigating the selection process, and may reopen invitations to tender.

Elbit was expected to receive contracts worth about $200 million to integrate new Huzar avionics and cockpit upgrades with Rafael's NT-D Long Spike helicopter-launched development of its new Gill anti-tank missile family. NT-D design features including electro-optical guidance through a fibre-optic link, and a tandem HEAT warhead to penetrate explosive reactive armour over a range of up to 6 km (4 miles). Firings from IDF/AF Bell AH-1s have already been conducted with the NT-D, of which about 2,000 air-launched versions are expected to be ordered for the Huzar programme. Around 3,000 more NT-Ds were planned for licensed production at the Mesko factory in southern Poland, for use by the Polish army.

PORTUGAL:

More F-16s sought

A second FAP F-16 squadron is planned from reported negotiations with Washington for up to 25 surplus USAF F-16A/Bs. They would follow 1994 deliveries of 17 Block 15 F-16As and three F-16B trainers with Operational Capability Upgrades (OCU), but would require similar or greater modernisation.

Above: This 349 Mira RF-5A was painted in a special scheme to commemorate the unit's disbandment, in September 1997, and 30 years of continuous F-5 operations.

Below: Doubt surrounds the future of Greece's F-4 force. The Phantoms may be upgraded or completely replaced.

ROMANIA:

Bell AH-1 production hitch

IAR Brasov plans to licence-build 96 Bell AH-1RO helicopters from a $1.4 billion contract were put on hold towards the end of 1997, following the government's inability to provide financial guarantees to the IMF. Alternative financial backing was then sought, but a programme go-ahead was not expected until some time in 1998.

RUSSIA:

Sukhoi S-37 details

As previously reported, rumours at Russia's biennial MAKS '97 air show at Zhukhovskii in August 1997 that AVPK Sukhoi was about to fly a radical new twin-turbofan combat aircraft proved well founded with the November appearance of the forward-swept wing S-37 Berkut (Golden Eagle) prototype. Originally referred to as the S-32, the prototype of what appears to be a high-performance technology demonstrator first flew at the Zhukhovskii test base near Moscow on 25 September, little more than two weeks after the Lockheed Martin F-22's initial flight. S-37 development is believed to be mainly financed by Sukhoi from commercial sales of its Su-27/30 series to China, India, Indonesia and Vietnam, but also appears to have received some government funding and possible Russian naval interest.

As suspected, the S-37 appears to be almost as big as the MIG MAPO 1.42/1.44, with a normal take-off weight of 25670 kg (56,592 lb), and a max weight of 34000 kg (75,000 lb).

Dimensions include a span of 16.7 m (54.8 ft), a length of 22.6 m (74.15 ft), and a height of 6.4 m (14.6 ft). The S-37's twin MiG-31M-type Perm/Shvetsov D-30F6 turbofans of 152 kN (34,172 lb) thrust may apparently be replaced by the MiG 1.42's newer and thrust-vectored 196 kN (44,092 lb) Saturn/Lyul'ka AL-41F powerplants. Its semi-circular cheek intakes appear to be of fixed geometry, although with auxiliary intake doors. Apart from its unusual forward-swept 90 per cent composite wings, with cranked leading edges, the S-32 retains similar swept canard foreplanes and the 'integrated triplane' layout with rear stabilators of the Su-35. It appears to make use of a number of Su-27 series parts, including the outward-canted vertical fins, forward fuselage and Su-33 undercarriage components. It also incorporates several stealthy features, including RAM covering and conformal underfuselage weapons stowage. Its avionics are said to be produced by the Ramenskoya Instrument Building Design Bureau.

Claimed performance for the S-37 includes a maximum sea level speed of 1400 km/h (870 mph) or 2200 km/h (1,367 mph) at altitude; a service ceiling of 18000 m (59,055 ft); and a 3300-km (2,050-mile) range.

More MiG-AT Larzac orders

Contracts worth some FF100 million ($17 million) were received in late 1997 by SNECMA from MIG MAPO for another 20 Larzac 04R20 turbofans, following initial orders in November 1996 for 10, to be used in the 15 pre-production MiG-AT advanced trainers now being built. Four Larzacs were also donated by

SNECMA for the two MiG-AT flight prototypes, the second of which made its first flight in late October last year.

Sextant Avionique also has a contract to supply 30 shipsets of nav/attack systems and associated equipment for the MiG-ATs, which include 10 ordered for Russian air force (V-VS) fly-off evaluation against a similar number of Yak/AEM-130s. If selected for V-VS use, the MiG-AT may be powered by the new Soyuz RD 1700 turbofan, claimed by the Russian engine company to be 2.5 times cheaper than the Larzac.

Upgraded MiG-29 flies

Private-venture development is continuing of VPK MAPO's upgraded MiG-29SMT (Article 9-17) prototype, shown in static form at Russia's MAKS '97 air show at Zhukhovskii in August, which made its first flight there on 27 November 1997. Several MiG-29SMT prototypes, redesignated MiG-29-917s, are planned for the flight development programme, which is scheduled for completion by August 1998, and the new 'Fulcrum' version is already being actively promoted by Rosvoorouzhenie for export.

For improved combat capabilities, the new MiG-29 has a redesigned cockpit and digital open-architecture avionics, including twin Western or Russian multi-function liquid-crystal colour cockpit displays and a wide-angle HUD. GosNIIASS INS/GPS equipment and uprated Phazotron NO10ME Topaz radar with added ground mapping, plus additional systems, are linked by a dual-redundant Mil Std 1553B databus to ensure compatibility with Kh-25ML (AS-12 'Kegler'), Kh-29T (AS-14 'Kedge') and Kh-31A/P (AS-17 'Krypton') ASMs, plus KAB-500KR laser-guided bombs, or similar Western weapons.

Based on the humped-back 9-13 'Fulcrum-C', the MiG-29SMT rectifies earlier range limitations with about 1000 litres (220 Imp gal) or 800 kg (1,760 lb) more internal fuel from equipment and intake bay changes. They are claimed to provide a range increase of up to 600 km (372 miles), to 3500 km (2,175 miles), as an alternative to double the original weapon load to 4000 kg (8,800 lb).

An-124 loss

The crash of a Russian air force (V-VS) An-124 (believed to be 'Black 8') during an Su-27 delivery flight from Irkutsk to Vietnam on 6 December 1997 (see Vietnam) was reported as the first military Ruslan loss to date from 27 originally delivered. At least two more have crashed, however, from deliveries of 21 civil-operated An-124s. Following a second Russian military transport accident on 11 December, when a V-VS An-12 collided in the air with a civil Mi-8, air force commander General Pyotr Deinekin restricted all military flights to essential operations pending further investigations.

SWEDEN:

Gripen is operational

Sweden's first JAS 39 squadron – 2 Divisionen of F7 Skaraborgs Flygflottilj (wing) at Sätenäs, on the Baltic, which received its first Gripens in June 1996 – was declared fully operational in September. 1 Divisionen, F7, is now converting to the Gripen from its AJS 37 Viggens, which will be fully replaced by late 1998. Re-equipment of three squadrons of J 35 Drakens and AJS 37s will then start with F10 at Angelhölm, followed by further wings at about one per year to complete the planned SAF combat strength of 12 multi-role Gripen squadrons, plus one air defence squadron with JA 37 Mod D Viggens, by 2007.

Some 204 Gripens have been ordered to date, comprising 30 initial production versions; 110, including 14 two-seat JAS 39Bs, in the second batch; and 64 (with 14 more JAS 39Bs) in the recently-ordered third batch costing SKr28 billion ($3.7 billion). The last batch will be delivered between 2003 and 2007, probably as JAS 39Cs, incorporating features of BAe's NATO-compatible Gripen version. The Gripen's Microturbo APU turbine is also being changed for a Sundstrand Aerospace T46C/APS1000-derived APU meeting more stringent emission standards.

A Gripen mid-life upgrade from about 2012 may include an advanced electronically-scanned array antenna (AESA) X-band development of the Ericsson PS-05/A radar. This features up to 1,500 gallium arsenide active transceiver modules in a new antenna within the existing radome, plus two-axis gimbals to supplement the resulting limitations on electronic steering.

Equally long-term is SAF interest in thrust-vectoring for the Gripen, following Swedish participation in the $90 million second-phase X-31 Vector flight-test research vehicle programme. Meanwhile, negotiations are in progress for the possible sale of the export Saab/BAe Gripen to Austria, Brazil, Chile, the Czech Republic, Hungary, the Philippines, Poland, Slovenia and South Africa. In 1997 trials, the JAS 39B was flown by General Fernando Rojas Vender, Lieutenant General Ladislav Klima and General Attila Kositzky, the Cs-in-C respectively of the Chilean, Czech and Hungarian air forces.

TURKEY:

Large-scale military procurement planned

Government spending is planned of over $30 billion on new military equipment over the next decade, to match similar Greek expansion. Funding is included for programmes already approved, such as the $632.5 million contract with IAI to upgrade 54 F-4Es; licensed production by Tusas Aerospace Industries (TAI) of 30 SA 532UL/AL Cougar helicopters costing $430 million for the Turkish army and air

Above and right: These two Moldovan air force types, an An-72 and an Mi-8MTV, participated in exercise Co-operative Key '97, held at Sliac, Slovakia, in July 1997.

Below right: This new-build IAR-330H Puma of the Romanian air force is wearing a new overall grey scheme and base titles on the fuselage.

force; $290 million to modernise seven ex-USAF KC-135 tankers; and co-production of 50-100 Rafael Popeye heavy air-to-surface missiles.

New programme funding is planned for up to $3.5 billion for 145 new attack and reconnaissance helicopters to supplement 38 current Turkish Army Aviation Bell AH-1P/Ws; $850 million for four AWACS aircraft and ground stations; some $500 million for another 24 TAI-built F-16C/Ds; around $140 million for 10 more TAI/CASA CN.235Ms, with requirements for another 30; and $150 million for new F-16 defensive and EW subsystems. Other allocations are earmarked towards payment for the 20-26 FLA transports required for military transport by Turkey, for which TAI recently became the sixth full partner in the FLA consortium.

Also sought is $500 million for 10-20 heavy-lift helicopters, for which IAI-upgraded surplus US Sikorsky CH-53s are being considered, against Boeing Chinooks and Mil Mi-26s. Four more Sikorsky S-70B-28 ASW helicopters are planned for the Turkish navy, towards total requirements for 28. Five Agusta AB 412s costing $49 million have also been ordered for Turkish Coast Guard service.

About $120 million has been earmarked to upgrade 48 F-5A/Bs for extended THK service. SAGEM in France and a Singapore Aerospace/IAI/Elbit consortium have been shortlisted from five contenders, which also included Eidetics, Northrop Grumman/CASA and Sierra Technologies, for selection in 1998.

Now nearing completion, TAI's $650 million co-production programme for 52 CN.235Ms may be extended by at least 10 more, including one transport and six maritime patrol versions for the Turkish navy, plus three for army use. Installation and integration of surveillance and sensor equipment will require a further $200 million for the maritime patrol aircraft programme. Another three CN.235M

maritime versions are envisaged with less complex equipment for Coast Guard operation, plus at least 13 for possible export to Croatia (three) and Pakistan.

KC-135s enter service

The THK was due to take delivery of its KC-135Rs in December 1997, with 58-0110 the first to be handed over. Turkey is to receive seven former KC-135As, consisting of 57-2592, 58-0110, 60-0325, 60-0326, 62-3539, 62-3563, and 62-3567. The aircraft were all removed from storage, for overhaul at the Oklahoma City Air Logistics Centre at Tinker AFB, Oklahoma. However following completion of this work, they were once again returned to AMARC for a short time pending delivery to Boeing at Wichita for conversion to KC-135R standard.

UKRAINE:

Russian bombers scrapped

Despite several reported agreements up to early 1997, for Russian repurchase of the 19 Tupolev Tu-160 'Blackjack' and 23 Tu-95MS 'Bear-H' strategic nuclear bombers left behind at Priluki and Uzin in Ukraine after the 1991

break-up of the USSR, no funding has been forthcoming from Moscow. Having earlier returned to Russia or destroyed its nuclear weapons and warheads, the Ukraine government has now announced its decision to scrap all these aircraft. It is retaining, however, an undisclosed number of 'Scud-B' tactical ballistic missiles. The V-VS appears to have decided that available funding would be better spent on completing five or six undelivered Tu-160s from Tupolev's Kazan production line, to supplement the five in Russian service at Engels Air Base.

UNITED KINGDOM:

First Chinook HC.Mk 2A

Boeing delivered a new HC.Mk 2A Chinook to the RAF on 6 December 1997. It is the first of 14 HC.Mk 2A and HC.Mk 3s manufactured for the RAF under a 1995 contract. Deliveries will continue through 2000.

The HC.Mk 2A incorporates several technology improvements, including addition of single precision machined fuselage frames and structural elements that add strength to the aircraft while eliminating hundreds of parts and fasteners. Boeing verified the performance of the new frames through extensive vibration and flight tests.

This is the first flying MiG-29SMT development aircraft. The example exhibited at the 1997 Moscow air show ('Blue 25') was a mock-up. This aircraft made its first flight on 29 November 1997.

Below and bottom: Recent additions to the Swiss Air Force include this F/A-18D, seen at Payerne, carrying wingtip AIM-9 acquisition rounds, and a Falcon 50 which has replaced one of the Learjet 35As previously in use.

Tornado GR.Mk 4 arrives

The RAF's first two production-standard upgraded Tornado GR.Mk 4 interdictor-strike aircraft were delivered by British Aerospace for DERA service trials at Boscombe Down in late 1997. They comprised two of the original development aircraft, in the form of ZD708 (build standard 112) and ZG773 (b/s 186), and will be followed by 140 more GR.Mk 1/1As converted to similar standards. Deliveries from the £1 billion programme will continue at up to 32 per year by 2002.

The MoD's original 1984 SR(A) 417 mid-life upgrade (MLU) requirement was to update 161 of the 228 RAF Tornado GR.Mk 1s, mainly to attain a covert or 'stealthy' low-level all-weather day/night attack capability from non-emitting passive target-navigation systems, to supplement the original active terrain-following radar. Funding restrictions have since cut programme totals to 142 aircraft, and negated plans to install TERPROM.

Covert approach equipment now includes FLIR/TV systems, integrated with TIALD, NVGs, plus raster image HUD and colour cockpit MFDs. New and mainly GEC-Marconi Mil Std 1553/1760 digital avionics also include GPS/INS, an improved passive/active DAS, and provision for new stand-off weapons and further MLU packages.

Package 1 will include Raytheon/TI Paveway III laser-guided bombs in conjunction with upgraded 400 series TIALD to meet the MoD's SR(A) 1242 requirement, and BAeD Sea

Eagle anti-ship missile for the MER(A) 6/94 programme, for integration by early 2000. In 2001, Package 2 will add MATRA/BAeD's medium-range Storm Shadow ASM to meet SR(A) 1236; GEC-Marconi Brimstone for the SR(A) 1238 anti-armour requirement; and the eight Hughes UK RAPTOR EO/IR tactical-reconnaissance pods ordered for the RAF GR.Mk 1 SR(A)1368 requirement.

Seven different RAF GR.Mk 1 variants currently operated in the

RAF's Tornado fleet will now become standardised as GR.Mk 4/4As. From September 1998, they will eventually re-equip the entire RAF Tornado IDS force, comprising two TIALD-fitted and two ALARM-carrying GR.Mk 1 squadrons at Bruggen; two GR.Mk 1A strike/reconnaissance squadrons at Marham; and the two Sea Eagle-armed GR.Mk 1B maritime strike/reconnaissance squadrons at Lossiemouth, for service until at least 2018. Replacement is then planned by the as-yet-

undefined piloted or unmanned Future Offensive Air System.

Two more upgrade packages are planned for integration by 2003 and 2004, and will include new IFF, secure data transfer (MIDS), and hands-on-throttle-and-stick (HOTAS) controls among other updates. Interest in the RAF's Tornado MLU is also being shown by Saudi Arabia, which received an initial batch of 48 IDS aircraft from 1986, and is currently taking delivery of another 48.

C-130J delivery schedules

As lead customer, the UK now expects delivery of the first of 15 stretched C-130J-30s from March 1998 (immediately after FAA civil certification), followed by 10 short-fuselage C-130Js, with options on five more. This is over 18 months behind schedule from the original 1995 order, because of stall-warning and electronic flight-instrumentation problems during the development programme. Two of four USAF C-130Js on order have been used for development and certification trials, and all four will continue on test and training roles.

Goodbye to RAF Gazelles

Retirement on 30 September 1997 of the last SA 341 Gazelles from the Central Flying School (Helicopters) at Shawbury marked the end of 24 years of RAF service. CFS(H) and No. 2 FTS had flown about 19 Gazelle HT.Mk 3s, prior to their replacement by 26 of 38 AS 350BA Squirrel HT.Mk 1s for the newly-formed Defence Helicopter Flying School, operated commercially by the FBS group. Delivery of the last HT.Mk 1 was due by February 1998. Gazelle HT.Mk 1s continue to be operated in some numbers, however, by the Army Air Corps, although 32 in the School of Army Aviation are being replaced at Middle Wallop by FBS-operated Squirrel HT.Mk 2s.

Middle East

EGYPT:

Helicopter deliveries

As launch export customer for remanufactured Kaman SH-2Gs, the Egyptian navy took formal delivery on 21 October 1997 of the first of 10 Super Seasprite ASW helicopters ordered from a $150 million Foreign Military Sales (FMS) contract. Kaman is modernising Egypt's ex-US Navy SH-2Fs with new General Electric T700-401 turboshafts, cockpit instrumentation, avionics, FLIR and ESM systems. They are also the sole export versions to date to replace the USN's original MAD systems with AlliedSignal AQS-18A dipping sonar. The Egyptian government is considering ordering another 10 SH-2G(E)s, to counter Iran's 'Kilo'-class submarines.

Egypt has also taken delivery in the past year or so of 12 Mil Mi-17-1V transport helicopters with uprated Klimov TV3-117VM turboshafts for tropical operation. They were produced in Russia by Kazan Helicopters, and supplemented Egypt's earlier procurement of a quantity of Soviet Mil Mi-8s.

IRAQ:

Counter-stealth technology?

Iraq was reported to be negotiating with Tesla-Pardubice in the Czech Republic to buy five of its mobile MCS-93 Tamara passive electronic monitoring and surveillance systems (incorrectly described as radar), which is claimed to be effective against stealth aircraft. However, Tamara functions by

detecting and tracking the electronic emissions of up to 24 approaching targets over ranges of up to 260 nm (300 miles; 480 km), so it has no real inherent or innovative 'anti-stealth' capabilities. It is undoubtedly effective in acquiring position information from the use of any emissions from search and navigation or terrain-following radars, IFF, radar altimeters or communications systems by aircraft over a very wide area from its location.

ISRAEL:

First F-15Is delivered

Formal delivery of the first two of 25 MDC F-15I long-range strike fighters on order for Israel took place at the Boeing/McDonnell Douglas St Louis factory on 6 November 1997 to senior Israeli officials, including IDF/AF C-in-C Major General Eitan Ben-Eliahu. Designated Raam (Thunder) by the

IDF/AF, the F100-PW-229-powered F-15I was developed from the original F-15E, but has an integrated Israeli EW package and some weapons systems changes. Among these are provision for Rafael Python-4 advanced close-combat AAMs, as well as for AIM-120.

F-15I delivery completion is due by late 1999, and more orders may follow from 10-year IDF/AF modernisation plans to allocate up to $3 billion for about 100 new fighters to replace A-4s and F-4s. Israeli orders are also planned for more Apache attack helicopters, comprising new AH-64Ds with Longbow radar, plus US support helicopters and transport aircraft.

JORDAN:

First F-16s arrive

The Royal Jordanian Air Force received their initial complement of F-16s during December 1997. Jordan

Right: Switzerland's upgraded Mirage IIIRS reconnaissance aircraft have retained their grey/green camouflage, unlike the upgraded Mirage IIIS fighters and IIIBS trainers.

Right, centre: Bond Helicopters currently perform the Royal Navy's FOST Flag Officer training requirement, using two SA.3655N Dauphins, based at Plymouth.

Right: On 31 October 1997 the first production (service) Tornado GR.Mk 4 (ZG750/BT051) was handed over to the RAF, at BAe Warton.

was set to obtain its first six F-16A/Bs before the end of 1997, with two further batches of five each scheduled for delivery during January and February 1998. The five year lease consists of twelve F-16As and four F-16Bs, all of which were previously in USAF service before retirement to AMARC for storage. Twelve of the F-16As and one of the F-16Bs were previously ADF versions. All 16 have been overhauled and received structural upgrade by the Ogden Air Logistics Centre at Hill AFB, Utah before delivery. The first aircraft to emerge from refurbishing was F-16A 222 previously 80-0547, which was operated by the 119th FS of the New Jersey ANG at Atlantic City until retired to AMARC on November 17, 1994.

OMAN:

RAFO procurement plans

Main Royal Air Force of Oman requirements in a new five-year national defence plan, now being prepared for implementation from 2001, include up to 30 new transport helicopters. Several medium-lift helicopters, including the Bell 412EP, AS 532 Cougar and Sikorsky S-70, are being evaluated as possible replacements for some 20 AB 205s, three AB 212s, and five Bell 214s in current RAFO service. The RAFO's long-standing lack of a basic training capability may also be rectified from a requirement for up to 16 turboprop types in the EMBRAER Tucano or Pilatus PC-9 category. Another RAFO requirement is to double its current fleet of three Lockheed C-130H transports.

SAUDI ARABIA:

AB 412 contract plans

An SR600 million ($160 million) Saudi government order for up to 36 AB 412EP helicopters was being finalised with Agusta in late 1997, for RSAF SAR roles. The planned contract included four more AB 412EPs for VIP use with the Saudi Royal Flight.

UNITED ARAB EMIRATES:

Mirage 2000-9 order

A FF16 billion ($2.7 billion) contract for up to 34 Dassault Mirage 2000-9 multi-role combat aircraft, signed in

December 1997 by French President Jacques Chirac in Abu Dhabi, will effectively fulfil the first phase of the long-standing UAE requirement for 100 or more new combat aircraft costing $6-8 billion. Their delivery between 1998-2001 will supplement original mid-1980s Abu Dhabi air force receipts of 22 Mirage 2000AD air defence fighters, eight Mirage 2000RAD tactical-reconnaissance fighters, and six Mirage 2000DAD two-seat combat trainers.

Some of the Mirage 2000-9s, including two-seat trainer versions, will also equip more ADAF combat units between 1999 and 2001. With a total value of FF20 billion ($3.44 billion), the new contract includes additional funding to upgrade the ADAF's 33 remaining original Mirage 2000s, now referred to as AD-8s, to 2000-9 standard. As well as new-build examples, up to half of the ADAF Mirage 2000-9s may be converted and upgraded by

Dassault from surplus French air force Mirage 2000C air defence interceptors of earlier vintage, to minimise programme costs.

Derived from the Mirage 2000-5, the 2000-9 retains the Thomson-CSF RDY multi-mode radar, digital avionics and other improvements to operate with smart weapons, but incorporates additional systems hardware and software changes for ADAF requirements. These are to ensure compatibility with the UAE's Al Hakim range of air-to-surface missiles, from the GEC-Marconi group, for dedicated strike roles.

Additional weapons to the UAE Mirage 2000-9 package, costing some $700 million, include MICA and ASRAAM AAMs. MATRA/BAeD is also offering a version of its Storm Shadow long-range ASM known as Black Shadow, as an alternative to Al Hakim. Other new equipment will include Thomson-CSF's Damocles laser designation and FLIR systems.

Africa

BOTSWANA:

Air force equipment changes

Following the late 1996 arrival of the first of 10 Canadair/Northrop CF-5A fighters and three two-seat CF-5Ds from Canada, the Air Arm of the Botswana Defence Force has retired its half-dozen or so remaining BAC 167 Strikemaster armed jet-trainers. Several have been seen with warbird dealers in the UK, and are expected to continue flying with civil operators.

The two CASA/IPTN CN.235Ms of the BDFAW transport wing were supplemented late in 1997 by two ex-USAF C-130Bs from AMARC storage from American aid programmes.

SOUTH AFRICA:

RFPs for modernisation

National Defence Force (SANDF) joint-service requests for proposals issued in September for a comprehensive Rnd10 billion ($2.14 billion) equipment modernisation package over the next few years attracted responses from no fewer than 10 global arms-producing countries. They have included Canada, the Czech Republic, Spain and Sweden, as well as Britain, France, Germany, Italy, Russia and the US, although some are involved in joint proposals. The proposed modernisation programme, with costs exceeding the entire South African annual defence budget (reduced to Rnd9.5 billion for 1997-98), covers new frigates, submarines, main battle tanks, combat aircraft, and support equipment, although priority is expected for the SAAF. This service has urgent requirements for 32 new multi-role combat aircraft and 16 advanced jet-trainers, to replace Mirage F1AZs, Atlas Cheetah Cs and Impala Mk 1/2s, as well as maritime patrol and transport aircraft, plus 61 support helicopters.

DASA is apparently looking to South Africa as a possible development partner and launch customer for its next-generation AT-2000 jet-trainer/light combat aircraft. This would be a Mach 1.5 tandem-seat low-observable fly-by-wire design powered by a single Eurojet EJ200 turbofan, and of mainly composite construction. R&D is an estimated $1.35 billion, with target fly-away unit costs of $16-20 million.

This anonymous Boeing 707 (4X-JYB), wearing only the serial '255', is an IDF/AF aircraft that passed through RAF Mildenhall in November 1997, supporting a visit by Israel's President Netanyahu to the USA.

Southern Asia

INDIA:

Russian air-refuelling tankers ordered

India's new force of 40 Sukhoi Su-30MKI multi-role fighters, of which the first eight have already been delivered in basic Su-30K form, is to be supported by six Ilyushin Il-78 'Midas' tankers, for a package cost of only about $100 million. Orders for the first two IAF Il-78s were recently finalised via Russia's Rosvoorouzhenie,

and are expected to be two new Il-76 'Candid' conversions produced by the Chkalov Tashkent factory in Uzbekistan. The IAF already operates the Il-76, some 24 having been acquired between 1985-1989.

US procurement prospects

Reports from Delhi indicate that traditional Russian equipment procurement policies may be abandoned by the Indian Navy for replacement of its five

Ilyushin Il-38 'May' maritime patrol aircraft operated by INAS 315 from Dabolim since 1977. Three Lockheed Martin P-3C Orions are reportedly under consideration for this requirement, which would represent India's first-ever US operational aircraft procurement.

SRI LANKA:

SLAF C-130K interest

Negotiations by the Sri Lanka government have been reported with the UK MoD for the possible purchase for SLAF operation of three of the four recently-retired RAF Lockheed C-130K

Hercules converted for tanker/transport roles. Six ex-RAF C-130Ks have also been offered to Angola by Lockheed Martin, which is taking them back in part-exchange for new C-130J Hercules IIs.

'Hinds' back in business

Following their refurbishment in Ukraine, two of three SLAF Mil Mi-24 'Hind' attack helicopters recently resumed combat operations against Tamil separatists. The SLAF's remaining Mi-24 has been awaiting repair to damage received from ground fire in September.

Far East

CHINA:

AWACS still open?

While Israel Aircraft Industries has a development contract for a prototype AWACS Ilyushin Il-76, similar to Russia's A-50 'Mainstay' but with an IAI-installed Elta Electronics' Phalcon active phased-array radar for China's AEW&C requirements, Britain's GEC-Marconi is apparently still involved in some aspects of this programme. With BAe and Ilyushin, GEC-Marconi reportedly resumed earlier negotiations with China in 1997 for the supply of its Argus 2000 radar developed for the Nimrod AEW.Mk 3 programme, for similar installation in an Il-76. As in the AEW Nimrod, installation is apparently proposed in nose and rear-fuselage mountings, to achieve full azimuth coverage, as against IAI/Elta plans for planar installations in a triangular configuration within a fixed dorsal radome. After three years of prototype development, China's future requirements are for at least three more AWACS aircraft, costing up to $250 million each.

Stretched Y-8 certificated

Recently certificated by the Chinese Civil Aviation Administration, a stretched version of the Shaanxi

Aircraft Company's Y-8 development of the Antonov An-12 military freighter, designated the Y-8F-200, is being offered for both civil and military use. Fuselage inserts of almost 2.5 m (8 ft) increase overall length of the Y-8F-200 to 36.3 m (119 ft), and its pressurised cargo compartment from 13.5 m (44.3 ft) to 15.7 m (51.5 ft). More than 60 Y-8s have now been delivered by Shaanxi.

JAPAN:

E-767 certified

The Boeing E-767 AWACS aircraft for Japan has completed qualification and FAA certification testing using the first aircraft (No. 502). The aircraft began 1998 in its Production Acceptance Test phase. The first two E-767s are scheduled to be delivered to the Japanese on 11 March 1998, followed by the two additional aircraft in late 1998 and early 1999.

KOREAN REPUBLIC:

GE404 to power KTX-2

Despite severe financial problems, including more than 50 per cent devaluation of its currency in 1997, the Seoul government is continuing its Won1,600 billion ($1.65 billion) Samsung KTX-2 supersonic advanced jet-trainer and light combat aircraft project. Further progress with this joint project, in which Lockheed Martin has a 13 per cent financial share as part of

its F-16 production offset commitments, was made late in 1997 with selection of the GE F404-402 turbofan in preference to the SNECMA M88-2 as KTX-2 powerplant. A $50 million initial contract with General Electric then followed on 24 November, for six F404s to power the four prototypes planned for the flight development programme, with spares, from 2001.

The RoK government is providing some 70 per cent of KTX-2 funding, with the remainder from Samsung and its RoK industry partners. Lockheed Martin will undertake integration and development of its fly-by-wire control and avionics installations, plus its alloy mainplanes. Its design assistance also includes incorporating features allowing the KTX-2 to meet the USAF's future Bomber/Fighter Training System requirement for a Northrop T-38 replacement from about 2010 onwards.

If production funding becomes available, the RoKAF is planning to buy an initial batch of 94 KTX-2s for delivery from Samsung from about 2004 onwards, with options for up to 100 more. Samsung would also co-produce 104 F404 engines for its KTX-2s.

AWACS and tanker/transport doubts

Up to $3 billion has been earmarked in RoKAF defence appropriations to buy four AWACS aircraft, for which the Boeing E-767, IAI's Phalcon and the Saab/Ericsson Erieye systems are being

evaluated. However, the future of this programme, plus a RoKAF requirement for four tanker/transports, may now be uncertain because of South Korean economic problems. The requirement for eight CN.235-220s, was finalised in November by a $143 million contract with IPTN, for delivery from 1999.

Army helicopter and SAM orders

Eurocopter Germany has received a $110 million contract from the defence ministry in Seoul for an initial 12 BO 105s, to be assembled by Daewoo Heavy Industries. In 1989, it was planned to acquire up to 120 scout/reconnaissance helicopters to support RoK army Bell AH-1S HueyCobras, but may now be scaled down because of South Korean economic problems.

A Won250 billion ($258 million) follow-up order for 1,294 MATRA/BAe Dynamics Mistral short-range portable air-defence missiles was announced in Seoul in October 1997 for the South Korean armed forces.

MALAYSIA:

MiG-29 upgrade contract

Having acquired 16 MiG-29SDs, plus two two-seat MiG-29UB trainers, in 1995, the RMAF is now supplementing the original $550 million contract by a $34.4 million upgrade. This will be undertaken locally by the Aerospace

Above: This Mil Mi-8TV 'Hip-H' carries the cockpit armour, exhaust shrouds and nose machine-gun mount that are the hallmarks of this variant. Seen at Entebbe, Uganda, during 1997, it wears a Zambian air force serial.

Above right: This Harbin Y-12 II is one of a pair serving with the Tanzanian People's Defence Force Air Wing, and was seen at Dar-es-Salaam in October 1997.

Right: This Xian Y7H-500 (5T-MAG, with temporary Chinese registration B3719) of the Mauretanian Islamic Air Force was seen routing through Luqa, Malta in October 1997.

Technology Systems Corp, a new Russian/Malaysian joint-venture company. It will involve installation of a retractable port-side NATO-compatible air-refuelling probe, using AN/APN-118 TACAN for tanker rendezvous; provision for new and higher-capacity (1150-litre/253-Imp gal) drop tanks; and updates to the original avionics and Phazotron N019 'Slot Back' pulse-Doppler radar. In addition to conferring a simultaneous twin-target air-to-air engagement capability, the N019M radar changes will also allow operation of the Vympel R-77E (AA-12 'Adder') medium-range active radar-guided AAM, for which Malaysia is reportedly the first export customer.

To support its new fighters, the RMAF is seeking more air-refuelling tankers, to supplement two of the RMAF's nine Lockheed C-130Hs and five new C-130H-30s converted by Airod and Lockheed Martin Aircraft Services from a $15 million contract with twin underwing Flight Refuelling Mk 32B hose and drogue pods, plus extra fuselage fuel tanks. Other RMAF support reinforcements may include 12 more IPTN CN.235M-220s to follow six now replacing 12 DHC-4 Caribou STOL tactical transports.

Helicopter plans reined in

Following the formal inauguration of the Malaysian Army Aviation Corps at Keluang base in March 1997 with 10 former RMAF Aérospatiale AS 316B Alouette IIIs, procurement of up to 300 new attack and transport helicopters was planned over the next 15 years. Prior to the recent budget cuts resulting from Far East economic problems and major currency devaluations, the Kuala Lumpur defence ministry

had confirmed proposals to buy eight Denel CSH-2 Rooivalk attack helicopters costing some $350 million. They were to be the basis of an aviation regiment to undertake airlift, tactical support and reconnaissance for Malaysia's Rapid Deployment Force, but the programme has now been put on hold.

All new planned helicopter procurement is likely to be similarly affected by the recent currency crisis. This includes the Royal Malaysian Navy Air Wing's urgent requirement to replace its 10 ex-RN Westland Wasp HAS.Mk 1s. Up to six new frigate-operated anti-submarine helicopters are being sought to operate from the RMN's two new GEC Yarrow-built frigates, due for imminent delivery. Twelve similar ASW helicopters are also required over the longer term for the RMN's planned offshore-patrol combatant vessels.

In late 1997, Westland's proposed LHTEC T800-powered Super Lynx Srs 300, which also features a new electronic flight-instrumentation system, appeared to be leading Kaman's SH-2G Super Seasprite as front-runner for this programme. Submissions have also been made by Eurocopter for its AS 565SA, and Sikorsky with its S-70B Seahawk, for a planned early 1998 decision.

PHILIPPINES:

Re-equipment reviewed

Although the Philippines is sharing many of the economic woes of its ASEAN partners, its FY98 budget allocations from the 15-year Pso164.5

billion Armed Forces Modernisation Programme (AFMP) were reportedly more than doubled in September, over 1997. Currency devaluation, however, has reduced the real-terms AFMP budget from its original $6.5 billion to around $4.5 billion. Attempts are being intensified to restore the Mutual Defence Treaty with the US, following the 1991-92 expulsion of American forces from the major bases at Clark AFB and Subic Bay Naval Complex.

The Philippine air force (PhilAF), currently operates only eight F-5As and two F-5Bs. These and 24 more used F-5s now being sought may be upgraded as lead-in trainers for the planned new fighters, if the necessary funding becomes available.

Other PhilAF priorities have been listed as 12 ground-attack fighters, six long-range maritime-patrol aircraft, more surplus USAF C-130B transports to follow recent deliveries of two, 12 SAR helicopters, and six new air defence ground radars. Following recent PhilAF receipt of four VIP Bell Textron 412 helicopters, a maritime version is competing with the Eurocopter AS 565 Panther, Eurocopter BO 105C, and LHTEC T800-engined GKN Westland Super Lynx to replace the Philippine navy's eight BO 105s and 12 PhilAF UH-1Hs operated on SAR roles.

SINGAPORE:

More US equipment orders

A new $350 million contract placed in late 1997 with Lockheed Martin for 12 new Block 52 F-16C/Ds, for delivery in 1999, has reportedly been followed

by a second lease/purchase agreement for 12 more Block 42 F-16C/Ds. If confirmed, the latter will be additional to 12 similar Fighting Falcons, for which the RepSAF signed a commercial lease-to-buy contract with Lockheed Martin in early 1996, increasing overall RSAF procurement to 62 F-16s. Of these, the first batch of 12 lease/purchase F-16C/Ds will replace nine leased USAF F-16A/Bs to extend RSAF training beyond 1999 at Luke AFB, AZ. The second batch is also scheduled to remain initially in the US, for similar training at Cannon AFB, NM. In Singapore, the remaining seven of four each Block 15 OCU F-16A/Bs delivered in 1988, now undergoing 'Falcon Up' structural upgrades by USAF civilian technicians at Tengah air base, will be supplemented in 1998 by eight F100-PW-229-powered Block 52 F-16Cs and 10 F-16Ds, ordered in 1994.

In late 1997, Singapore was also finalising an FMS contract for its long-planned second batch of six Boeing CH-47D Chinooks, with options for another four. They will equip the first Singapore-based RSAF Chinook unit, supplementing the six operated for training at Grand Prairie, TX, with orders expected for eight to 10 more.

First KC-135 readied for delivery

The first KC-135A due for conversion to KC-135R standard for the RSAF is 61-0325, which was removed from storage at AMARC during October 1997. The aircraft was then flown to the Boeing facility at Wichita, Kansas

These South African Air Force C-47TPs were unveiled at the SAAF's Test Flight & Development Centre in November 1997. The two-tone grey aircraft (6828) is an 'EW trainer'. The second aircraft (6882) was the development airframe for a maritime patrol version. This project has now been shelved due to lack of funding.

for conversion. This is one of two RSAF tankers funded as part of a $68.4 million contract with Boeing to convert eight more aircraft with the installation of the General Electric F108-CF-100 engines. The remaining six consist of four RC-135V/Ws, and two more KC-135Es, for the USAF.

TAIWAN:

Army helicopter contract

Recent US Foreign Military Sales notifications have included a $172 million contract with Taiwan for another 13 Bell OH-58D Kiowa Warriors. Like the 24 OH-58Ds previously supplied to Taiwanese army aviation, the follow-up batch will be equipped for anti-tank/ground-attack operations, with AGM-114A Hellfires and a mast-mounted sight. The new package will also include 13 Lycoming T703-AD-700 turboshafts, Hydra 70 rockets and launchers, ammunition, spares and support equipment.

THAILAND:

RTAF Hornets abandoned

The Royal Thai Air Force has indicated that it will scrap plans to buy eight F/A-18 Hornet fighters from the US because the cash-strapped Thai government cannot afford them. Air Force Chief of Staff Air Chief Marshal Anek Puasuwan said he was preparing a letter to the US government asking it to look for a new buyer for half of the squadron of 16 jet fighters Thailand had promised to acquire. "In this option we are willing to lose the $74 million we already spent for the down payment," Anek declared.

In 1996, Thailand signed a deal to buy the squadron of Hornets from McDonnell Douglas, since absorbed by the Boeing Company. The sale was held up for a while because of initial Thai insistence that the AIM-120A AMRAAM be included in a package deal.

VIETNAM:

Su-27 delivery losses

A Russian air force Antonov An-124 heavy-lift transport (c/n 82005), which crashed within seconds of taking off from Irkutsk airport on 6 December 1997 for Vladivostok and Hanoi, was carrying two of four two-seat Sukhoi Su-27UBK trainers and two Su-27SK 'Flanker' multi-role fighters ordered for the Vietnamese air force on January 31 of last year. It had delivered the first two Su-27UBKs to Vietnam only on 1 December 1997, and had picked up the second pair from the Irkutsk Aviation Industrial Association Joint Stock Company in the Siberian region of Russia, immediately before the accident. IAIA is responsible for producing all two-seat versions of the Su-27 series, now comprising the Su-30MKs being delivered to India, plus other Su-30 deliveries claimed by IAIA to China. Both Su-27UBKs were completely destroyed, together with the An-124, when it crashed into an Irkutsk apartment block following power loss in two, or possibly three of its D-18T turbofans, perhaps through contaminated or unsuitable fuel. Among the 23 crew and passengers killed in the crash were technicians and other members of a Russian air force training mission accompanying the Su-27s. At least 44 people were also reported killed on the ground when the An-124's 140-tonne fuel load exploded on impact.

The two Vietnamese Su-27UBKs were insured for some $56 million (though the An-124 was reportedly uninsured), but as Su-27UB production has reportedly been completed by IAIA, the VNAF is now expected to receive two twin-stick Su-30Ks in their place. Vietnam's two Su-27SKs were expected from Komsomolsk-on-Amur (KnAAPO) production by 31 December, and to be followed by orders for a further 18 by 2001.

Australasia

AUSTRALIA:

AWACS progress

The three competing teams for the RAAF's $A1.2 billion ($888 million) Project Wedgetail (Project Air 5077) requirement for four AWACS aircraft, plus options on two more, were awarded initial design activity (IDA) contracts each worth some $US6 million by the Australian Defence Department in Canberra towards the end of 1997. IDA funding will allow critical initial design work to precede full tenders later in 1998. Project Wedgetail bids include one from a Raytheon E-Systems-led team for an Airbus A310 with an Elta 360° Phalcon phased-array dorsal radar. Lockheed Martin, Northrop Grumman and Transfield Defense Systems are proposing a modified C-130J with E-2C APS-145 radar, while Boeing, with BAe Australia, is submitting the E737-700 with Northrop Grumman MESA radar. Selection is due in 1999, for deliveries from 2002, and aircraft commonality is being sought for six RAAF-required tanker/transports.

RAN SH-2 upgrade

Kaman's current upgrading of 11 surplus USN SH-2Fs to SH-2G(A) standard for ASW and over-the-horizon surveillance and targeting roles with the Royal Australian Navy will incorporate the most advanced Litton-integrated digital avionics and other features of any of the current export Super Seasprites. New equipment will include Telephonics APS-143 ISAR radar, EFIS cockpit with four LCD displays, Litton GPS/INS, Hughes AN/AAQ-27 IR imaging system, an Elisra EW suite, and composite main-rotor blades. Like all other export SH-2Gs, other than those of Egypt, the RAN's SH-2G(A)s retain the MAD anti-submarine equipment, as part of an integrated tactical aviation system (ITAS) for launching Penguin or Maverick anti-ship missiles.

The RAN has a requirement for at least 12 more utility versions of the SH-2G, while others are being considered for the army's Air 87 armed-reconnaissance helicopter programme.

C-130J deliveries imminent

As the second Lockheed Martin Hercules II customer after the RAF, the RAAF is expecting 12 stretched C-130J-30s from a late 1995 $A900 million ($670 million) order in mid-1998, to replace its dozen C-130Es, with options on 24 more. With Alenia, Lockheed Martin is also submitting the Allison AE2100-engined C-27J version of the G222 for the RAAF's Project Air 5190 Light Transport Aircraft requirement for 12-18 DHC-4, BAe 748 and Douglas C-47B replacements, in competition with the CASA/IPTN CN.235M and projected stretched CASA CN.295M.

NEW ZEALAND:

New five-year defence plan

Five-year defence plans by the New Zealand government for 1998-2002 currently exclude funding for two more ANZAC frigates, on which options are held, although the original pair are to be equipped with Evolved Sea Sparrow air defence missiles. Another Kaman SH-2G ASW helicopter will also be ordered, increasing the RNZN commitment to five. Finance is also included for five C-130Js to replace the RNZAF's C-130Hs, and for further upgrades of the nav/attack systems of its 19 A-4K/TA-4K Skyhawk. Another type earmarked for replacement are the RNZAF's Boeing 727s, which may give way to new-build Boeing 737s.

South America

ARGENTINA:

New helicopters for air force and army aviation

The Fuerza Aérea Argentina is in the process of receiving eight US Army surplus Bell UH-1Hs. These helicopters will be assigned to Escuadrón 1 de Helicópteros of Grupo Aéreo 7. The first two examples (marked as H-09 and H-10) arrived on 11 September 1997 on a FAA Hercules. Currently, Escuadrón 1 has a strength of only two Bell UH-1D/Hs and six Bell 212 IFRs, so the eight additional Hueys represent an important increase in their line-up. The Fuerza Aérea is considering the purchase of another six to eight twin-engined helicopters (the most likely type being second-hand Bell UH-1Ns) to be used as SAR machines on detachments at V and VI Brigadas Aéreas. A number of RACA/Hughes 500Ds currently fulfill that role.

The Aviación de Ejército Argentino has recently confirmed the purchase of another 10 surplus UH-1Hs, to be serialled AE-437 to AE-446. Their arrival coincides with the disbandment of the Escuadrón de Aviación de Exploración y Ataque 602 based at Campo de Mayo airfield. This unit flew armed Agusta A 109s and UH-1H gunships. Those helicopters, plus the 'new' ones, will be assigned to four new Secciones de Aviación (Aviation Detachments) to support land units in northern Argentina. One Sección de Aviación will be based at Salta. Since February 1970, when the first Bell UH-1HBF was delivered to the Argentine army, 41 UH-1D/H have been delivered, plus seven Bell 205A-1 and two Bell 212s.

P-3 acquisition

The Argentine Navy is in the process of obtaining six former US Navy P-3Bs which have been in storage at

Right: 63-0002 is the second prototype Mitsubishi XF-2, which first flew in December 1995, and is now operating with the TRDI test and development unit. Two two-seat XF-2Bs also serve with TRDI.

Below: This Japanese Ground Self-Defence Force UH-60J (43102) is one of two bailed back to Mitsubishi for ski testing until March 1998.

AMARC. The first two aircraft, (152746 and 152763) were being prepared for departure during October 1997, destined for the Naval Air Depot at NAS Jacksonville, Florida for overhaul. Brazil is also interested in obtaining P-3s, although it is unclear if these would be ex US Navy aircraft or new-build models.

CHILE:

New equipment evaluations and 737 delivery

Evaluations of new combat aircraft are being completed by the Chilean air force (FACh) to select up to 24 by mid-1998 as replacements for its Mirage III/5/50s and F-5E/Fs. Final selection will be between the Mirage 2000-5, Saab/BAe Gripen and two American types, pending US State Department clearance. During a late 1997 European tour, FACh C-in-C General Fernando Rojas Vender flew

the combat trainer versions of the Mirage 2000-5 and Gripen, which, with the F-16C/D or F/A-18, have been short-listed for procurement.

In December 1997 the delivery took place to the FACh of a Boeing 737-500 costing $31 million, to replace a VIP Boeing 707-320 for presidential and government use.

COLOMBIA:

UH-1P programme begins

Flight development started in late 1997 of the first of eight Colombian air force (FAC) Bell UH-1As to be upgraded to UH-1P Huey II standard by Bell Helicopter Textron. Apart from uprating the original Lycoming 1,400-shp (1044-kW) T53-L-13B engine to T53-L-703 standard by 400 shp (300 kW) for improved hot-and-high performance, the UH-1P has Bell 212 main and tail rotor systems, gearboxes and transmission, conferring a

27-39 per cent increase in payload. After prototype conversion, Bell Huey II kits will be installed by the Corporación de la Industria Aeronáutica (CIAC) in Colombia.

VENEZUELA:

Naval helicopter plans

Twelve Agusta-Bell AB 212ASW helicopters operated by Venezuelan naval aviation, some recently upgraded with new avionics by Israel Aircraft Industries, will be supplemented by a half-dozen Bell 412EPs, according to government plans announced late in 1997.

ENAER have fitted the first of the FAC's upgraded Tiger III fighters with an inflight refuelling probe. The probes were supplied as kits by Tiger Century Aircraft Co. ENAER has also begun to undertake airframe and engine overhauls on Royal Thai Air Force F-5Es.

This aircraft (515) is the first Fuerza Aérea de Chile (FAC) Mirage 50DC to be converted to Pantera standard. It was redelivered to Grupo 4 in December 1997. The Pantera upgrade adds canards, an IFR probe, Elta 2001B radar, Caiquén RWR, Eclipse chaff/flare dispensers and a new radio system. Pantera aircraft are also compatible with the Python 3 AAM and LGBs.

North America

CANADA:

Hawks and Texan IIs ordered for NFTC

Following prolonged negotiations, a 20-year \$C2.85 billion (\$US2 billion) contract was received by the Defense Systems Division of Bombardier Inc. in late 1997 from the Canadian government, to provide the aircraft and infrastructure to operate NATO Flying Training in Canada (NFTC) at Canadian Forces Base Moose Jaw, Saskatchewan. As expected, British Aerospace Military Aircraft & Aerostructures will supply 18 Hawk Mk 115 lead-in fighter trainers and through-life spares support for the advanced stage of this programme. BAe's contract from the \$C1.3 billion (\$926 million) to be spent on NFTC aircraft will include an immediate option for another seven Hawks, plus participation in the programme build-up and on-going marketing initiatives.

As one of the NFTC partners, EMBRAER in Brazil had been expected to receive an order for 24 EMB-314 Super Tucanos, for the basic and some advanced stages of the proposed training programme. Raytheon's announcement on 18 December 1997 of its first firm export order, from Bombardier Services for 24 Beech/Pilatus T-6A-1 Texan IIs with twin VHF/VOR/ADF for NFTC use, therefore caused major surprise. T-6A and Hawk deliveries are planned for courses to start in early 2000.

CF-18 deployment ends

Canadian CF-18 Hornets completed a three-month deployment with the NATO Stabilisation Force (SFOR) at Aviano AFB, Italy on 15 November 1997. One hundred and fourteen personnel, primarily from 416 'Lynx' Squadron, 1 Air Maintenance Squadron, 441 Squadron and 4 Wing, CFB Cold Lake, accompanied six CF-18s on Operation Mirador, Canada's first operational fighter deployment

since the Gulf War. The Canadian Air Component, part of the Canadian Air Contingent (which also controlled a Hercules tactical airlift component out of Rimini), carried out close air support, monitoring of airspace, and protection of NATO and 1,200 Canadian ground troops stationed in the Balkans.

The Hornets were also carrying out Canada's first deployment with newly acquired Loral AN/AAS-38B NITE Hawk pods, GBU-12 Paveway III LGBs, and AGM-65G Mavericks. Operational capability had only just been declared with the precision-guided munitions on the CF-18, and 416 Squadron had trained with the new equipment and ordnance immediately before the deployment. AIM-7s and AIM-9s were carried for air-to-air operations by the CF-18s during the Bosnian deployment.

The six-ship departed Canada from CFB Bagotville on 14 August, employing the services of a USAF KC-10 tanker for the nine-hour non-stop transatlantic flight to Aviano. The first operational mission took place on 22 August, flown by 416's commanding officer Lieutenant Colonel Jim Grecco, and Major Steve Charbonneau. Ten pilots flew missions, rotating 45 days into the deployment in order to give the rest of 416's pilots a chance at the action. Some 261 operational missions were conducted over three months, with no shots fired in anger, and the 100 per cent serviceability rate was marred only by bad weather. Missions included a mix of air-to-air, air-to-

ground and air presence flights. Average mission duration was about three hours and most included air-to-air refuelling with NATO partners. In addition, 77 training missions were carried out, which included the deployment of two aircraft to Laage Air Base in Germany from 2 to 6 November to conduct dissimilar air combat exercises with Luftwaffe MiG-29s. The six CF-18s returned from Aviano to Bagotville on Saturday 15 November, again accompanied by a KC-10. A welcome-home ceremony took place in Ottawa two days later. The success of the effort will put Canada in a much better position to support NATO and UN taskings

Above: During 1996 and 1997, Chile supplied UH-1H helicopters and 41 crew (from Grupo 9) to the UN monitoring mission in Iraq. In 1998, Chile will begin to replace its UH-1s, perhaps with UH-60s.

Below: The flight inspection aircraft of Brazil's GEIV are being repainted in a red and white scheme. This is an EC-95 Bandeirante. An old-scheme EU-93 (HS 125) is visible in the background.

requiring fighter participation in the future.

UNITED STATES:

Joint-STARS gains IOC

The 93rd Air Control Wing at Robins AFB, Georgia, received the third E-8C Joint-STARS aircraft which was delivered from the Northrop Grumman Surveillance and Battle Management Systems facility at Melbourne, Florida on 25 November. The Wing subsequently received its initial operational capability (IOC) on 18 December, enabling the unit to deploy for worldwide operations. Despite the IOC not having been established previously, the unit has performed two deployments to Europe for inclusion in Operation Deliberate Guard over Bosnia. In addition, an E-8 was temporarily deployed to Kadena AB, Okinawa, during late October/early November for inclusion in Exercise 'Foal Eagle 97', the first occasion that a J-STARS has been involved in any Pacific operations.

The wing took delivery of a Boeing 707 trainer on 14 October, enabling additional crews to become proficient in handling an aircraft the size of J-STARS. The 707 lacks the mission kit of the E-8, but has the same grey colour scheme and unit insignia as the Joint-STARS.

C-141C enters service

The USAF received its first C-141C StarLifter when 65-9414 was rolled out of the Warner Robins Air Logistics

Above left: This RC-135V Rivet Joint is the first upgraded Block 6C ('baseline 6 complete') aircraft to enter service. Note the additional Satcom antennas.

Left: This mysterious USAF Boeing 707 is reportedly a C-18 operated by AFMC, at Wright-Patterson AFB. It visited RAF Mildenhall during December 1997.

Center at Robins AFB, Georgia, on 31 October, 1997. The aircraft has been modified with a 'glass cockpit', including touch-sensitive screens and digital displays. The aircraft has also been fitted with GPS, an all-weather flight control system, and a new fuel status system. A defensive system has been incorporated, which includes the installation of missile warning receivers.

The first aircraft has been delivered to the 452nd AMW at March ARB, California, for Air Force Reserve Command. Subsequently, 65-0245 and 66-0152 have been completed and rejoined the 452nd AMW. A further 61 will be modified by the Warner Robins ALC, with the programme due to be completed by August 1999. The Reserves will operate the C-141C exclusively, with other units slated for the upgraded StarLifter including the 445th AW at Wright Patterson AFB, Ohio, 459th AW at Andrews AFB, Maryland (both part of AFRC), together with the 155th AS/Tennessee ANG at Memphis IAP and the 183rd AS/Mississippi ANG at Allen C Thompson Field. The modification has been a joint development between personnel of the C-141 System Programme Office at the Warner Robins ALC, and Raytheon E-Systems of Waco, Texas.

Latest C-130J orders

The US has ordered 10 more C-130Js, increasing to 42 the number of new aircraft sold by Lockheed Martin 1997, including 28 for US forces. The first four US C-130J aircraft will be used for operational testing and training, and have not yet been assigned to an operational unit. Assignments that have been disclosed include eight aircraft to the Maryland Air National Guard (including four from the new order), nine outfitted as WC-130J weather reconnaissance aircraft, commonly known as 'hurricane hunters' (including two from the new order) for the Air Force Reserve at Keesler AFB, Mississippi, and two configured as EC-130J special-ops aircraft and assigned to the 193rd Special Operations Wing, Pennsylvania Air National Guard, Harrisburg, PA. Five aircraft (including two from the new order) will become US Marine Corps KC-130J tankers, used both for aerial refuelling of helicopters and fixed-wing aircraft and for rapid ground refuelling (RGR). The Marine Corps now has a total of five KC-130s on order, and operates 52 KC-130s that are among the oldest C-130 Hercules in US service.

SR-71 funds denied in FY98

In an unexpected move, President Bill Clinton exercised his 'line item veto' on October 14 to cut the $39 million operating budget for the two SR-71s for fiscal year 1998. In effect the veto denies Detachment 2, of the 9th Reconnaissance Wing at Edwards AFB its operating capability. Included in the veto are proposed modifications to the

Above and right: This HSL-46 SH-60B (RAPTOR 465) was detached aboard the USS Ticonderoga, in late 1997, for drug interdiction and anti-smuggling tasks.

Right: This F-14A is the new CAG bird for VF-201 'Hunters', at NAS Fort Worth. In 1998, this unit will transition to the F/A-18A and hand its F-14s over to other units.

cameras installed in the SR-71, as well as an enhancement of radar processing, and installation of a global positioning system and an improved electronic intelligence gathering suite.

The two SR-71s were only declared operational in January 1997, and had yet to deploy overseas on an operational mission. The aircraft were originally returned to service to redress the anticipated shortfall in reconnaissance assets, pending the introduction into service of the various UAVs, such as the Global Hawk and DarkStar. Should the veto stand, as is likely, the SR-71s will be flown the short distance from their home at Edwards AFB to Palmdale for storage at the Lockheed Martin 'Skunk Works', for a second time.

DarkStar and Global Hawk advance

The second prototype Lockheed Martin/Boeing RQ-3A Tier III Minus DarkStar stealthy Unmanned Aerial Vehicle (UAV) – serial 696 – was transported from the Skunk Works at Palmdale to Edwards AFB on October 15, 1997. After reassembly and initial evaluation, the RQ-3 was due to have made its first flight before the end of 1997. The first DarkStar was allocated serial 695, which was the date it was rolled out in June 1995, and in keeping with the pattern set, the second has serial 696 as it emerged in June 1996. RQ-3A 695 performed its maiden flight on March 29, 1996, but crashed on its second flight just under a month later on April 22. RQ-3A 696 has had redesigned flight controls installed and the undercarriage has been strengthened. A further two prototypes are under construction at Palmdale, with these joining the programme in 1999.

DarkStar is being developed jointly by the two corporations and assembled at Palmdale for a requirement by the Defense Airborne Reconnaissance Office (DARO) to obtain 'responsive and sustained' data from anywhere behind enemy lines, both day and night, and within any weather condi-

tions. The UAV is designed to be a highly survivable, high altitude craft. The Lockheed Martin/Boeing team is under a cost plus, fixed fee contract for a unit flyaway price of $10 million based on an average production run of between 11 and 20 units.

DarkStar is to be evaluated alongside the Teledyne Ryan RQ-4A Global Hawk, as this UAV is capable of higher altitude, combined with longer range and endurance for the Tier II Plus section of the DARPA/DARO high altitude endurance requirement. Once evaluation has been completed a decision will be made sometime during the next decade as to the quantity of each type to be acquired. The prototype RQ-4A was dismantled at the Teledyne Ryan plant at San Diego and transported by road to Edwards AFB during August 1997. Following reassembly, the RQ-4A commenced taxi trials in preparation for its first flight early in 1998.

C-27 withdrawal

The 24th Wing at Howard AFB, Panama has begun to retire the C-27A (Alenia G.222) from service, with the first example arriving with AMARC, At Davis Monthan AFB, in July 1997 followed two months later by a further pair. All 10 have been declared surplus, and are being prepared for possible US government agency use. The wing has also replaced its handful of Lockheed C-130Es with the C-130H, resulting in these being the only transport version of the Hercules remaining in service with Air Combat Command. The C-130Hs are believed to have been obtained from the 317th AW at Dyess AFB, Texas.

Scaled's Proteus

Burt Rutan's Scaled Composites is building a high-altitude, long-endurance aircraft for military and commercial missions ranging from data relay services to launching small satellites into low-Earth orbit. The Proteus aircraft resembles a scaled-up version of Rutan's earlier ARES attack aircraft and is scheduled to fly in mid-1998. The all-composite Proteus features a three-section modular structure that can be tailored for different missions. The aircraft has a 79-ft (24-m) wing span that can be increased to 92 ft (28 m) by adding longer wingtips for certain payloads. The Proteus is powered by two Williams/Rolls-Royce FJ44-2 turbofan engines and expected to have a time on station of up to 18 hours for missions at an altitude of about 60,000 ft (18290 m). The Proteus can be crewed by two or configured as a UAV.

CH-60 makes maiden flight

The prototype Sikorsky CH-60 fleet combat support helicopter made its first flight from the company's Stratford, Connecticut facility on October 6, 1997. The CH-60 is a combination of the Navy's SH-60 Seahawk with the Army UH-60L Black Hawk to provide the Fleet with a helicopter to replace the CH-46 Sea Knight. The Navy awarded Sikorsky a contract in April 1997 to build a CH-60 demonstrator, which has been constructed using an Army UH-60L loaned from the Army and a Navy SH-60F. A 35-hour flight test programme will be carried out by an crew composed of a pilot from the manufacturer and the Navy to evaluate the primary mission of vertical resupply

Military Aviation Review

Left: This EP-3J Orion is seen in the markings of newly-established VQ-11, based at NAS Brunswick. VQ-11 have taken over the 'LP' tailcode previously used by VP-49.

Right: This ex-USAF T-39A (formerly 62-4480) is operated as a systems testbed by Tracor Flight Systems. It is seen here in Malta during late 1997, undertaking radar tests for Italy's FIAR.

(VERTREP). The USN has a requirement for up to 250 CH-60s, with a decision on low-rate initial production expected to have been taken by the end of 1997. Two aircraft had already been funded from the fiscal year 1998 budget. Provided the CH-60 is given the go ahead, production funding for six helicopters will be included in fiscal year 1999, followed by a further 18 per year subsequently.

T-45C digital Cockpit 21 introduced

A production Boeing T-45C Goshawk trainer with a new digital cockpit known as Cockpit 21 was rolled out in a ceremony at St Louis, MO, on 31 October 1997. Cockpit 21 will replace the T-45's existing analog cockpit, to enhance the Navy's ability to train pilots destined for future aircraft.

Cockpit 21 uses a MIL-STD 1553 bus and has two MFDs in each cockpit, which provide navigation, weapon delivery, aircraft performance and communications data. It also has a GPS/INS navigation system, and a HUD in the forward cockpit. Cockpit 21 has a growth capacity in spare memory and throughput.

The first production aircraft to be equipped with Cockpit 21 is No. 84 (BuNo. 165080), and was delivered in October 1997 to NAS Patuxent River, MD, for testing. Delivery of T-45 No. 85 to NAS Meridian, FL – where the aircraft is sorely needed to replace fatigue-troubled T-2C Buckeyes and to replace relatively low-hour TA-4J Skyhawks – took place in November 1997 and was celebrated in a 15 December ceremony. Follow-on deliveries were scheduled to occur monthly. A total of 104 production T-45Cs are planned, with all due for assignment to CTW-1 joining VT-7, VT-19 and VT-23 to replace the TA-4J and T-2C. The Wing is due to commence the first training syllabus on the new Goshawk in July 1998. The 84 T-45As in service with VT-21 and VT-22 of Training Wing 2 at NAS Kingsville, Texas will be upgraded to T-45C standard in due course.

USAF 'Huey' replacement

The US Air Force is considering leasing rather than buying helicopters as it looks to replace the ageing fleet of Bell UH-1N 'Hueys' it now uses for support of ICBM fields and other operations. Missions include nuclear weapon convoy escort and emergency security response force insertion at three ICBM wings. Air Force Space Command has been consulting with industry since August 1997, and the USAF is seeking information on two different lease options. The first would be for a fleet operated by a contractor, which would be responsible for helicopters, crews, and maintenance; the second option would be to lease only the helicopters. If the USAF pursues the lease option, it would be a blow to Sikorsky which had hoped the Air Force would join the Army and Navy in a multi-service H-60 procurement programme.

C-17A news

The 97th AMW at Altus AFB, Oklahoma, received its eighth C-17A on 12 November, 1997, thereby completing the full unit establishment of the 58th AS. The squadron has a mixed complement including 88-0265 inscribed '97th AMW' on the tail, 89-1191, 90-0535, 92-3293, 93-0603 marked '58th AS' on the fin, 93-0604, 94-0068, plus one. However, the unit exchanges aircraft with the 437th AW at Charleston AFB, South Carolina on a regular basis to harmonise flight hours devoted to operational missions with those of flying training.

The 437th AW received the 34th C-17A serial 96-0002 on 2 October, 1997 in a ceremony at Long Beach, California. The aircraft was christened 'The Spirit of the Air Force' in honour of the 50th anniversary of the USAF becoming a separate service. 96-0003 had been delivered to the 437th AW by the end of November, from the batch which extends to 96-0008. With deliveries to the 437th AW nearing completion, the 62nd AW at McChord AFB, Washington, is preparing to receive its first aircraft some time during 1998.

The US Air Force apparently needs one more squadron of C-17s than is being procured under the current purchase of 120 aircraft. General Walter Kross, who heads US Transportation Command and Air Mobility Command, said in November 1997 that the purchase should increase to 135 aircraft by 2005 to accommodate a need for C-17s in Special Operations forces.

Command KC-135Rs

Seven Boeing KC-135Rs modified to carry C^3 equipment will replace seven other aircraft now used to support the US military's Commanders in Chief. The KC-135Rs will replace an EC-135Y, an EC-135 and a CT-43A at MacDill AFB, FL, a KC-135E at Offutt AFB, NB, a C-135E and C-135K at Hickam AFB, HI, and a C-141 at Kadena AB, Japan. The KC-135Rs will give US field commanders 'unhindered worldwide transportation', according to the USAF. Meanwhile, the EC-135C fleet responsible for the strategic command and control mission was being supplanted in November 1997 by US Navy E-6B Mercurys in the airborne command post role.

Upgraded E-6B delivered

The first Boeing E-6B Mercury upgraded to act as the command module for all three components of the US nuclear triad, has been accepted into service by VQ-3 during a ceremony at Tinker AFB, Oklahoma on October 10, 1997. The modification performed by Raytheon E-Systems at Majors Field, Greenville, Texas now allow the E-6B to directly command and control all strategic assets such as ICBMs, B-1B, B-2A and B-52H bombers and ballistic missile submarines. Previously the command and control element for the USAF was installed in the EC-135C. The E-6B modification adds secure satellite communications via the Milstar system, housed in a large oval fairing aft of the cockpit. To enable a smooth transition of operations from the Air Force to the Navy (which in effect undertakes two thirds of the role), E-6 crews have performed work up sorties with EC-135Cs. This has included both EC-135s and E-6s deploying overseas together to perform missions simultaneously. A further 15 E-6As will be upgraded enabling full integration by the year 2001.

All operational E-6s are assigned to the Navy's Strategic Communications Wing One (SCW-1) at Tinker AFB. Crews are assigned to either VQ-3 or VQ-4, with operations dedicated to the Pacific and Atlantic Fleets respectively, although none of the aircraft carries any form of squadron insignia externally. However, E-6s of VQ-4 carry the last five digits of their serial on the tail, whereas those of VQ-3 display their serial on the nosewheel door only.

Compass Call upgrade

The USAF plans future upgrades of its EC-130H Compass Call aircraft even as the newest version, the Block 30, is being fielded with the 41st ECS, at Davis Monthan AFB, AZ. The EC-130H, with a crew of 13, performs tactical command, control, and communications countermeasures. The USAF has taken delivery of the first three of six Block 30s which feature a local area network (LAN) replacing a number of stand-alone systems. In addition, a single large amplifier is being replaced by two smaller amplifiers

Military Aviation Review

to increase capability against certain unspecified types of radios. The companion 43rd ECS still operates Block 20s, but could get the Block 30 aircraft now being contemplated for 2000, which will have a digital Tactical Radio and Countermeasures System.

X-36 progress

The Boeing/McDonnell Douglas/ NASA X-36-1 unmanned, tailless fighter agility research aircraft has faired well since its first flight on 17 May, 1997. The prototype performed 22 flights with the Dryden Centre at Edwards AFB totalling almost 11 hours to complete Phase 2 testing during September. This involved planned low and high-g agility manoeuvres which were all successfully completed, including 360° rolls at angles of attack (AoA) up to 15°, and rapid turning/ rolling manoeuvres up to 35° AoA. Flights were carried out to a maximum of 4.86g at 40° AoA, 177 kt (216 km/h, 134 mph) and at altitudes up to 20,500 ft (6,248 m). This test phase led to some flight control software updates. Phase 3 was completed on November 12 with nine flights, including those devoted to lower speeds and high AoA, along with higher speeds and low AoA, relying heavily upon thrust vectoring to maintain stability and performance. By the end of Phase 3 the X-36 had accumulated 15 hours and 38 minutes of flight time, and had used four different versions of flight control software. The maximum altitude of 20,200 ft (6,156 m) was reached, with the highest AoA being 40°. The fastest speed achieved was 206 kt (381 km/h, 237 mph). The goals, to develop and demonstrate enhanced technologies to improve manoeuvrability and survivability of future fighter aircraft, were either met or exceeded according to project manager Mark Sumich of the NASA Ames Research Centre based at Moffett Field, California. The second test aircraft, X-36-2, was delivered to Edwards AFB in mid-October, but only performed a limited number of flights as the programme had been largely completed by this time. With flight testing complete, the two aircraft were placed in flyable storage with NASA at the Dryden Centre pending a decision on their future.

OH-58D(I) funding cut

Funding for additional Bell OH-58D(I) Kiowa Warriors is to be terminated after the 13 budgeted in the fiscal year 1997 appropriation have been completed. Instead of the 507 which the Army had anticipated, the number delivered will be 413. Furthermore, the programme designed to integrate the latest digital technology into the Kiowa Warrior fleet will also not be completed due to the cost involved. The programme was to have incorporated a GPS with a digital map capability and video downlink. However, the Army is anxious that funding for its state of the art RAH-66 Comanche

Above: Howard AFB, Panama is the headquarters of the US-led Joint Inter Agency Task Force which manages all drug interdiction missions in the eastern Pacific (EPAC), western Caribbean (WCAR) and 'in country' (Peru, Colombia, Venezuela). Howard hosts a wide range of aircraft including US Customs Service P-3 AEW (six aircraft equipped with APS-138 and APS-145 radars), US Coast Guard HU-25Cs (equipped with APG-66 radars and FLIR), and a variety of US Navy Orions equipped with APS-137 ISAR radar, APG-66 radar, Elint systems and the AN/AVX-1 long-range daylight imaging system. The aircraft seen here are US Army EO-5B ARL-C (Airborne Reconnaissance Low-Comint) platforms. The ARL family comprises eight modified DHC-7s, configured for specific missions: ARL-I (O-5A), image gathering; ARL-C (EO-5B), Comint gathering; ARL-M (RC-7B), multi-function surveillance tasks. Five ARLs are based at Howard AFB.

project is not affected by further budget cuts, which together with consideration of the age of the Kiowa, were major factors in the decision.

AH-6/MH-6 upgrade

The small number of Special Forces AH-6 and MH-6 helicopters are to be upgraded under a programme entitled Mission Enhancement Little Bird. 15 AH-6Js and a similar number of MH-6Js operated exclusively by the 160th Special Operations Aviation Regiment at Fort Campbell, Kentucky are involved in the upgrade. Known by their crews as 'killer eggs' due to their shape and role, the H-6s are operated in a wide variety of special operations duties. The upgrade includes the fitting of a new Allison 250-C30R-3 engine and a six-bladed tail rotor to improve performance as well as ensuring the helicopter can operate with an additional mission kit installed. The new engines were originally developed for the OH-58D and are fitted with FADEC to ease the workload on the pilot.
Mission equipment includes the installation of lightweight planks to the fuselage side to provide a universal mounting for weapons, fuel tanks and external personnel carriage systems. Amongst the weapons carried are Hellfire missiles and an integrated weapon management system. The night vision capability will be improved, as will navigation and communications equipment, although this will vary between the two models.

Below: This Cessna 550 Citation II is one of several modified Citations operating with the US Customs Service. Based at Howard AFB, it is equipped with an AN/APG-66 multi-mode radar, FLIR (housed in a ball turret under the fuselage) and Satcom capabilities (note the black antenna on the spine). These aircraft are used for all-weather interception and tracking of suspect aircraft and have reportedly been allocated the designation 'OT-47'.

F-16CJ for SEAD

The USAF has unofficially adopted the designation F-16CJ for the Block 50 Fighting Falcons which are fully HARM capable. Approximately 90 have been modified with the installation of the HARM Targeting System (HTS) pod for the suppression of enemy air defences (SEAD) mission. At present four wings are equipped for the role, consisting of the 77th, 78th, and 79th FS's of the 20th FW at Shaw AFB, South Carolina; 13th and 14th FS's of the 35th FW at Misawa AB, Japan; 22nd and 23rd FS's of the 52nd FW at Spangdahlem AB, Germany; and the 389th FS, 366th Wing at Mountain Home AFB, Idaho.

Deliberate Guard tankers redeployed

The detachment of Reserve KC-135s supporting Operation Deliberate Guard, the air exclusion zone over Bosnia moved from Pisa AB, Italy to Istres AB, France on 28 November, 1997. Despite being crewed by personnel and aircraft drawn from Air National Guard and Air Force Reserve Command units, the detachment is organised by the 100th ARW with headquarters at RAF Mildenhall.

Torrejon AFB closed

The US military ended its permanent presence at Torrejon Air Base, near Madrid in Spain at the end of 1997. The facility was officially returned to the Spanish Government, although there had been no US military or civilian personnel there for some time. The base was constructed primarily to house SAC bombers forward deployed in Europe, and was activated on 1 June, 1957. The base was occupied by B-47s until the reflex operation at Torrejon ceased on 31 March, 1965. SAC KC-135s continued to rotate to

the base until 31 December 1976. The 401st TFW was resident from 27 April 1966 until the unit left in 1992 as part of an overall withdrawal of USAFE assets from Spain.

EF-111 deployment ends

EF-111As of the 429th ECS, 27th FW ceased to be detached to Incirlik AB, Turkey for Operation Northern Watch when the final three departed on 24 June 1997 with a refuelling stop at Lajes AB in the Azores. Two days earlier three EA-6Bs of VMAQ-1 arrived at Incirlik AB to perform the EW/SEAD mission. During the six-month detachment by the Marine squadron, crews were rotated from the USA. The squadron was relieved of duty during the second week of December when the mission was taken over by VAQ-134 which is manned jointly by USN and USAF personnel.

E-2/C-2 upgrade

The Navy's existing fleet of C-2A Greyhounds and E-2C Hawkeyes will be retrofitted with new composite eight-bladed propellers commencing in the year 2000. The programme will be conducted by the Naval Air Logistics Centre at NAS North Island, as aircraft are cycled through for depot level maintenance.

Harrier force adjustment

The USMC has implemented a reduction in the complement of its AV-8B squadrons from 20 to 16 aircraft each as a method of stabilising flight hours on the type. The Corps is also considering increasing the number of aircraft to be remanufactured to AV-8B Plus standard from the 72 planned, to 96. The additional conversion is seen as the most effective method of ensuring a credible force until the Joint Strike Fighter becomes available.

BRIEFING

Islamic Republic of Iran Air Force

An embargoed air force at war

Volume 30 of *World Air Power Journal* carried a photographic briefing on the modern Islamic Republic of Iran Air Force (IRIAF). The newly uncovered photographs presented below predate those previously published by perhaps 10 years. They reflect the state of the IRIAF in the late 1980s/early 1990s, as it was emerging from its arduous war with Iraq, which began in 1988.

Despite their vintage they are important for several reasons. Firstly, they indicate that the combat capability of the IRIAF remained potent. Though an arms embargo was imposed on Iran after the Islamic Revolution of February 1979, Iran obviously retained the technical proficiency to keep a substantial proportion of its air force in action. Many publicly available sources have credited the IRIAF with little combat potential – and what little it had was always

assumed to have declined rapidly, once sanctions began to bite. The material presented here would seem to indicate that this was not the case, and that Iran had the technical resources to keep a substantial proportion of its air force in service and in action.

Furthermore, there is now clear evidence that Iran received outside help in its efforts to wage war against Iraq. This assistance ranged from the supply of weapons and material to technical and engineering assistance to maintain and modify aircraft and weapons. Some of the operational solutions Iran found to its military isolation were unique, and hitherto unreported. These photographs give some small insight into the way the IRIAF has retained its teeth, and provide pointers to the ability of the enlarged and rearmed IRIAF of today. **Robert Hewson**

*Above: An enthusiastic **IRIAF** F-4E crew returns from a successful mission over Iraq. Perhaps the most noteworthy aspect of this photo is the way Western trappings such as squadron badges have been retained, suggesting a high ésprit de corps within the unit.*

*Left: This **TISEO**-equipped F-4E fires an unidentified air-to-surface missile – with a second still under the wing. This completely unknown weapon appears to combine elements of the **US HOBO** (**HO**ming **BO**mb) guidance system and warhead shape (it most resembles the 2,000-lb **GBU-8 HOBO** bomb) but with a new fin assembly and rocket motor. **GBU-8** is known to have been exported to Israel and Turkey. However, the **GBU-8** was a **LOBL** (**L**ock-**O**n **B**efore **L**aunch) weapon with an early-model seeker. The Phantom does not appear to be carrying the datalink pod required to control a **GBU-15**-type weapon. Therefore, this weapon may only have been effective against high-contrast targets, such as oil refineries, powerplants or perhaps ships – and it remains a mystery.*

Below left: This formation of F-5E and F-5F is seen over typical Iranian terrain. Iran has now modified its F-5s to carry a new generation of weapons.

The status of Iran's Tomcat fleet has always been the most hotly debated aspect of *IRIAF* operations, after 1979. The point has been well made that Iran had tremendous difficulty in keeping aircraft serviceable even with unlimited *US* help, and once this vanished Iran's Tomcats must have become unserviceable virtually overnight. Yet many aircraft did remain active and Iran obviously found other sources for the technical assistance it needed to maintain its F-14s. Aircraft, such as the one seen right, were forced to fly with reduced warloads, as *AIM-54 Phoenix* and even *AIM-7 Sparrow* missiles could not be made serviceable – but Iran found ingenious solutions to these problems. Another aircraft (below and below right) carries an *MIM-23 Hawk SAM* – a missile delivered to the Iranian army before 1979 and one which was later resupplied to Iran, by the *US*, as part of the *CIA*-sponsored arms-for-hostages deal ('Irangate') in 1985/86. This extraordinary modification may have entailed using the Tomcat's *AWG-9* radar as a *CW* illuminator for the Hawk, but there is no information available on whether the combination was ever used operationally.

Above: This *TISEO*-equipped (Target Identification Sensor – Electro Optical) *F-4E* is carrying a *Standard* missile on a makeshift *MER* bomb rack mounting. The Standard is an anti-radiation missile developed during the Vietnam War. The air-launched version was designated *AGM-78*, but it is uncertain if any were ever delivered to Iran. This example may be a sea-launched *RIM-66 Standard*, taken from one of the Iranian navy's 'Babr'-class (US 'Sumner'-class) destoyers and modified for airborne carriage. These Iranian missiles were an anti-aircraft version (with a limited air-to-surface capability). They may have been modified for *CW*-homing air-to-air use, but only against large, slow-moving targets.

Right: Iran's increasing domination of the strategic waterways of the Persian Gulf is causing widespread concern. The *IRIAF* is now believed to have introduced an F-4/anti-shipping cruise missile combination into service, with Chinese aid.

Left: Under the *Peace Station* programme Iran received 14 Boeing 707-3JC's, six of which were fitted with air-to-air refuelling booms. Most of the fleet were also modified to carry wingtip-mounted hose-and-drogue refuelling pods. Iran was the first operator to routinely combine both these systems in a single airframe, allowing one 707 to refuel several different types at once.

Above: Iranian F-4s and F-14s were co-located at Mehrabad, Tabriz, Hamada and Dezful air bases.

Below: This US M117 750-lb bomb is fitted with an MAU-91 high-drag fin. The MAU-91 fin is not designed to be released at high speed (it was mostly used by B-52s) and is very 'draggy'.

Above: An F-4E with a load of Mk 82s fitted with Mk 15 Snakeye retarding fins approaches the boom of an IRIAF tanker – Iran has both Boeing 707s and 747s configured with refuelling booms. Note the unusual rear-view mirrors fixed to the side of the canopy on this aircraft, and the one seen below.

Below: Iran took delivery of nearly 3,000 early-model AGM-65A Maverick missiles, and this F-4E is carrying pairs of missiles on three-rail LAU-88 launchers. None of Iran's F-4Ds was Maverick-capable. The AGM-65A uses electro-optical (TV) guidance and is fitted with a 125-lb (56.7-kg) high-explosive, shaped-charge warhead.

Above: This F-4E is carrying pairs of British-supplied BL755 cluster bombs – a weapon little-seen outside the RAF inventory even though it has been widely exported. Two versions of the BL755 have been developed. One is a fragmentation weapon (BL755 No. 1 or GP) and the other is a dedicated anti-armour bomblet weapon (BL755 No. 2 or AAA).

Below: Several nations have upgraded their F-5s to carry AN/ALE-40 chaff/flare dispensers, scabbed on to the rear fuselage. This unique Iranian modification appears to use a side-firing Tracor AN/ALE-39 dispenser – a first generation analog system – fixed to a pylon.

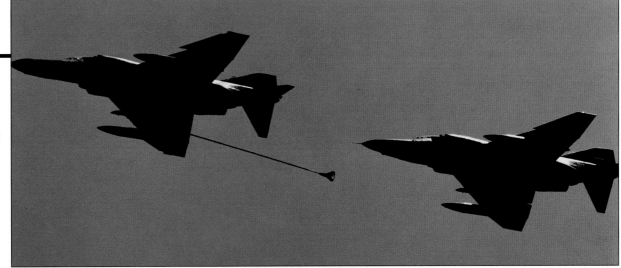

*Right: Though it may not be immediately apparent from this photograph, the lead Phantom in this formation is carrying a large **HDU** refuelling pod on its centreline station. The pod closely resembles the Beech wingtip pods fitted to the IRIAF's Boeing 707 tankers. Though of little use to the trailing F-4, an aircraft equipped with such an adapted system could refuel the Iranian F-5s, F-14s, MiG-29s or Su-24s.*

Above: The Boeing-Vertol CH-47 Chinook is still an active type in the Iranian inventory. A total of 68 CH-47s was delivered to Iran (mostly to the army, though a handful did enter air force service) – 54 arrived before the revolution, six later in 1979 and a further eight in 1981. The US arms embargo ultimately blocked the delivery of another 11 aircraft which had been built for Iran.

Below: Though Iran took delivery of F-4Ds and F-4Es, only the latter (along with RF-4Es) are likely to remain in service today. At the peak of its strength Iran had 225 aircraft operating with over 12 squadrons. Since then, spares and technical help has been received via Israel and the USA.

Above (two): Like many of the IRIAF aircraft seen here, these Northrop F-5s still wear all the serials and squadron codes allocated to them in the days of the Imperial Iranian Air Force. The F-5 was originally seen by the USA as the perfect aircraft for an air force such as Iran – it was cheap to acquire and operate, technically straightforward and easy to train crews for, while still being an effective combat type. Iran acquired 104 early-model F-5As and 23 two-seat F-5Bs, followed by 140 F-5Es and 28 F-5F trainers (above, uppermost). The F-5A/Bs are all believed to have been rapidly disposed of to other nations. Even the more advanced F-5E had been deemed to be no longer of use by the late 1970s, and Iran was negotating for their wholesale replacement by F-16s or F-18Ls. The advent of the revolution quickly stopped any such plans and the F-5 became an important element in the IRIAF's campaign against Iraq. The aircraft above is seen carrying US-supplied Mk 82 500-lb Snakeye retarded bombs.

BRIEFING

Dassault Mirage IIIEA

Twenty-five years of Fuerza Aérea Argentina operations

In a ceremony held on 7 November 1997, at Base Aérea Militar Tandil, the Fuerza Aérea Argentina (FAA) commemorated the 25th anniversary of the Mirage IIIE's entry into Argentine service. For the first time in FAA history, an aircraft was specially marked for the event, a tribute to the fighter which – despite its age – is still the backbone of the air force.

In the late 1960s, the FAA was in need of a new fighter to replace its Gloster Meteor F.Mk 4s. The new type had to be equipped with an airborne radar and air-to-air missiles as its main weapon system. At that time, the contenders for the Argentine contract included the English Electric Lightning, the Saab 35 Draken, and the Lockheed F-104 Starfighter.

On 14 July 1970, a contract was awarded to Avions Marcel Dassault for 10 Mirage IIIEA and two Mirage IIIDA trainers to be delivered during 1972. Under a separate contract, the FAA also acquired a significant number of MATRA R530 medium-range missiles of the IR-homing and SARH variants. The Mirage IIIEA was the first Mach 2 aircraft for the FAA, and the brand new aircraft were initially assigned to Escuadrón 1 de Caza Interceptora, at BAM Mariano Moreno (Buenos Aires).

During the Falklands War, two operational detachments of Mirages undertook a total of 47 combat sorties. Despite its well-trained crews, however, harsh reality showed that the Mirage was not suited to that operational environment – in the first day of combat, the Argentine unit lost two aircraft: one killed by a Royal Navy Sea Harrier, the other a victim of the Argentine anti-aircraft defence.

Currently, a total of 12 Mirage IIIEA fighters plus two Mirage IIIDA two-seaters remains in service with Grupo Aérea 6 de Caza, based at BAM Tandil. The

Left: The Argentine Mirage fleet – which includes upgraded IAI Fingers and Mirage 5PA Maras – is based at BAM Tandil. However, deployments to other air bases or civil airports – such as Ezeiza International airport, as seen here – are routinely conducted throughout the year.

Mirages share the VIᵃ Brigada Aérea facilities with IAI Fingers (an upgraded IAI Dagger, itself based on the Mirage 5), which are dedicated to the attack role. Grupo 6 also operates all the FAA's Mirage 5PA Maras (ex-Peruvian air force Mirage 5Ps), transferred from the now deactivated Grupo Aéreo 10, at BAM Rio Gallegos. In its 25 years of operations, the Argentine Mirage force has completed 172,000 flight hours and has been responsible for the graduation of 158 pilots – including 25 from the Spanish, Venezuelan and Peruvian air forces.

Argentina's Mirages are the only ones in South America not to have received any modernisation package, mainly due to the heavy postwar budget cuts. However, as this Mirage fleet still has a significant residual airframe life, several upgrade projects are now under consideration. One of these is the replacement of the outdated Thomson-CSF Cyrano radar with the lightweight, multi-mode FIAR Grifo F3 set, while another includes the installation of new engines, although the type to be installed has not yet been disclosed. If a decision is not taken in the near future, even these limited upgrade packages may not come to fruition. This is because the United States has now sanctioned the release of the Lockheed Martin F-16 to South American nations and the prospect of acquiring such a 'new' aircraft, coupled with Lockheed Martin's growing commercial operations in Argentina, may prove to be persuasive.

Jorge F. Núñez Padin

At a ceremony held on 7 November 1997, at BAM Tandil, the Fuerza Aérea Argentina marked 25 years of Mirage III operations. For the occasion, Mirage IIIEA (I-006) of Grupo Aéreo 6 de Caza/VIᵃ Brigada Aérea, became the first FAA aircraft to ever wear a special paint scheme.

Eclipse tow-launch demonstration project

Unique role for QF-106 and C-141

Unveiled at the Edwards AFB USAF 50th anniversary air show, on 18-19 October 1997, was a QF-106A which might have gone unnoticed were it not for the NASA logo on the tail and a 'rope' dangling from its nose. This modified QF-106A, known as EXD-01, is the centrepiece of a bold new project – carrying the name of Eclipse – which aims to demonstrate a reusable horizontal tow-launch space vehicle concept.

The NASA Dryden Flight Research Center is hosting and supporting this joint Kelly Space & Technology, Inc. (KST) and US Air Force project. Data gleaned from the tests will be used by KST to develop the Eclipse family of low-cost, reusable tow-launch vehicles. Moreover, these tests will demonstrate the viability of towing delta-wing aircraft, validate the tow simulation model, and develop various operational procedures, including ground processing, inflight manoeuvres, and emergency abort scenarios.

In July 1995, KST was awarded a contract with the USAF Phillips Laboratory (now the AF Research Laboratory) under a Phase I Small Business Innovation Research (SBIR) programme, to conduct a feasibility study for flight testing of its Eclipse launch technique. Studies, which were completed by KST and Tracor Aerospace in 1996, proved the technique's viability and led to an SBIR Phase II contract on 18 July 1996. This contract required KST to match all USAF funding. The contract included modifications to the QF-106 and NC-141A to incorporate tow line provisions for the two aircraft.

Soon after the Phase II contract was awarded, the EXD (Eclipse eXperimental Demonstrator) team, consisting of KST, NASA Dryden and the AFFTC, was established at Edwards AFB to co-ordinate and conduct the test flights. KST provided concept, design and hardware for the tow system, and performed modifications to the QF-106. NASA Dryden converted the QF-106 into the piloted EXD-01 (Eclipse eXperimental Demonstrator-

The early demonstration phase of the Eclipse project called for close formations to be flown with the (manned) QF-106 and NC-141 to establish the influence of wake turbulence on the QF-106's stability.

01). As the responsible test organisation, NASA Dryden was assigned flight safety responsibility for the project, and to provide range support, engineering, instrumentation, simulation, maintenance, research pilots and chase aircraft. The Air Force Flight Test Center (AFFTC) was to supply the NC-141A tow aircraft, aircrew and engineering support to configure the aircraft for the tow tests.

The QF-106 was selected as the test aircraft by KST because its delta wing planform is representative of the Eclipse Astroliner satellite launcher the company plans to build. Two aircraft were provided as goverment-furnished equipment (GFE) from the USAF 475th Weapons Evaluation Group target drone inventory and delivered from Holloman AFB, NM to Mojave Airport, CA on 2 August and 11 September 1996 for temporary storage. As F-106As, 59-0130 and 59-0010 were last operated by the 5th FIS, prior to their convertion to drones by Honeywell (conversion numbers AD 152 and AD 246 respectively). The pair was then delivered to nearby NASA Dryden in April and May 1997 where 59-0130 was modified by NASA personnel, and designated EXD-01 by KST. Delivery and familiarisation flights were conducted by NASA Dryden research pilot Mark Stuckey, later to fly EXD-01.

The most obvious modification to the QF-106 is the tow rope attachment and release mechanism mounted on the upper nose, just forward of the windscreen but aft of the radome. This unit was modified from a B-52G drag chute release mechanism. The nose boom was shortened to prevent interference with the tow rope, and a video camera was installed near the nose to provide the ground station with a view of the tow rope during flight. Finally, a research instrumentation system was installed to obtain airspeed, aircraft motion, tow rope tension, and tow rope angle measurements. The second QF-106A (59-0010) was not modified but was acquired to provide back-up and serve as a pilot proficiency aircraft.

The first towed flight of EXD-01 was made on 20 December 1997, from Edwards AFB. The NC-141A hauled the modified QF-106 to a height of 10,000 ft (3048 m) over the course of the 18-minute maiden flight.

The tow train assembly linking the two aircraft comes in two configurations. For the first flight tests, the tow rope, consisting of a 1,000-ft (304.8-m) long, ¾-in (1.9-cm) thick Vectran synthetic fibre rope is bisected by a 50-ft (15.24-m) section of 8-ply nylon strap. This nylon segment was requested by NASA to improve damping of the tow train. Flight testing will later proceed to the single Vectran rope. A 3-ft (0.91-m) nylon web strap adapter is added at one end of the rope to enable cutting by the guillotine in the C-141. At the other end, an adapter fitting hooks up to EXD-01 and includes a frangible link to limit loads in the tow train.

The NC-141A (61-2775 from the 412th Test Wing) was a suitable tow vehicle as it was readily available at Edwards AFB, had the necessary size and performance for towing, and offered an aft cargo ramp ideal for securing the tow pallet assembly – and for observing tow tests. No significant modifications were made to the NC-141A except for the removal of the aft clamshell cargo doors to eliminate interference with the towing operation. The towing and tow rope jettison equipment, consisting of a Type I tub pallet and guillotine, was mounted on a standard Type V LAPES (low-altitude parachute extraction) pallet and secured to the rear cargo. A video display of the tow rope and EXD-01 was

installed, as well as a flight test instrumentation pallet to obtain NC-141A parameters. Differential GPS was used to determine the distance between the two.

NC-141A 61-2775, which first flew on 17 December 1963, was the first StarLifter built, and was one of four A-model C-141s to arrive from Wright-Patterson AFB at Edwards AFB in the spring of 1993 to join the 418th Flight Test Squadron (FLTS). Owing to design changes, and non-standard egress doors, these aircraft had formed the original C-141 flight test fleet and did not enter regular airlift service. Instead, they were used as airframes for a variety of tests and designated NC-141A. It was originally planned to consign NC-141A 61-2775 to the AMARC at Davis-Monthan AFB, AZ, for storage on conclusion of the Eclipse demonstration project. However, the aircraft now appears to have had a reprieve, as Kelly Space may lease it from the Air Force to serve initially as a tow transport for the Eclipse, Sprint and Express vehicles, pending replacement by a commercial type.

As a prelude to the Eclipse test flights, KST initiated the Sprint Experimental Demonstrator (SXD). This phase started in August 1997, and culminated in towing a Dyke Delta JD-2 home-built aircraft with a Maule high-performance lightplane on 9 September 1997.

The Eclipse test programme was

structured in three phases: wake turbulence assessment, air data calibration, and tethered operations. The first two of these were successfully completed during 1996 and 1997, while the latter was initiated towards the end of 1997.

The first phase in the Eclipse demonstration project was to evaluate the vortex environment and effects of wake turbulence of the NC-141 on the handling qualities of the QF-106. A joint flight test between NASA Dryden, the AFFTC and KST was successfully conducted in late October 1996 in which a NASA Dryden F/A-18A chase aircraft flew wake probing flights at various distances between 500-2000 ft (152-610 m), and at lateral positions behind the NC-141A to map the wake turbulence environment. On one of these tests, in December 1996, smoke-generating devices were mounted under the C-141's wings to show its wake vortices.

This flight test phase was repeated in July 1997 using the unmodified QF-106. From these probing flights, it was determined that proper positioning of an aircraft behind the wake turbulence provided stable and very controllable flight conditions, especially for the QF-106. These tests also confirmed viability of the selected tow rope length and the low-tow position.

In autumn 1997, EXD-01 was flown to obtain air data calibration with the modified nose boom, which was shortened to prevent interference with the tow rope. NASA Dryden research pilot, Mark Stuckey, flew both the F/A-18A and QF-106A on these probe flights and was the designated research pilot for EXD-01 tow test flights.

Throughout 1997, a series of tests was conducted on all tow train components, culminating in a hook-up Combined Systems Test

(CST) on 1 November 1997. The CST was conducted with EXD-01 and the NC-141 connected by the tow train to test the attachment and release mechanisms and to validate tow procedures prior to the first tethered taxi tow test. The final ground test was conducted on EXD-01 on 7 November 1997 to measure canopy deflections and binding under simulated tow loads.

On 13 December 1997, the two aircraft were staged on the Edwards runway and were prepared for their first tethered take-off test, short of a full flight together. Rope attachment and pre-flight checks were conducted and the StarLifter ran up its engines for a slow taxi forward to add tension to the tow rope. The pair began its acceleration down the runway, and just as the StarLifter was about to rotate and take off, Mark Stuckey released the rope from EXD-01. The

StarLifter continued on its take-off and go-around with the rope trailing from the aft end. It then proceeded to a drop zone where the loadmaster released the rope to validate tow train jettison procedures, prior to a return landing at Edwards AFB.

The first tow flight of EXD-01 was achieved on the morning of 20 December 1997 and was deemed highly successful. The tow flight profile called for take-off and climb to a target altitude, where a series of flight and dynamic manoeuvres were planned prior to rope separation and landing. The NC-141 and EXD-01 were positioned on the runway, for attachment and pre-flight checks. As a flight safety contingency, EXD-01's J75 engine was also run up but remained idle at 60 per cent thrust. This was done to facilitate rapid spool-up to military power for an abort

manoeuvre and fly-off following rope release at any stage.

The tow train began to accelerate and, at 120 kt (222 km/h; 138 mph) airspeed, the StarLifter was the first to rotate and level off at 300 ft (91 m). This was done to ensure that EXD-01 stayed clear of wake effects during take-off. The pair continued in this attitude for about 30 seconds until EXD-01 began its rotation at 130 kt (241 km/h; 150 mph) and take-off at 170 kt (315 km/h; 196 mph). Take-off under tow was smooth and uneventful for a climb to a target altitude of 10,000 ft (3048 m). Removal of the clamshell doors on the C-141 had imposed a tow speed limit of 200 kt (370 km/h; 230 mph). Throughout all portions of towed flight, EXD-01 pilot, Mark Stuckey, flew in a high-drag configuration with landing gear and speed brakes extended while maintaining a 'low

tow' position at -20° elevation angle. Stuckey conducted a series of excursion manoeuvres into the C-141 wake and vortex field to map this environment and to investigate rope dynamics (vibration, damping, spring tendencies, etc.). All flight under tow and test manoeuvres was reported stable, providing good flight data, and the measured rope tension was very close to predicted values. The tow flight was concluded when Stuckey released the rope, completed engine power-up procedures to normal flight operations and conducted an off-tow test manoeuvre to clear the rope. Both aircraft concluded their successful 18-minute test flight with a normal landing at Edwards AFB.

The second tow flight was successfully conducted on 21 January 1998 using a configuration and flight profile similar to that of the first flight. On the third tow on 23 January, however, a one-piece all-Vectran rope replaced the two-segment/nylon mid-section configuration. This approach was conducted to define the differences in dynamic behaviour between the two for simulation validation. Instead of conducting an off-tow release as in the first two flights, the frangible link, designed to break at 24,000 lb (106.8 kN) tension, was intentionally broken to release the rope. This technique proved to be successful.

The Eclipse family of reusable vehicles includes the Sprint, Express and Astroliner sub-orbital launchers. The tow-launch method calls for a modified aircraft (C-130, C-141, DC-9 or 747) to tow an Eclipse vehicle to launch altitude from a conventional runway. A tow line between 1,000 and 5,000 ft (305 and 1524 m) long will ensure that the two avoid any hazardous interaction. During take-off and initial flight, the Eclipse vehicle is, in effect, an unpowered glider as it is towed to the required launch altitude. Releasing a vehicle at this altitude will result in greater fuel economy for launch than conventional ground methods.

Terry Panopalis

Chile

Aviación Naval Chilena

Above: The AS 332s in service with HA-1 of the Aviación Naval are not Cougars, as has been reported elsewhere, but locally-modified Super Pumas.

Chile's 800-man Aviación Naval has recently undergone modest expansion and reorganisation, and now consists of approximately 60 aircraft, organised into two naval air forces rather than into two groups as it was before. The principal naval air base remains at Concón, 20 km (12 miles) to the north of Viña del Mar, with a minor base at Punta Arenas and air stations at Iquique, Talcahuano, Puerto Montt, Puerto Williams and Isla Dawson.

Naval Air Force No. 1 has its headquarters at Concón and comprises Maritime Reconnaissance Squadron VP-1, equipped with three Lockheed P-3A Orions, three EMBRAER EMB-111ANs and a single Dassault Falcon 200; Transport Squadron VC-1, with two CASA 212 Aviocars, three EMB-110CN Bandeirantes and a Lockheed UP-3, converted for use as a VIP transport; General Purpose Helicopter Squadron HU-1, with three MBB BO 105s and six Bell 206Bs; and Squadron VT-1, the flying element of the Naval Aviation School, with 10 Pilatus PC-7s, which also double in the light strike role. All major maintenance is carried out at Concón.

Naval Air Force No. 2 has its headquarters at Punta Arenas and seems to be mainly an administrative

rather than an operational entity. It consists only of Attack Helicopter Squadron HA-1, equipped with seven heavily-modified AS 332 Super Pumas, which are usually erroneously identified as Cougars. Although nominally based at Punta Arenas, the force's aircraft are dispersed for the most part among the helicopter-capable elements of the fleet.

The naval air stations at Iquique, Talcahuano and Puerto Montt each have an attached flight, consisting of an EMB-111AN fixed-wing maritime patrol aircraft and an MBB BO 105 helicopter. A BO 105 is also, in theory, based at Puerto Williams although it is usually to be found at Punta Arenas, where a CASA 212 is also located. The Isla Dawson Naval Air Station has no permanently assigned aircraft.

The P-3s and the EMB-111 maritime patrol aircraft have all been completely refitted with new, locally-developed electronic, avionic and sensor systems, as have the AS 332 helicopters. Two of the eight P-3As, which were originally intended for cannibalisation when transferred from the United States in 1993/94, are in a state of preservation. They are likely to undergo an upgrade similar to the three serviceable maritime patrol aircraft of this type when funds become

available. One of the PC-7s was completely rebuilt and restored to full operational status following a serious crash and, of 10 recently-acquired Cessna 337 Skymasters, two are scheduled for cannibalisation, with the remainder to be distributed between the naval air stations, for inshore patrol.

Adrian J. English

Aviación Naval

Naval Air Force 1

VC-1	CASA 212, EMB-110CN, Falcon 200, UP-3A	Concón
VP-1	P-3A, EMB-111AN,	Concón
VT-1	Pilatus PC-7, Cessna 337	Concón
HU-1	MBB BO 105, Bell 206B	Concón

Iquique Air Station Flight

EMB-111AN, MBB BO 105	Iquique

Talcahuano Air Station Flight

EMB-111AN, MBB BO 105	Talcahuano

Puerto Montt Air Station Flight

EMB-111AN, MBB BO 105	Puerto Montt

Naval Air Force 2

HA-1	AS 332 Super Puma	Punta Arenas

Punta Arenas Base Flight

CASA 212	Punta Arenas

Puerto Williams Air Station Flight

MBB BO 105	Puerto Williams

Inventory

P-3A	Maritime reconnaissance (plus 2 transport conversion and two in storage)	4
EMB-111AN	Maritime reconnaissance	6
Falcon 200	Maritime reconnaissance	1
CASA 212	Utility transport	3
EMB-110CN	Communications	3
Cessna 337	Inshore patrol (Two to be cannibalised)	10
Pilatus PC-7	Trainer/light attack	10
AS 332SC	Attack/ASW helicopter	
MBB BO 105C	Utility helicopter	
Bell 206B	Utility helicopter	6

Above: Chile acquired a total of eight ex-US Navy Orions, beginning in 1993. Two are now in storage, two serve as UP-3A transports and four are tasked with maritime patrol duties, as part of VP-1.

Above: The EMB-111ANs in service with VP-1 wear a mix of overall sea grey schemes (as seen here) and a much darker blue/black finish.

Above: In December 1997 VT-1 acquired the first of 10 Cessna O-2As. After overhaul in Chile they will be tasked with SAR and EEZ patrol duties.

Above: Four CASA 212A transports were delivered to the Aviación Naval in August-November 1978, and three remain in service with VC-1.

Above: Three EMB-110CN Bandeirantes were acquired by VC-1 in August 1976. At the time, the squadron operated only a single PA-31 Navajo.

Above and right: HU-1 operates a mix of MBB BO 105Cs and Bell 206B JetRangers, which undertake regular ship-board deployments.

Thailand

Royal Thai Naval Air Division (Kongbin Tha Han Lur Thai)

With the arrival of the Royal Thai Naval Division's (RTND's) first aircraft-carrier, HTMS *Chakri Naruebet*, and its associated aircraft in the latter part of 1997, the RTND has been re-organised. A third operational wing has been established to accommodate two new carrier-based squadrons. At the same time, two new squadrons were added to the two existing wings, with aircraft reassigned among these squadrons. With these changes the RTND now comprises nine mission-specific squadrons, attached to three wings.

The four squadrons of 1 Wing all have a combat role. The aircraft of the former 101 Squadron are now split between two squadrons.

101 Squadron still operates some S-2F Trackers, for flight training and surveillance missions, alongside its three Dornier Do 228-212s (delivered in 1991), which are used for coastal and border patrol. The newly-established 102 Squadron is tasked with anti-submarine warfare and maritime reconnaissance. It is equipped with two Lockheed P-3T Orions (delivered in 1995), one UP-3T Orion and three Fokker F27-200MEs, which can be armed with the AGM-84 Harpoon anti-ship missile. Two P-3As are used as spares ships. 103 Squadron has a liaison, training and secondary light attack tasking, for which it operates five Cessna O-1Gs, four Cessna U-17Bs and 11 Cessna T-337SPs. The Cessna 337s are each fitted

with four underwing hardpoints, for rocket or machine-gun pods, and are used on anti-piracy and COIN missions. The RTND's first jet squadron was 104 Squadron, which operates the A-7E and TA-7C Corsair. A total of 18 A-7E/ TA-7C aircraft was acquired in 1995 and two additional A-7Es were acquired for spares.

The second wing of the RTND has three squadrons, all tasked with second-line duties. 201 Squadron operates the former 202 Squadron fixed-wing aircraft. The oldest type on strength is the C-47, used for transport duties, while two Fokker F27-400Ms are used for SAR. Two Canadair CL-215-IIIs undertake fire-fighting/ SAR missions. Five N-24A Searchmasters (fitted with APS-504 search radar) are in use for coastal patrol. They will be joined by three Do 228-200s.

With the establishment of 201 Squadron as a purely fixed-wing unit, 202 Squadron became a support helicopter unit, acquiring some of the aircraft previously operated by 203 Squadron. 202 Squadron is now equipped with four Bell UH-1Hs and eight Bell 212s, while 203 Squadron retains the five Bell 214STs and six Sikorsky S-76Bs (delivered in 1996). All of the helicopters are used as transports but do have a secondary SAR tasking.

Above: Radar-equipped Dornier Do 228s serve with 101 Squadron on maritime patrol duties.

Right: 101 Squadron also operates Thailand's remaining S-2F Trackers.

Above: The former assets of 101 Squadron have been split between 101 and the new 102 Squadron.

Right: Fokker F27-200MEs undertake armed patrol missions with 102 Squadron.

Above: RTND O-1 Bird Dogs serve with 103 Squadron on training and liaison tasks.

Right: Thailand operates two P-3T Orions, delivered from ex-US Navy stocks in 1995.

In 1997 the third wing, the Carrier Air Wing, stood up with an establishment of two squadrons. 301 Squdron was formed to operate Thailand's seven ex-Spanish AV-8S and two TAV-8S Matadors (Harriers). All the Harriers arrived in Thailand on board HTMS *Chakri Naruebet*, which was built in Spain by Bazan, in September 1997. Earlier that year six Sikorsky S-70B Seahawks were delivered to 302 Squadron. They are tasked with SAR and ASW missions onboard the carrier.

All RTND aviation units are home-based at U-Tapao in central Thailand, where the RTND Headquarters is also located. Detachments are maintained at the RTND's secondary base of Songkhla and at Narathiwat, both in the south of the country.

Royal Thai Naval Air Division

1 Wing, U-Tapao

101 Squadron	Dornier Do 228-212, Grumman S-2F
102 Squadron	Lockheed P-3T/UP-3T, Fokker F27-200ME
103 Squadron	Cessna O-1G, U-17B, T-337SP
104 Squadron	Vought A-7E, TA-7C

2 Wing, U-Tapao

201 Squadron	CL-215-III, F27-400M, N24A, C-47, (Do 228-200)
202 Squadron	Bell 212, UH-1H
203 Squadron	Bell 214ST, Sikorsky S-76B

3 Wing (Carrier Air Wing), U-Tapao

301 Squadron	McDonnell Douglas AV-8S, TAV-8S
302 Squadron	Sikorsky S-70B

Roland van Maarseveen and Cees-Jan van der Ende, with additional material by **Simon Watson**.

Above and below: RTND Cessna O-1s (above) and U-17s (Cessna Model 185s) wear a mix of olive drab and two-tone green/brown camouflage.

Above: Thailand acquired a total of 10 armed Cessna/Summit T-337SPs between 1980 and 1983.

Right: The RTND's first combat jets came in the shape of the A-7E Corsair. All are operated by 104 Squadron.

Above: The RTND's two transport-dedicated Fokker F27-400Ms are operated by 201 Squadron. Note the forward cargo door.

Above: The weapons-capable Searchmaster Ls of 201 Squadron can carry SSQ-801 Barra sonobuoys, but they no longer have a primary ASW tasking.

Above: The C-47 continues to soldier on with 201 Squadron as a general transport, though several have been withdrawn from use at U-Tapao.

Above: The four Bell UH-1Hs in service with 202 Squadron were all transferred from the army aviation branch (originally to 4 Squadron).

Above: The Bell 214STs now serving with 203 Squadron were ordered in 1986 and delivered to the RTND in March-May 1987.

Above: The twin-engined Sikorsky S-76B is a relatively recent RTND acquisition. Six were delivered in 1996 and all serve with 203 Squadron.

Left: 301 Squadron now operates all the RTND's AV-8S Harriers, as part of the carrier-based 3 Wing.

Above: Carrier-based ASW and SAR capability is provided by the S-70Bs of 302 Squadron.

Since the introduction of the Gulfstream II in 1968, these sleek twin-engined jets have become a symbol of prestige. As a result, Gulfstreams have sold well to military and government customers. To a military operator, the design also offers a tantalising combination of high speed and long endurance, coupled with impressive high-altitude performance and handling. It is these qualities that give the Gulfstream II, III, IV and V the potential to be far more than just 'mini-airliners'. After nearly 20 years of development and promotion, today's Gulfstreams are emerging as ideal special missions platforms for a wide range of tasks – with several little-known but highly-capable variants already in worldwide military service.

Gulfstream jets serve the armed forces and governments of 35 nations, from Algeria to Venezuela, and 24 of these countries use the aircraft for head of state transportation. The supremacy of the Gulfstream II/III/IV in their commercial market made it inevitable that military customers would turn towards these aircraft for their own VIP transport duties. This is where the perception of most observers stops, as far as this aircraft is concerned. In fact, even this seemingly innocuous transport role masks clandestine and little-discussed missions for the Gulfstream. The Gulfstream Aerospace Corporation has also developed a range of dedicated military variants, derived from the Gulfstream II, III and IV. With the Gulfstream V now coming on line, that list is set to grow – perhaps dramatically, if programmes such as the UK's ASTOR project bear fruit. The first Gulfstream jet to enter military service was a GII, acquired by the United States Coast Guard in April 1969 (as a VC-11A transport), but the full story of the 'Gulfstream in uniform' predates even this. It can be traced back to the earliest days of the design, which was born at the Grumman Aircraft Corporation's Bethpage factory, on Long Island, in the mid-1950s.

Grumman was justifiably famous for its wartime military aircraft, but the company had little experience in designing civil aircraft (other than amphibians). Grumman nevertheless set out to develop a purpose-built business aircraft, to fill what it alone at the time perceived as a gap in the market. Abandoning a high-winged design based on the TF-1 Trader, Grumman incorporated newly developed but proven Rolls-Royce Dart 529-8 turboprops into a low-winged aircraft that was unveiled, in June 1957, as the Grumman G.159 Gulfstream (later Gulfstream I). The G.159 made its first flight on 14 August 1958 and confounded its critics by selling well, despite its high price tag. A total of 200 was built until 1969, when the G.159 was replaced by the G.1159 Gulfstream II jet.

A certain amount of confusion surrounds the origin of the unusual Gulfstream name, which was chosen by Leroy Grumman himself. It is

widely believed that the name was intended to give an impression of the new aircraft's comfort, speed and long range, but no-one knows for sure. The aircraft started out with Grumman model numbers, which were carried through from the G.159 to the G.1159A Gulfstream III, despite several changes in the ownership of the company over the years. With the advent of the Gulfstream IV, these model designations were finally abandoned. The family is universally known by the shorthand titles of GI, GII, GIII, GIV and GV.

TC-4C: The first of many

The US Navy ordered a highly-modified version of the Gulfstream I as the TC-4C Academe. The Academe was used to train Grumman A-6 Intruder bombardier/navigators and in its rear cabin was a complete replica of an A-6 cockpit, a fully-functional navigation/attack suite and four A-6 bombardier/navigation consoles. In a huge extended nose radome the TC-4C carried the A-6A's Norden AN/APQ-148 radar, and in 1978 the TC-4C fleet was given the same TRAM upgrade as the A-6E, complete with undernose FLIR turret. Seven aircraft were delivered, between June and December 1967, to VA-128 'Golden Intruders' (NAS Whidbey Island) and VA-42 'Green Pawns' (NAS Oceana). Two TC-4Cs were delivered to the USMC (VMAT(AW)-202), and a third was transferred from VA-42. One USMC aircraft was written off in 1975. When the Intruder was withdrawn from US service in 1996/97 the TC-4Cs became surplus to requirements and were flown to the AMARC 'boneyard'. A handful of Gulfstream Is were

acquired as military VIP transports and airways calibration aircraft by Austria, Greece, Japan, Mexico, Sweden, Switzerland, the United States, and Venezuela.

The advent of the Rolls-Royce Spey-powered G.1159 transformed the market place, and the future, for the Gulfstream. The Gulfstream II made its maiden flight on 2 October 1966. The T-tailed jet retained the cabin of the Gulfstream I in a slightly longer airframe with a new wing design, swept to 25°. The Spey Mk 511-8 turbofans were rated at 11,400 lb (62.3 kN) and gave the GII an impressive thrust-to-weight ratio – the GII could reach 41,000 ft (12,500 m) from brake release inside 15 minutes. The first GII was delivered in November 1967, and 256 were built until production ended in December 1979, in favour of the Gulfstream III. In the early days of the GII, to make way for the F-14 Tomcat line, production was shifted from Bethpage to Savannah, Georgia. After s/n 40 no more Gulfstreams were built on Long Island, and

Gulfstream
Special Missions

from January 1973 they were rolled out under the banner of the newly-established Grumman American Aviation Corporation.

Attempts to improve the range/payload capabilities of the GII led to the Gulfstream II(TT) modification, which added extra fuel in tip tanks, and increased its range by 300 nm (345 miles; 555 km). GII(TT) development began in 1976 with the first flight of a company prototype. The tip tank modification was applied to several new-build aircraft after s/n 173 and was retrofitted to others, for a total of 18. GII(TT)s have served with the air forces and governments of Bahrain, Morocco, Oman, Saudi Arabia and Uganda.

NASA's STAs

Several GIIs have been modified for specialist tasks, the best known of which are the aircraft delivered to NASA. To train Space Shuttle pilots in the art of high-speed, no power and no second-chance landings from orbit, NASA acquired two GIIs and had them modified by Grumman to become its Shuttle Training Aircraft (STAs). Several other aircraft types, including the Lockheed JetStar, were considered for this mission. The GII acquisition was announced in December 1973 and the first example was delivered 'green' for modification in May 1974. This aircraft (N946NA, s/n 146) made its first flight in full STA configuration on 15 September 1976. The second STA (N947NA, s/n 147) first flew in June 1974 and then as an STA on 1 March 1976. Both aircraft were delivered to the Johnson Space Center, Texas, and flew from nearby Ellington AFB. Initial training sorties were flown at the Northrup Strip, a dry lake bed runway on the White Sands Missile Range. Operations later moved to Edwards AFB and its lake bed Runway 17. In 1983 a third STA (N944NA, s/n 144) was acquired.

The STA featured several obvious changes over the basic GII. First among them was the addition of two large airfoils under the centre fuselage to act as side force generators (SFGs), simulating the lateral control forces of the (much larger) Shuttle orbiter. In the Shuttle the pilot sits 13 ft (4 m) above the roll axis and can experience significant lateral acceleration, as a result. There is no great lag in control input and, despite its size, the Shuttle rolls readily. To simulate this, the SFGs slewed to 'lurch' the STA into Q (lateral acceleration), upon input by the pilot. However, after several years of successful operation, the requirement for the SFGs was felt to be outweighed by the safety implications of their use. If, for example, an aircraft suffered a hard landing which burst tyres – or, worse, experienced a gear failure and collapse – there was a danger that the SFGs would catch on a runway safety barrier and damage the aircraft. As the actuators for the SFGs were routed all the way through the wing, they might rip open fuel tanks and cause a fire. As a result, the SFGs have been removed.

The STA is fitted with direct lift flaps, modified thrust reversers (internal clamshell rather than target type, to avoid tail buffet) and speed

brakes, allowing it to simulate the high-speed, high-angle approach of the Shuttle. Inside the STA the port cockpit area has been replaced by a fully-functional Shuttle cockpit with HUD and controls routed through a computerised flight control system (FCS) – the Ada-based Advanced Digital Avionics System – that replicates the Shuttle's handling characteristics. The starboard cockpit remains unchanged and is always occupied by a second (safety) pilot. A quadruple-redundant fly-by-wire FCS was developed for the STA with a manual backup, linked to the SFGs and modified flaps which can be deployed up and down (in a slow or rapid action) to better simulate the Shuttle's large delta wing. The combination is successful, and astronauts typically say that 'the Shuttle flew just like the STA'.

STA mission

A textbook STA training mission begins at altitude, perhaps FL430 (43,000 ft/13106 m altitude) – or as high as possible. A descending spiral is flown around a TACAN beacon, following a 'heading alignment cone'. The STA follows the alignment cone around (by as much as 270° or more) to join the runway centreline at approximately FL200, 7 nm (8 miles; 13 km) from the runway threshold, with the pilot looking for the runway PAPIs (Precision

Approach Path Indicators). A standard airliner approach is flown at a glide path angle of 3°. The STA flies at 21° glideslope with main gear down and engines at 93 per cent reverse thrust to simulate the Shuttle. This outer glideslope approach is flown until approximately 1,750 ft (533 m), when the STA enters a 1.5g pull-up, the 'pre-flare', to reduce airspeed and enter a 3° inner glideslope. Speed drops from 290 to 190 kt (333 to 218 mph; 537 to 352 km/h) at this point and, with such a dramatic change in approach speed and angle, correct entry into the pre-flare is the most important element of any Shuttle approach. The nosegear is only deployed at 300 ft (91 m). The STA aims to touch down 2,500 ft (762 m) past the threshold, but is not flown all the way to a landing. In the Shuttle, the pilot sits 35 ft (10 m) above the ground at touchdown, compared to 12 ft (3.6 m) in the STA. This height difference accounts for a major difference in depth perception by the pilot so, to keep an STA mission as realistic as possible, each approach ends with a radar altimeter warning at 35 ft to signify a 'safe landing'. A typical training sortie might continue with another 10 approaches from FL200 to save time, and end with another all the way from FL430. It is a demanding two hours in the air.

The Space Shuttle has an autoland capability but pilots are reluctant to use it, and so a huge amount of training time has been spent in the STA by all Shuttle pilots. A minimum of 500 landings is required to qualify as a Shuttle co-pilot, and 1,000 as a commander. The STA was designed with a notional fatigue life of 5,000 hours which is now being extended to 10,000. The STA fleet is now receiving the same digital 'glass' cockpit upgrade as the orbiters themselves.

In association with Lockheed (Marietta), NASA operated a single GII (N650PF/NASA 650) as a propfan testbed, during 1987. As part of the NASA Propfan Test Assessment programme, this aircraft flew for 150 hours fitted with an eight-bladed Hamilton Standard propfan, fitted to an Allison 570-M78 engine which was mounted on the GII's port wing. The aircraft retained its own Spey engines. Modified by Gulfstream on behalf of Lockheed Georgia, the GII made its first flight from Savannah in this revised configuration on 29 April 1987. The fuselage of this aircraft was later mated with the wings and wing box of a second and third GII for modification to STA standard. It was redelivered to NASA in December 1990, becoming the fourth STA.

More military GIIs

A single Gulfstream II transport serves with the US Army. It was delivered to a commercial customer in February 1969 and, after several changes of ownership, it was sold to the Corps of Engineers, US Army in May 1981. It was allocated the civil registration N40CE and designated as a VC-11A (in line with the single GII operated by the US Coast Guard). In November 1989 this registration was cancelled and the current military serial (89-0266) was allocated. The C-20J designation was allocated in 1993. This aircraft has since undergone the Aviation Partners winglet modification (Gulfstream IIW).

Other GIIs have served as testbeds for expressly military purposes. Between 1987/88 Gulfstream modified a GII (s/n 066, N720F later N165W) for Norden Systems Inc. (later Westinghouse Norden Systems) as a Multi-

Mission Radar Testbed. This aircraft had a distinctive extended nose radome and could also carry removable underwing pods. It was sold to a commercial leasing company in 1996 and the registration has been allocated to a Boeing 737-247, operated by Northrop Grumman.

One particular aircraft has served with the Lincoln Laboratories division of the Massachussetts Institute of Technology (MIT) since 1993, on highly classified research work for the US Air Force's Electronic Systems Center (ESC), part of Air Force Material Command. ESC is based at Hanscom AFB. Lincoln Labs is a federally-funded R&D centre of MIT, established in 1951, for (military) electronics research. Today it works closely with ESC and the DARPA Sensor Technology Office on new AEW systems, and other projects. For example, the laboratory will confirm that it was heavily involved in developing an MTI (moving target indicator) radar for a US UAV project, in the late 1980s. It will not, however, comment on any of the current activities of its extensively-modified Gulfstream II – or its companion (and equally modified) Dassault Falcon 20. The Gulfstream II was registered on 10 May 1993, to AFMC, and has an experimental-class airworthiness certificate, approved for research and development flying.

Another GII (s/n 132, N400M) was leased to Northrop Grumman for a year between 12 August 1994 and 11 August 1995 (from its listed owners Eckhert Cold Storage). This aircraft was radically modified with large fairings above and below the forward cabin, plus a 'pannier-type' fairing wrapped around the underside. The timing of the lease suggests that the aircraft was involved in the B-2 programme. This aircraft has now been demodified and sold on.

In January 1997 Gulfstream was conducting studies for NASA's Jet Propulsion Laboratory to modify a GII for its GeoSar radar survey project. This involved design studies for an aircraft with UHF antenna pods on the wingtips and conformal radar antennas on the wing leading edge. An X-band conformal antenna array (with a 60° look angle) would be mounted on the port forward fuselage. Gulfstream has amassed considerable design experience with conformal antennas, which have obvious benefits for 'discreet' surveillance applications.

The arrival of the G.1159A Gulfstream III, in 1978, heralded the beginnings of a serious military career for the aircraft. Gulfstream had first proposed a stretched development of the GII, with a supercritical wing, in 1974. A few days before this proposal was to be launched at the 1977 Paris air show, it was abandoned (although it had 40 paid deposits, the manufacturer feared an uncertain market), and Grumman returned to the drawing board to design a less ambitious successor to the GII.

The Gulfstream III (and the IIB)

The GIII that was relaunched in 1978 featured a more affordable modification of the basic GII wing, but with distinctive drag-reducing 'Whitcomb' winglets. Conventional Collins avionics were fitted in the cockpit, though the GIII was later certified for use with the Collins EFIS-85 system, in 1983. The Rolls-Royce Spey engines could not be surpassed, and were retained. The cabin of the GIII was 2 ft (0.6 m) longer than its predecessor and the fuselage was 3 ft (0.9 m) longer, overall. The nose was given a sleeker, more pointed profile and the cockpit windows became wrap-round. As a result of its much improved aerodynamics, the GIII offered a maximum range of 3,691 nm (6831 km; 4,245 miles), a cruising speed of Mach 0.77 and a maximum speed of Mach 0.85. The GII, by comparison, could cover only 2,613 nm (4836 km; 3,005 miles).

The first GIII made its maiden flight on 2 December 1979 and deliveries began in 1980. So successful were the changes made to the GIII that existing GII customers sought a modification for their aircraft to bring them up to the new standard. As a result, the G.1159B Gulfstream IIB conversion was developed, adding the new wing design and cockpit avionics to GIIs – which retain their original rounded nose shape and split side cockpit windows. Between 1981 and 1987, 43 GIIB conversions were undertaken.

In July 1978 the Grumman Corporation began negotiations with Allen Paulson's American Jet Industries, to sell its 80 per cent stake in Grumman American. This deal was completed by August and Grumman American became the Gulfstream American Corporation – a wholly-owned subsidiary of AJI. Grumman

The USAF acquired a trio of C-20As in 1983, which was followed by seven C-20Bs (seen here) in 1987. As the C-20Bs were introduced, the C-20As were reassigned to duties in Germany.

continued to supply design assistance for the Gulfstream, at Bethpage.

The GIII had its public debut at the Hannover air show in April 1980, followed by the NBAA convention, Kansas City, in September. The GIII quickly began to chalk up performance records, including a 'biz jet' absolute altitude record of 52,000 ft (15850 m). In 1979 the GIII notched up its first 'real' military order (before any commercial deliveries had even begun), when the prototype airframe (s/n 249, actually a rebuilt GII) was sold to the Royal Danish Air Force (RDAF). The Danes bought three aircraft, but not as simple transports. The RDAF Gulfstreams were intended as 'fisheries patrol aircraft' and provided Denmark with a versatile yet unobtrusive long-range maritime patrol and surveillance aircraft. The three GIIIs were fitted with a Texas Instruments AN/APS-127 sea search radar (replacing the standard Bendix RDR-1400C weather radar) in a slightly recontoured nose. A radar operator's console was provided in the rear cabin, along with a dedicated navigator's station, and the cockpit layout was modified to accommodate additional radios and radar displays. Additional navigation aids fitted to the RDAF aircraft included a Litton 72R INS and VHF/Omega receivers.

The Danish aircraft were fitted with an air operable, inwards-opening door (the standard baggage door), in the rear port fuselage, to allow the dropping of life rafts and rescue equipment, for example. Provision was also made for flare dispensers in the rear fuselage, aft of the port wing trailing edge. The RDAF Gulfstreams were the first to be fitted with a cargo door – which was, and still is, a major structural modification. The door, measuring 83 x 63 in (2.11 x 1.6 m) can be used in conjunction with a removable cargo roller floor. These aircraft were the first multi-mission Gulfstreams and their acquisition by a NATO air force was an important stepping stone towards Gulfstream's emerging primary sales target – the United States Air Force.

Gulfstream III in Royal Danish Air Force service

For more than 15 years, Eskadrille (Squadron) 721 of the Kongelige Danske Flyvevåben (Royal Danish Air Force) has operated the Gulfstream III Special Mission Aircraft in a unique and demanding role. The geographic composition of Denmark – which includes Greenland and the Faroe Islands, with their surrounding waters, all at great distances from the Danish mainland – dictate very special operational responsibilities to the Royal Danish Air Force (RDAF).

In 1977 these zones were expanded to 200 nm (370 km, 230 miles) from the coastline. The area to be patrolled increased to the formidable size of more than 850000 km² (328,000 sq miles) – an area equivalent to Great Britain, France, Holland and Belgium combined. The RDAF started looking for an aircraft with sufficient speed, range and equipment to cope with this demanding task (to supplement its C-130s), and after thorough evaluation of the Boeing 737-200C, Canadair Challenger, Dassault Falcon 20G, de Havilland Canada Dash 7 Ranger, Fokker F27 and F28 Maritime, Grumman Gulfstream III, Hawker Siddeley HS.748 Coastguarder

and Lockheed C-130, the RDAF ordered three Gulfstream III Special Mission Aircraft on 29 June 1979.

When the RDAF order was placed, the GIII prototype had not yet flown. This allowed Grumman (Gulfstream Aerospace Corporation) to develop a special missions variant of the business jet design at an early stage.

While the Faroe Islands area is normally covered by Esk 721 flights from mainland Denmark, the far greater Greenland area is covered by a GIII permanently deployed to Luftgruppe Vest (Air Group West) at Søndre Strømfjord (Sonderstrom Air Base) on the west coast of Greenland, just north of the Arctic Circle. Every second week aircraft and crew of Luftgruppe Vest are exchanged on a rotational basis, and the detachment includes two technicians (an avionics specialist and a flight engineer) so that minor malfunctions on the GIII can be corrected immediately. Major malfunctions, which are very few, require assistance from the Værløse base.

Duties of the Sonderstrom AB detachment include fishery inspection, ice reconnaissance and a general presence to demonstrate sovereignty of

the Greenland airspace. Luftgruppe Vest also maintains a constant alert for possible medical evacuations and SAR operations.

The economic zone around Greenland covers 550000 km² (212,000 sq miles) and is patrolled in segments during fishery inspection. For optimum fuel economy, flights to and from the patrol areas are normally made at a cruising altitude of 39,000-41,000 ft (11890-12500 m) and a speed of about 475 kt (875 km/h; 544 mph), before descending to the area of interest, which is determined by the extent of the ice-pack, the current activity of the reported fishing vessels and the most probable concentration of fish.

Surveillance is typically executed from 5,000 ft (1525 m) at 300 kt (553 km/h; 343 mph) to optimise utilisation of the radar, which has an effective range of 80 nm (150 km; 93 miles) at this height. When the APS-127 radar has identified a target, its position is passed to the INS which controls the autopilot. The GIII can literally fly itself through a search profile determined by radar targets. However, manual control is resumed when visual

identification has to be made, with descent to as low as 100 ft (30 m) in order to register possible violations and make a photo confirmation, in the event that a violation is taken to court. The inspection is carried out in close liaison with Danish naval vessels and Lynx helicopters in the area, which have the task of actually boarding suspected violators.

Fishery inspection sorties around the Faroe Islands are flown from Værløse AB, with a refuelling stop at Vagar airfield on the Faroes. This is the only airfield on the islands able to take larger aircraft, and a visit here can be an exhilarating experience since the approach is flown through a narrow fjord between steep hillsides subject to unpredictable vertical winds.

The GIII is able to cover the entire patrol area around the Faroe Islands – some 300000 km² (115,000 sq miles) – and make the 2700-km (1,677-mile) round trip from/to Værløse in an eight-hour mission. Fishery inspections are normally flown twice a week by Esk 721, and nearly 85 per cent of the total number of GIII flying hours are spent in the North Atlantic area around Greenland and the Faroe Islands.

The main strengths of the GIII are its speed and range. On certain medical evacuation missions there is a requirement to maintain surface pressure in the cabin, which can be done if the cruise altitude is less than 22,000 ft (670 m). At that altitude, the GIII can still reach mainland Denmark in less than five hours from even the remotest points of Greenland. During a search and rescue mission that originates from Sonderstrom, the GIII can reach any point of the Greenland territory in less than two hours. It can

Denmark's hard-working Gulfstream IIIs undertake a host of long-range patrol missions, in harsh North Atlantic conditions – in addition to more routine VIP and transport duties. These GIIIs also provided invaluable special mission engineering experience for their manufacturer.

US military interest in Gulfstream began with the August 1982 request for proposals for a new special air missions aircraft (C-SAM), to replace the VC-140 JetStars then in service with the USAF's 89th MAW. The initial requirement was for three aircraft, with additional options (up to eight). Gulfstream submitted the GIII in a stiff competition that saw it pitted against other types such as the Boeing 737-200 and a version of the Fokker F28. A contract was awarded to Gulfstream on 7 June 1983, calling for the delivery of three C-20A aircraft, to be leased for a 12-month period. These aircraft were delivered 'green', without the mission communications system (UHF/dual HF radios). The option on a second batch of eight aircraft, designated C-20B, was soon taken up, although only seven were delivered. The third was diverted to become one of the three C-20C war readiness aircraft. The C-20Bs were delivered with UHF satcom equipment, dual HF radios

and all necessary switching installed, but are essentially identical to the C-20As. The only important difference between the two is their electrical systems. All GIIIs before s/n 401 were built with a DC power supply. After that point (December 1982) a new 48-KVa/115-volt AC system was certified by the FAA, and became standard on all GIIIs. The new system was 200 lb (90 kg) lighter than the previous one and could still provide DC power, if required. The C-20A fleet was based at Andrews AFB until 1987, but with the arrival of the C-20Bs the earlier aircraft were retasked and transferred to the 58th MAS, at Ramstein AFB. All C-20s have received a communications fit under the super-

vision of the little-known White House Communications Agency (WHCA), which oversaw the design and installation of approximately 2,000 lb (907 kg) of secure comms equipment for each aircraft. The three specialist C-20Cs delivered in 1985 (which are covered elsewhere in this article) were the last C-20s to be delivered to the USAF for several years, but by then the success of the GIII in USAF service had aroused the interest of the other services.

In 1986 the US Navy ordered two C-20Ds, which were delivered without a (VHF/UHF) comms system, but with antenna provision for a portable satcom set. The C-20D acquisition was made possible under the terms of the original

conduct a three-hour search before heading for the nearest airfield, and still maintain the required fuel reserve for diversion to an alternate field.

Once a month, the GIII of Luftgruppe Vest performs a surveillance flight round the entire Greenland coastline to demonstrate Danish sovereignty. These two-day missions are flown at an altitude of only 5,000-10,000 ft (1524-3048 m) and are very popular among aircrews because they give a spectacular view of the dramatic Greenland landscape.

Although the main duties of the GIII lie in the North Atlantic, the aircraft has retained its executive jet capability and is frequently used for VIP transport of the Royal Family and Cabinet ministers. In VIP configuration, seating can be arranged to suit the specific requirement and on such flights a cabin attendant is usually included in the crew.

With an area of 2.2 million km² (850,000 sq miles), Greenland is the world's largest island, about the size of central Europe but with only 55,000 inhabitants (and fewer than 3,500 registered cars!). More than 85 per cent of Greenland is permanently covered by an ice cap up to 3000 m (9,842 ft) thick, and only during summer do the snow and ice melt from areas along the coast. Summer in Greenland is very brief and beautiful, but for the rest of the time this unique island is dominated by Arctic winter with freezing temperatures and darkness most of the time.

The Faroe Islands is a small group of rocky islands situated in the stormy Northern Atlantic, approximately midway between Greenland and mainland Denmark. The Faroes have the same political ties to Denmark as does Greenland, and as a result Esk 721 has special commitments to these islands.

The Arctic region is an extremely harsh environment, facing freezing temperatures, stormy winds and darkness during the winter. The facilities to predict weather in remote areas are limited, and the crews are often presented with unpleasant surprises. The number of airfields that can accommodate the GIII are limited

This pair of Esk 721 Gulfstreams is seen here on detachment at Søndre Strømfjord.

and are located far apart. In addition to Sonderstrom, there are only two airfields on Greenland with facilities for overnight stops: Thule Air Base in the north and Narssarssuaq Airfield in the south. Nearby Keflavik, in Iceland, is often used for staging and diversion.

Thule Air Base is the only military air base in Greenland but it has a comprehensive infrastructure with a long runway and large facilities for aircraft parking. Today, the only resident unit at Thule is the 12th Space Warning Squadron of USAF Space Command, with its large radar complex, but ESK 721 often uses the base for overnight stops during missions in northern Greenland.

Under optimal conditions, the GIII requires only 600 m (1,970 ft) for take-off and 400 m (1,310 ft) for landing, making certain secondary airfields acceptable for refuelling stops. They include Station North, Mestersvig and Kulusuk, all featuring short, gravel runways. No special modifications were required to the engines or landing gear of the GIII to allow these operations.

With its 1600-m (5,250-ft) gravel runway covered by snow or ice most of the year, Station North is the world's northernmost permanently manned airfield, located at a latitude of 83° North – only 560 miles (900 km) from the North Pole. A minimum of five voluntary military personnel are based at Station North around the year; among other duties, they support the Sirius patrol, which is a small Danish military unit patrolling the freezing wilderness of northern Greenland with dog sleds.

In order to make Station North suitable for aircraft operations, Esk 721 deposits one year's worth of aviation fuel at the base every spring. During Operation Brilliant Ice, some 400 tonnes (393 tons) of aviation fuel is airlifted from Thule to Station North in a six-week operation that requires at least 40 C-130 return flights.

Its size, stability and excess electrical power make the GIII a very popular

platform for testing different kinds of new equipment, and through the years Esk 721 has been involved in many military as well as civil aviation related projects. Most comprehensive of these has been the test and evaluation of new advanced radar principles. In 1989 F-249 was used as a testbed for a synthetic aperture radar (SAR) developed by the Danish Technical University. The SAR radar was installed in a drop tank from a Saab Draken and carried on a pylon below the GIII's central fuselage. In 1991 a sideways-looking airborne radar (SLAR) developed by the Danish company Terma Elektronik was tested on G-III F-330, mounted on a special rack below the aircraft fuselage.

Esk721 can perform Open Skies missions with a GIII configured with a special surveillance radar mounted on the fuselage side.

On 3 August 1996 Esk 721 lost one of its GIIIs when F-330 crashed on approach to Vagar airport on the Faroe Islands, on a flight from Keflavik, Iceland. Vagar is regarded as one of the world's most difficult and dangerous airports from which to operate, being situated at the end of the Sørvågs Fjord. The final 5-10 km (3-6 miles) of the approach take aircraft down through the narrow fjord, low over the water, with up to 460-m (1,500-ft) high steep mountains on either side. The harsh northern Atlantic weather conditions often result in a cloud base considerably below the top of the mountains, and extreme turbulence and powerful gusts often develop between the mountain sides over the fjord.

The Gulfstream was transporting a five-man high-ranking military delegation, including the Danish Defence Chief, Admiral Hans Jørgen Garde. All on board including the four-man crew, were tragically killed.

The crash investigation team concluded that the most probable cause of the crash was that F-330 had flown into deteriorating weather conditions and encountered such heavy turbulence that it was impossible to maintain control of the aircraft.

With three GIIIs at its disposal, Esk 721 has always been hard-pressed to fulfil its operational roles. One GIII is permanently detached to Sonderstrom Air Base on Greenland, one is used operationally from its Værløse base, and the last is used for crew training or as a spare. After the Vagar crash, with only two GIIIs remaining, it was impossible for Esk 721 to perform its missions effectively, and as a temporary solution, the RDAF leased a GIII for a period of one year. The aircraft (s/n 401), was delivered to Værløse on 21 December 1996. Under normal practice its RDAF serial should have been F-401, but because the number 401 is already used by another aircraft (T-17 Supporter T-401) it was serialled F-400 instead. The aircraft was configured for VIP transport – and due to the limited lease period no mission-specific equipment was installed – so Esk 721 only used F-400 for crew training and transport of personnel or minor cargo. The aircraft left Værløse again on 3 December 1997 for return to its owner.

Jan Jørgensen

USAF C-20 contract as the pricing matrix offered by Gulfstream actually allowed for more than the eight aircraft specified. Next, the Army acquired its own GIIIs in the shape of two C-20Es. These aircraft were essentially identical to the C-20Ds (but were bought outright by the Army under a separate contract). One member of the sales team remembers the deal as "the best brief anyone ever had. The Army just said 'give us the exact same specs as the Navy'." The C-20Es were delivered with provision for a microwave landing system. The two C-20Es were the last Gulfstream IIIs to roll off the production line, and were handed over in June 1986. US forces now have one Gulfstream II (C-20), 17 Gulfstream IIIs (C-20s) and eight Gulfstream IVs (also C-20s), and will soon add two Gulfstream Vs (C-37s). The roles and missions of these aircraft, and also the details of the next-generation Gulfstream IV and V, are dealt with later in this article.

The successful introduction into service of the RDAF GIIIs and the USAF C-20s heralded the beginning of a major sales effort by Gulfstream to develop and build a family of special missions aircraft. Two distinct approaches were considered: a multi-mission transport based on the Danish experience, dubbed the SMA-3 (Support Missions Aircraft); and a dedicated surveillance/reconnaissance aircraft with the potential for combat use, the SRA-1 (Special Reconnaissance Aircraft).

Multi-mission SMA-3

Of the two concepts, the SMA-3 was the most straightforward. Gulfstream offered an aircraft with a 3,600-nm (4,140-mile; 6662-km) range operating at maximum take-off weight and with full IFR fuel reserves for a mission endurance of eight hours. The SMA-3 could cruise at Mach 0.77 at FL450 yet still operate from short fields with as little as 5,850 ft (1783 m) of runway (needing only 3,400 ft/1036 m in which to land). It had a large cabin with over 6 ft (1.8 m) of constant headroom, plus a cargo door, integral airstairs and APU – all required for autonomous operations. Just like the Danish aircraft, the SMA-3 could be configured to carry up to 19 passengers, 15 litter patients with a medical aid station and attendants, or 4,630 lb

(2100 kg) of cargo (with no centre of gravity limitations), or to air drop supplies or undertake maritime patrol missions. The RDAF aircraft were used heavily in the marketing efforts for the SMA-3 and this designation has been widely applied to them. However, they are not true 'SMA' aircraft as that programme was launched after their delivery.

Special-mission SRA-1

The second special missions concept pursued by Gulfstream in the mid-1980s was the SRA-1 (which has sometimes been incorrectly referred to as the SRA-3). While the SMA-3 had its foundations firmly in an existing aircraft design, the SRA-1 programme broke new ground in its attempt to provide an airborne platform for which customers could then write their own job description. Based on the Gulfstream III airframe, the SRA-1 'prototype' was rolled out at Savannah in May 1984, at a ceremony attended by military officials from 31 countries. The SRA-1 (N47449) temporarily wore the false US-style serial '40420', which was a reflection of its manufacturer's serial number (construction number) of 420 and was soon replaced by its correct civil identity. The SRA-1 made its maiden flight on 14 August 1984.

The gloss sea-grey SRA-1 that was rolled out in Savannah had several obvious differences compared to the baseline Gulfstream III. It was fitted with a cargo door, and thus had only two windows on the starboard side. Underneath the fuselage was a large (mock-up) pod for the Motorola-built SLAMMR (Sideways-Looking Airborne Multi-Mode Radar). The SRA-1 had six (mocked-up) underwing hardpoints, with pylons, and dispensed with the GIII's distinctive 'winglets'. Their place was taken by composite wingtip pods, to house ESM equipment (the winglets were later refitted during the flight test programme). The SRA-1 was intended to provide all the airframe capability required to fulfil a wide range of missions, but the precise mission fit would be selected by the customer. Gulfstream would deliver an aircraft (at a 1984

Substantial development effort went into the FEWSG project, to develop a stand-off EW 'aggressor' trainer for the US Navy. The single Gulfstream IV-based FEWSG/SRA-4 is seen here with a DF antenna fitted above the fin. Flight tests soon forced its removal from this position.

price of approximately $12.5 million) and aid in systems integration, if required, but did not involve itself in developing a range of mission fits 'from scratch'. Gulfstream did include several other specialist firms and named them as preferred partners in any real systems selection.

At this juncture, it should perhaps be pointed out that Gulfstream never actually sold any SRA-1, or SMA-3, aircraft – at least not in the form in which they appeared in copious company brochures. The reasons for this are not readily apparent. It may be that Gulfstream fell victim to its own concept of producing many enticing designs, but no actual hardware. The company also attempted to enter a very specialist market as an outsider, with little experience and no partners. While its product was obviously a good one (throughout the lifespan of the SRA-1 and its successors, military/government orders for basic Gulfstreams never slackened), Gulfstream's 'full-up' SRA-1 never managed to gain that vital launch customer, which others surely would have followed. Nonetheless, the SRA-1 was extremely important to Gulfstream because it laid the foundations for the different breeds of special mission aircraft that were built, as well as providing valuable experience for several future developments. For that reason, it is worth examining the various missions and systems earmarked for the SRA-1 as they provide an insight into the capabilities of the few, secretive, aircraft that did evolve from the programme.

When the SRA-1 made its debut at the Farnborough air show in September 1984, it was displayed with a range of (dummy) stores on the underwing pylons. They included GEC

Marconi Stingray torpedoes, AGM-84 Harpoon anti-ship missiles, AGM-65B Maverick ASMs and GBU-12 500-lb LGBs. Gulfstream did not pursue armed options for the SRA-1 very far, although the capability was retained and the options returned when the LRAACA/P-X design was later offered to the US Navy.

SRA-1 surveillance systems

The primary role for the SRA-1 would have been high-altitude reconnaissance and electronic surveillance. The SRA-1 was fitted with a CAI KS-146 LOROP (LOng-Range OPtical) camera, with a 66-in (128-cm) focal length. At Farnborough the SRA-1 photographed the airfield using an even larger 94-in (2.38-m) ITEK LOROP system. An optional palletised antenna system could be carried on the opposite side of the fuselage to the LOROP system. The LOROP system was fitted in the forward port cabin, behind an optically flat window panel. Both the LOROP and the antenna system might not be immediately apparent to an observer. Under the fuselage a Goodyear AN/UPD-8 synthetic aperture radar (SAR) could be carried in a small canoe fairing (approximately 5 ft/1.5 m), or replaced by the larger podded SLAMMR radar (approximately 9 ft/2.7 m). The ESM fit (with internal and wingtip antennas) would provide emitter identification, classification and location over a frequency band from 0.5 GHz to 40 GHz. Inside the rear cabin were four consoles for an ESM, communication collection, SLAR and maritime surveillance radar operator, for example. Since the SRA-1 existed for the most part only on paper, internal configurations could, and did, change regularly. The reconnaissance-configured SRA-1 offered a cruising altitude of FL500, with a range of 3,500 nm (4,025 miles; 6477 km) at 430 kt (374 mph; 602 km/h) TAS. At altitudes above 25,000 ft (7620 m) it had a loiter endurance of 9.7 hours.

In the electronic surveillance role, the SRA-1 could be outfitted with a communications intercept system covering frequencies from 20 MHz to 1200 MHz, the same ESM system as outlined above, and a full VHF/UHF/HF radio for command and control functions. Inside, the cabin would be configured for two communications consoles, four equipment operators/signals analysts, a C^3 console and a mission director. In such a configuration, the SRA-1 offered an endurance of 9.6 hours at a loiter altitude of 37,000 ft (11277 m).

The SRA-1 offered a maritime patrol option, based on the SMA-3 but with several changes. The most obvious was an extended radome to house a sea search radar – typically the Texas Instruments AN/APS-134(V)2. A FLIR turret was also provided under the forward fuselage. Sonobuoy launchers could be housed in the rear fuselage (behind the engines), with two manually-operated tubes inside the rear cabin itself. A retractable MAD was fitted to the tailcone. Any maritime version of the SRA-1 would also have the full ESM fit. The cabin was configured for two observers, a radar operator, ESM operator, sensor operator and tactical co-ordinator.

The companies chosen to 'provide' the SRA-1's mission equipment included Recon Optical, CAI Division (LOROP), California Microwave (communications collection), EM Systems (ESM), Goodyear Aerospace (SAR), ITEK Optical Systems (long-range cameras), Motorola (SLAMMR) and Texas Instruments (maritime surveillance radar).

Gulfstream entered into serious negotiations with several governments and made proposals to many more. Particular attention was paid to

This view of the FEWSG prototype gives a clearer view of its tailcone-mounted countermeasures dispenser. This airframe later became the SRA-4 demonstrator and it trialled several technical innovations that became important for the S 102B and ASTOR programmes.

Sweden's two S102B Korpens were delivered in 1995, after initial flight tests at Savannah (top). The ventral canoe fairing (left) can be removed (above left) and this is often the case if the aircraft returns to Savannah for maintenance, for example. The two S 102Bs (above left and right) are named Hugin and Munin, who were the ravens of Odin. The blind Norse God would send the two birds out into the world and on their return they would settle on his shoulder and whisper to him all they had seen and heard.

North African nations, such as Tunisia, and to the Middle East. Aircraft would be delivered with a baseline standard equipment fit (known as Phase I) with options of surveillance radar, Comint/ESM systems and operator consoles (Phase II/III). Plenty of onboard power-generating capability was provided for Phase IV expansion (SAR, SLAR, etc.). A variety of airframe configurations was considered, including aircraft with three or even four engines, an internal bomb bay and a carrier arrester hook. Every SRA-1 could still be configured as a transport, and the large cargo door allowed it to accommodate jet engines.

One contemporary story concerned a proposed sale to Argentina of a version armed with long-range stand-off weapons. The words of the customer were 'get us an export licence, change the engines and we'll take it'. In a post-Falklands War Argentina, the SRA-1's Rolls-Royce engines were unacceptable – but these terms were unacceptable to Gulfstream, and the deal was declined.

India's Gulfstream IIIs

The one (foreign) special missions (GIII) sale achieved via the SRA-1 programme was to India. Gulfstream will not comment on any aspect of this deal, but it is possible to piece together some details of what was a very extensive and specialist modification. Two Gulfstream IIIs were involved in this programme, but their current Indian Air Force (IAF) identities are uncertain (see serial/operators section below). India sought a high-altitude reconnaissance aircraft for border surveillance missions and chose Gulfstream to develop a specialist camera platform. Gulfstream had hitherto proposed using standard cabin windows (with flat optical glass) for any internal LOROP system. This was soon found to be impractical – the windows did not offer sufficient field of vision and were too high in the cabin to provide adequate downlook and 'grazing angle'. For the Indian LOROP installation, Gulfstream developed what would become the largest optical glass section ever used as part of an aircraft structure. The flight test programme was intended to provide an FAA-approved installation, but the FAA insisted on using two layers of glass, which was not acceptable. The redesign to get back to a single (but slightly thicker than planned) glass panel was a long drawn-out process and forced a major delay in the programme.

The new window design was coupled with a Gulfstream-led innovation to the camera layout. The LOROP (believed to be a modified Recon Optical KS-146 system) has an articulated head which can be rotated to look to port and starboard. The IAF GIIIs have camera windows on both sides (covered by sliding doors), allowing the aircraft to take up a racetrack pattern on station while maintaining almost constant surveillance. The LOROP is manually aimed and focused and can be removed or repositioned through a side cargo door on each aircraft. The IAF reconnaissance GIIIs were fitted with a new navigation system, based on a triple Litton LTN-72R INS, which later became standard on all Gulfstreams. The cabin floor has been reinforced to cope with the weight of the camera.

Such a LOROP system would allow the aircraft to look approximately 250 miles (400 km) into denied territory, from a high-altitude station. It is a simple matter to calculate exactly

Above: Alongside its two special mission S 102Bs the Flygvapnet operates a single Tp 102 for VIP transport missions. This aircraft was delivered in 1992, three years ahead of the much-modified S 102Bs, and is based at Broma airport.

Right: This is the second U-4 for the JASDF, seen at Marshall Aerospace, Cambridge, following its cargo door modifications. All Gulfstream cargo doors are 'cut' and fitted at Marshall. Adding the door removes three windows from the port cabin and is a major undertaking that, in one way or another, 'touches' 60 per cent of the airframe.

how far any airborne platform can 'see', by using the equation $d=\sqrt{1.5h}$ (where 'd' is the distance in miles and 'h' is the altitude above sea level, in feet). A LOROP-equipped GIII might typically operate at an altitude between 35,000 and 45,000 ft (10668 and 13716 m) – starting the mission at a lower level and climbing as fuel is burned off. Of more importance is the resolution of the camera. Initial tests with a KS 146 camera, using wet film, reportedly found the results to be 'grainy and disappointing', but they later improved. At maximum range a resolution of 5 m (16 ft) was reportedly obtained. It is possible, even likely, that the Indian aircraft no longer use a film-based system but have upgraded the cameras to an electro-optical-backed system. The IAF GIIIs are also believed to have other vertical- and sideways-looking cameras (perhaps paired ITEK RC-30s – ITEK is now Hughes Danbury Optical Systems) mounted in the underside of the fuselage, behind sliding covers. It is not known whether the IAF GIIIs have any Elint-gathering capabilities; at one time they may well have had, but this role has now likely passed to modified Boeing 707s in IAF service. These aircraft have been fitted with large cheek fairings similar to those found on Israeli and SAAF 707s. India's two specialist GIIIs were among the very last built, being the fourth (s/n 495) and fifth (s/n 494) from the end of the line, respectively. They were delivered in June 1986, but is not known where or by whom they were outfitted, or when they finally entered service. At the time of writing they have never been seen outside India. A footnote to this programme involves the third GIII in IAF service (VT-ENR). This aircraft is understood to be a standard VIP transport but was formerly the SRA-1 demonstration aircraft (s/n 420). It was delivered to the IAF in May 1987.

Many important sub-systems were trialled by the SRA-1 demonstrator. They included chaff/flare dispensers (in ventral mountings in the wing box) and a LORAL/Sanders IR countermeasures set (now integrated in the Swedish S 102B aircraft, and another for a undisclosed Middle Eastern customer). A refuelling probe

mock-up was fitted, chiefly to determine the correct positioning for maximum crew visibility. Even the possibility of a 'KC-20' tanker was explored, by fitting an aircraft with an under-wing HDU pod. This would allow it to refuel a probe-equipped Gulfstream, and significantly extend its already impressive time on station.

Gulfstream IV

The next step forward in the Gulfstream evolution came on 11 September 1985 with the first flight of the Gulfstream IV. The GIV offered an even greater advance than the GIII did over the GII. The new aircraft was first announced in March 1983 and combined a stretched fuselage (by 2 ft/0.6 m) with new Rolls-Royce Tay Mk 611-8 engines. The GIV boasted a maximum range of 4,220 nm (4,853 miles; 7810 km), cruising at Mach 0.80 (459 kt; 846 km/h). The GIV had a maximum speed of Mach 0.88 (519 kt; 957 km/h) and a maximum operating altitude of 51,000 ft (15545 m). The GIV soon started breaking records, such as its (class) absolute altitude record of 57,290 ft (17462 m). The GIV broke both westbound (12-14 June 1987) and eastbound (27-27 February 1988) round-the-world records. During one fuel stop in Dubai the turn-around time was a remarkable eight minutes, which while not normally a factor in day-to-day business jet operations, could be significant in military service. Gulfstream has made much of the high-altitude performance of its wing design. The low loading, combined with high-speed cruise capability, lets the aircraft operate at the optimum loiter speed within a wide manoeuvre margin. The GIV (and GV) wing is a large clean high-lift design, but with no complex high-lift devices. It uses a single Fowler flap (with no leading-edge slats or flaps), and the wing's relatively large size is given over to holding all of

the aircraft's fuel load (making any airframe modifications more straightforward).

The Gulfstream IV was the first Gulfstream to break away from using the old Grumman model numbers. Several sources use the designation G.1159C to describe the Gulfstream IV, but this is incorrect. The aircraft's FAA type certificate identifies it simply as the GIV. With the launch of the commercial Gulfstream IV came a military version, the SRA-4. This applied all the previous SRA-1 concepts – surveillance/reconnaissance, maritime patrol, medevac, priority cargo transport – to the new airframe.

SRA-4 and FEWSG

A new role was added to the SRA-4's repertoire, that of electronic warfare support/training. This came as a result of the FEWSG project, which was launched in the late 1980s for the US Navy. The Navy had a requirement to replace the varied and ageing aircraft operated by its Fleet Electronic Warfare Support Group (FEWSG), which included ERA-3 Skywarriors. In conjunction with Chrysler Technologies Airborne Systems, at Waco, Texas, Gulfstream made major airframe modifications to a GIV (s/n 1034, N413GA) to house an extensive emitter antenna array, countermeasures dispenser system (two ALE-39s) and triple the electrical power supply. The finished aircraft, which first flew in August 1988, was given the unofficial designation of 'EC-20F'. At the time, the US DoD had an outline requirement for three aircraft for delivery in 1988/89 (some sources reported this as a firm order, which was not the case). However, the decision was made to phase out the dedicated FEWSG squadrons (VAQ-33, 34 and 35) by 1993 and the requirement for the 'EC-20F' disappeared. The FEWSG GIV still undertook extensive tests and was later used as a company demonstrator for

the SRA-4. A three-piece antenna fairing, approximately 24-in (61-cm) in radius, 36-in (92-cm) long and 24-in (61 cm) deep, was fitted to the underside of the aircraft – containing all necessary real antenna elements. The FEWSG testbed never had any operational electronic warfare systems installed, but in March 1990 it began flying with two massive 90-KVa Bendix-built electric generators (one per engine) which were run at full power, into a 15-ft x 2-ft (4.6-m x 0.6-m) loadbank in the cabin, to prove that the Gulfstream IV could routinely generate such a massive amount of electrical power for onboard systems. The aircraft's Tay 611-8B engines were certified with a gearbox modification to run the generators. The variable-speed constant-frequency generator fitted to FEWSG provided up to 150-KVa of mission power above and beyond that required by all basic aircraft systems, and thus was a major technical innovation – of particular relevance to today's UK ASTOR requirement.

Several other serious paper studies of GIV derivatives were completed for the US Navy. The LRAACA study was based around the proposed Gulfstream IV-B. This was a stretched (by 18 ft 6 in/5.64 m) 26-seat aircraft, originally aimed at the US airline market. A long-range patrol version for the US Navy was to be fitted with a bomb bay, sonobuoy launchers and wingtip AIM-9 Sidewinder launchers. Several studies conducted for the Navy included a bomb bay, and one Gulfstream test pilot remembers conducting a low-level 450-kt (517-mph; 832-km/h) pull-up into a loft/toss manoeuvre in a GIII – with some very surprised passengers – to show that the airframe was easily capable of such a procedure.

LRAACA led to a more serious proposal, the P-X follow-on to the Lockheed P-3A/B Orion. A Gulfstream IV, fitted with P-3C Update IV avionics and ASW systems, was offered to counteract the cutbacks in the US Navy's VP squadrons. The GIV would be configured with a seven-man crew, extended radar nose, FLIR, weapons bay (using an extended wing box), 60 sonobuoys and two wing hardpoints. The idea was to develop a medium-range patrol/ASW version, and pave the way for a longer-range version to follow soon after. The P-X Gulfstream IV could carry four Mk 46 torpedoes (internally) or two AGM-84 Harpoons (externally), or two Mk 46s and two AGM-84s or six Mk 36 mines (four internal, two external). In the end, it was never built and all plans for an Orion replacement were shelved.

Sweden's special aircraft

The importance of the airframe development done under the FEWSG project became apparent in 10 July 1992 when Sweden's defence material administration (FMV/ Foersvarets Materielverk) announced a contract for three Gulfstream IVs for the Flygvapnet (Swedish air force). Two of these aircraft were to act as dedicated Sigint platforms, maintaining a valuable capability that the Flygvapnet has possessed for many years. Sweden's strategic position on Europe's northern edges – for many years wedged between NATO and the Warsaw Pact – put its military in an intelligence-gathering playground. Sweden maintained strong and capable defence forces fed with information from its own 'national technical means'. Such means included two SE.210 Caravelle aircraft (Flygvapnet designation Tp 85) which were modified with a plethora of antennas and operator/ analyst stations in the cabin. The Caravelles were acquired in 1971 and performed exactly the same task as the RAF's Nimrod R.Mk 1s or German Marineflieger Peace Peek Atlantic Sigint/Elint gathers, which they frequently encountered in northern patrols. However, by the mid-1980s the Tp 85 was becoming an increasingly expensive aircraft to support.

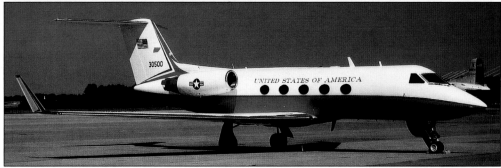

Above: The C-20B is still the backbone of the USAF's C-20 SAM fleet, with five aircraft in the current inventory. Seven were delivered, but one was later transferred to the Coast Guard and one to the Chilean air force.

Intensive secrecy surrounded the operations of the Tp 85 fleet and for many years the Swedish authorities refused to comment on their existence. Similar secrecy surrounded the search for a Tp 85 replacement, and Gulfstream will make no comment on any of the details surrounding this programme. Spurred by an interest in the SRA-1, Sweden's relationship with Gulfstream began in 1986. One member of the requirements team remembered how representatives from Gulfstream and the Swedish authorities conducted secret meetings where neither was supposed to know the identity of the other. FMV analysis concluded that the Gulfstream IV aircraft was the ideal Sigint platform for Sweden, and, together with TRW Avionics & Surveillance Group, Gulfstream launched Project Fresh Look to supply them. The programme was formally known by its Swedish acronym SF NY (Spanning Flygplan Ny/new reconnaissance aircraft).

In 1992, before the special mission Gulfstream IVs arrived, Sweden took delivery of a single VIP transport GIV, which received the local designation Tp 102A (Tp=Transportplan/ transport aircraft). The Sigint aircraft were initially referred to, in official Swedish documents, as Tp 102Bs, but this was later abandoned in favour of the more honest S 102B designation (S=Spanning/reconnaissance). The S 102B has since been named the Korpen (Raven – these birds were always the eyes of the gods in Norse mythology). Furthermore, each aircraft has received its own name: *Hugin* and *Munin*, the ravens of Odin – the supreme God of Norse mythology. All GIVs from s/n 1214 onwards were built to GIV-SP standard, with an increased maximum take-off weight of 74,600 lb (33838 kg). The S 102Bs are s/n 1215 and 1216 – almost the first of the new breed.

S 102B Korpen

The S 102B airframe modifications were conducted to Swedish specifications and undertaken in the US by Gulfstream and TRW. A three-month flight test programme, which drew heavily on FEWSG experience, validated the many changes to the basic Gulfstream IV. A canoe antenna fairing, approximately 25 in (64 cm) deep and 20 in (51 cm) wide, but slightly shorter than the FEWSG installation, was fitted under the forward fuselage. This fairing houses a

Above and below: Some speculation surrounds the full range of missions undertaken by the USAF's three C-20As, which have been based at Ramstein AFB, Germany, since 1986/87. A US DoD Publication Model Designation Of Military Aerospace Vehicles (June 1986) lists the designation EC-20A as a "C-20A modified with special avionics equipment installed for electronic surveillance." It may be possible that the C-20A had (or was intended to have) an intelligence-gathering capability, in addition to its primary transport mission – a situation not without precedent in USAFE . What is clear is that the C-20A fleet has undergone at least two major (communications) systems modifications since its delivery one at the hands of E-Systems and one at Gulfstream, Savannah. HF tail spikes were added to the C-20As on the latter occasion and the three aircraft today have an antenna fit that resembles the C-20B transports. The changes can be seen on these views of 83-0500, taken at Ramstein.

Sigint antenna and not a SLAR, as has been reported elsewhere. It necessitated the addition of a new ventral fin under the tail, to maintain lateral stability.

Other antenna fairings were added on either side of the nose, with larger antennas on the lower fuselage sides, ahead of the wing box. The aircraft retains its cabin windows, as the expense of deleting them was deemed not to be worthwhile. Neither S 102B has been fitted with a cargo door. A sizeable 'hockey stick' antenna farm is located under the fuselage and wings. Gulfstream undertook extensive CFD (computational fluid dynamics) airflow studies of the new airframe configuration, paying special attention to any icing hazards – a fact of life in the Swedish operational environment.

The S 102Bs were delivered empty to Sweden (in August and October 1995), where all mission equipment was fitted, by air force technicians at Linköping. This fit is based on the TRW Wideband Tactical Surveillance System (WTSS), although it is sure to contain much hardware of Swedish origin. WTSS can monitor frequencies from 20 MHz to 2 GHz, with options down to 2 MHz or up to 40 GHz. WTSS offers a signal search rate of between 15 and 45 GHz per second. At an operating altitude of 45,000 ft (13716 m), the S 102B would have a 'footprint' of some 212,000 sq miles (341172 km^2). Its radio horizon at the same altitude would be 260 nm (299 miles; 481 km). The onboard Sigint sensors are capable of fast signal search and rapid intercept, emitter classification/location, digital audio record and playback, co-channel mitigation and Elint processing. Between four and six operators are believed to be carried by the S 102B – significantly fewer then on the Tp 85. This is a reflection of the compact size of the aircraft's electronics, and also of its datalink capabilities. The Korpens are integrated into Sweden's TARAS digital datalink/radio system and will be capable of downlinking information (at a minimum rate of

US military C-20 fleet details

Entries are presented in the following order: US service designation, US military serial, manufacturer's serial and delivery date.

C-20A	83-0500	382	19 October 1983
C-20A	83-0501	383	16 September 1983
C-20A	83-0502	389	17 November 1983

All C-20As operated by USAFE, 76th AS, 86th AW, at Ramstein AFB. The C-20A originally lacked the tailcone HF antenna, or 'spike', found on the C-20B, C-20C and C-20H. C-20A has DC electrical system. All aircraft initially operated by 89th MAW.

C-20B	86-0200	465	30 January 1987
			(transferred to FAC)
C-20B	86-0202	468	29 April 1987
C-20B	86-0201	470	7 April 1987
C-20B	86-0203	475	18 May 1987
C-20B	86-0204	476	28 May 1987
C-20B	86-0205	477	24 July 1987
			(transferred to US Coast Guard)
C-20B	86-0206	478	16 September 1987

All C-20Bs delivered to 89th MAW, which was redesignated 89th AW on 1 October 1991. Currently operated by 99th AS, 89th AW, Andrews AFB. 86-0200 sold back to Gulfstream in March 1996. Transferred to the Fuerza Aérea de Chile to become FAC911. 86-0200 was traded in for C-20H 92-0375, as part of the leasing deal covering the C-20B fleet. 86-0205 transferred to the US Coast Guard on 31 June 1994 (date as recorded). Now based at Washington National Airport. 86-0206 noted in November 1990 in standard VIP colours, but in November 1997 was the only C-20B among five now in service to be painted not in standard VIP colours but in civil livery, with '60206' on tail (replaced 86-0205 in this role).

C-20C	85-0049	458	28 February 1985
C-20C	85-0050	456	5 March 1985
C-20C	86-0403	473	27 December 1985

All C-20Cs operated by 99th AS, 89th AW, Andrews AFB. 86-0403 observed in 1991, 1992 and again in December 1997 in overall gloss white with same cheat line as SAM C-20, gold with blue outline, white colour wraps under nose and to back of aircraft, under engines. Underside is highly polished silver metal. Wears corrupted version of full serial ('60403') on fin. All C-20Cs were delivered 'green' for outfitting with special mission equipment on the dates shown. Outfitting was undertaken by E-Systems.

C-20D	163691	480	13 May 1987
C-20D	163692	481	24 July 1987

Operated by VR-1 'Star Lifters', US Navy, Andrews AFB. Transferred to CFSLW (Commander Fleet Support Logistics Wing) which became VR-1 on 1 May 1997.
163691 is considered the personal aircraft of the Commandant of the Marine Corps. Wears 'Marines' titles on left side, 'Navy' on right (opposite of 163692). Seen 8 August 1987 and 23 November 1990 in 'Danish grey' with low-visibility national insignia. By 1 March 1996 it was in the same white scheme as its sister-ship.
163692 is considered the personal aircraft of the Secretary of the Navy and the Chief of Naval Operations. White, with 'Navy' on left side, 'Marines' on right (opposite of 163691).

C-20E	87-0139	497	17 June 1988
C-20E	87-0140	498	5 July 1988

Operated by US Army, OSAC, based at Hickam AFB. The C-20E was the first jet aircraft to be officially operated by the US Army. The two C-20Es were the last Gulfstream IIIs to be built.

C-20F	91-0108	1162	25 February 1992

Operated by US Army, OSAC. This aircraft was the first Gulfstream IV to be delivered to the US military.

C-20G	165093/JR	1187	9 March 1994
	(USN, VR-48 'Capitol Skyliners', Andrews AFB)		
C-20G	165094/JR	1189	4 February 1994
	(USN, VR-48 'Capitol Skyliners', Andrews AFB)		
C-20G	165151/RG	1199	17 December 1994
	(USN, VR-51 'Windjammers', MCB Kaneohe Bay)		
C-20G	165152/RG	1201	22 December 1994
	(USN, VR-51 'Windjammers', MCB Kaneohe Bay)		
C-20G	165153/VM	1200	17 December 1994
	(USMC, MASD)		

165093 is named *City of Annapolis*.
165094 is named *City of Baltimore*.
165151 and 165152 were delivered to CFLSW Kaneohe Bay Detachment, MCB (formerly MCAS) Kaneohe Bay, Hawaii, which became VR-51 'Windjammers' on 1 May 1997.
165153 wears 'Danish grey' with high-visibility national insignia and 'United States Marines' titles on fuselage. From about December 1994 to March 1995 it served at MCAS Futenma, Okinawa. Now allocated to MASD (Marine Aircraft Support Detachment) at Andrews AFB, but was badly damged on the ground, during a storm at Miami on 2 February 1998, and may not be returned to service.

C-20H	90-0300	1181	23 May 1994
C-20H	92-0375	1256	16 January 1996

Operated by USAF, 99th AS, 89th AW, Andrews AFB. The C-20H was once referred to as the C-20F in Congressional documents.
90-0300 duplicates a serial that has also been allocated to a US Army AH-64A Apache. This aircraft was later brought up to GIV-SP standard.

C-20J	89-0266	045	

Operated by US Army, USAPAT. Delivered to a commercial customer (as N711R) in February 1969. After several changes of ownership it was reacquired by Gulfstream in October 1980 and sold to the Corps of Engineers, US Army in May 1981. Allocated civil registration N40CE and designated as a VC-11A (in line with the single GII operated by the US Coast Guard from April 1969 until May 1995). In November 1989 this registration was cancelled and the current military serial was allocated. On 1 January 1992 the aircraft was transferred to USAPAT (US Army). The C-20J designation was allocated in 1993, and at the same time the aircraft was refurbished by Duncan Aviation.

C-37A	97-0400	521	(mid-1998)
C-37A	97-0401	542	(30 September 1998)

Will be operated by USAF 89th AW. The C-37 contract was announced on 5 May 1997. These aircraft will be the first Gulfstream Vs in military service. Planned delivery dates shown.

---

2 Mb per second) to as many as 25 ground workstations and other Flygvapnet aircraft, such as the S 100B Argus (Saab 340AEW). Sweden's operational concept for its future air force (FV2000) places great reliance on sophisticated C^3 and 'information warfare', and the S 102B fleet has received a controlled amount of official publicity, reflecting its important role in that plan.

While the first S 102B was being outfitted with its mission systems, the second aircraft was used for crew training. On 17 December 1997 the first S 102B was declared operational, and the second aircraft is now believed to be receiving its mission fit. FMV can be justifiably proud of delivering these aircraft on time and under budget to the Flygvapnet. The last Tp 85 is still in service, after several postponements of its fate, and will not be withdrawn until 1998, at least. The Tp 102A is attached to F16 Wing at Uppsala, but is routinely based at Broma, much closer to Stockholm. The S 102Bs are currently stationed at Malmen, near Linköping, alongside the Tp 85, and all are operated by the same unit, Malflygdivisionen 85. There has been some suggestion that the new aircraft and crews may be moved to Uppsala, north of Stockholm, to form a combined unit with the S 100B fleet – and perhaps safeguard Uppsala from closure.

Gulfstream IVs in Japan

Another important 'new' Gulfstream IV operator is Japan, which has acquired two quite different versions of the basic aircraft for military/government use. Spurred by the success and suitability of the C-20G in US Navy service, the Japan Air Self Defence Force (JASDF) opted to acquire similar aircraft for high-priority transport missions. In 1994 Gulfstream won the JASDF's U-X competition to replace its existing Beech Queen Airs (and other types) with a $72 million contract for two Gulfstream IV-MPAs (Multi-Purpose Aircraft), based on the GIV-SP airframe and with the local designation U-4. An order for a third aircraft was announced during the 1997 NBAA show, held in Dallas in September and a fourth followed before the end of the year. Japan's ultimate requirement is for nine U-4 aircraft and the GIV was chosen in the face of stiff competition from Dassault and Bombardier.

The JASDF's decision to acquire the GIV was undoubtedly influenced by the operation of two other aircraft by the Japan Civil Aviation Bureau (JCAB). The JCAB acquired two GIVs, in 1993 and 1995, for use as air navigation aid verification aircraft. The GIVs replaced a NAMC YS-11 and GII in this role, and were the first to be delivered to Japan. All foreign sales to the Japanese government require a Japanese 'trading partner' to act as an intermediary. GAC worked with Okura & Company Ltd who bought the aircraft from GAC and then sold them to the customer. Japan is meticulous in its requirements. On hand-over the first JCAB aircraft was subjected to unprecedented acceptance testing – two days were spent looking over the paperwork before the actual aircraft was even approached. All onboard avionics were bench-tested and then tested

Left: C-20A (83-0500) 99th Airlift Squadron, 89th Airlift Wing.

Right: C-20B (86-0200) 99th Airlift Squadron, 89th Airlift Wing.

Left: C-20D (163691) VR-1 'Star Lifters', (old scheme).

Right: C-20E (87-0140) US Army, OSAC.

again onboard. On predelivery flights from Savannah the first aircraft actually found and reported a problem with a local VOR. The GIV flew for 100 hours of testing, when 20 is the norm, and its first 150-hour inspection was thus due almost immediately after delivery.

The JCAB aircraft were system outfitted by Parker/Gull and equipped with the MFI-201 flight inspection system. Each carries GPS, MLS, VLF/Omega, DME/ILS, TCAS and a linescan camera system. The JCAB will have a very important role in proving the satellite-based FANs (Future Air Navigation System) and CNSATM (Communications Navigation Surveillance Air Traffic Management) programmes which will revolutionise air traffic control, particularly in the Pacific region. FANS/CNSATM will ultimately allow 'free flight' by commercial traffic using purely GPS navigation instead of existing methods.

The U-4 transport for the JASDF has a reconfigurable cabin, fitted with five seat tracks, and can be configured for up to 18 passengers or 2 medevac litters. Unlike the higher-density C-20G, the U-4 does not need additional Type II emergency exits and does not have a roller floor. The cockpit has been configured with TACAN, dual HF radio, three V/UHF radios, satcom, DF, GPS, IFF and GPWS. Each aircraft is fitted with a cargo door and was modified by

Marshall Aerospace. The U-4 door design is not the same as that fitted to the C-20G and was described by all involved as, 'a major modification'. The installation process took five months, as the cabin had to be stripped and every fuselage beam replaced. Gulfstream and Marshall have proved their expertise in this critical modification for several customers by now and it is a major advantage over other competing types such as the Falcon 900 or Challenger (which simply have no room for a similar installation). On completion by Marshall the U-4s were outfitted by Gulfstream, using a Hunting Engineering shell. Like the JCAB deal, the U-4 programme was conducted in association with Okura. A contract between Okura and the Japanese government was signed in March 1995 and the first two airframes were delivered 'green' to Cambridge in August 1995. They returned to Savannah, for final outfitting, in June 1996. The third U-4 was rolled out on 8 January 1997 and returned from Marshall in June.

Gulfstreams in US military service

Of course, the most important operator of military Gulfstreams today is the United States. The US 'order of battle' consists of 26 C-20s and soon two C-37A aircraft, in four distinct versions (Gulfstream II, III, IV, and V) used by all five branches of the armed forces (Air Force,

Two C-20Gs serve with VR-51 'Windjammers' at MCB Kaneohe Bay, Hawaii. VR-51 is the newest of the two US Navy Reserve C-20G-eqipped OSA units.

Army, Coast Guard, Marine Corps and Navy) – the only fixed-wing aircraft with this distinction. Until recently, these 26 aircraft also shared a trait with the B-52: the fleet consisted of eight C-20 variants, assigned letter suffixes A through H, with no experimental or one-off variants and no suffixes skipped. The tidiness of this was spoiled when the US Army's sole GII was redesignated as a C-20J. The Gulfstream also enjoys the distinction of having the very first A model and the last H model still in service. The current force consists of: C-20A – three USAF (GIII) OSA transports; C-20B – five USAF (GIII) SAM airlifters (of seven delivered); C-20C – three USAF (GIII) war readiness aircraft; C-20D – two US Navy (GIII) VIP transports; C-20E – two US Army (GIII) OSA transports; C-20F – one US Army (GIV) OSA transport; C-20G – four US Navy/one US Marines (GIV) OSA transports; C-20H – two USAF (GIV) SAM airlifter; C-20J – one US Army (GII, former VC-11A) OSA transport. To be added in 1998 are two Gulfstream V SAM airlifters, designated C-37A.

The Gulfstream IV has now entered US military service, in several forms. The first to

Left: C-20F (91-0108), US Army, OSAC.

Right: C-20G (165093/City of Annapolis), VR-48 'Capitol Skyliners'.

Left: C-20H (90-0300) 99th Airlift Squadron, 89th Airlift Wing.

Right: C-20B (01) United States Coast Guard.

Gulfstream: Special Missions

Gulfstream IV. This duty cements the Gulfstream's image as a sophisticated VIP aircraft, but it has two other roles not thought of as charismatic – a war readiness function so classified it can only be speculated on, and the very prosaic job of carrying out OSA (operational support airlift), the Pentagon's term for short- and medium-distance, intra-theatre transportation.

The natural mission for the C-20 – providing executive transportation for the elite – has three practitioners, all based in Washington, DC. The 'ultimate' VIP airline is the USAF's 89th Airlift Wing at Andrews AFB, which has the job of carrying the President, Vice President, members of the Cabinet and Congress, and other dignitaries, and uses five C-20Bs among other aircraft to do the job. The 89th is not alone: Naval Air Reserve squadron VR-1 'Star Lifters' operates two C-20Ds to transport the Secretary of the Navy, the Chief of Naval Operations, and the Commandant of the Marine Corps. Across the Potomac River at Washington National Airport, the Coast Guard's C-20B is also available to the Secretary of Transportation and of course to the Commandant of the Coast Guard.

89th Airlift Wing

But the 89th outshines the others. The wing operates two VC-25As (Boeing 747-200B) assigned solely for Presidential travel, five VC-137Cs (Boeing 707-320B) used for Vice Presidential and other VIP travel, three VC-9Cs (Douglas DC-9s) used by the Secretary of Defense and others, and seven Gulfstreams (five C-20Bs and two C-20Hs) used for a variety of dignitaries including the Speaker of the House and other representatives. The 89th no longer operates C-21As. The five VC-137Cs are in the process of being replaced by a six-aircraft

arrive was the US Army's C-20F, in 1992. Its introduction allowed one of the existing C-20Es to be transferred to Hickam AAF, Hawaii. GIVs arrived for the US Navy in 1994. The US Navy had originally intended to acquire one C-20G, to operate from Hawaii, and two for Okinawa, but this plan (and the acquisition total) was changed. Today two aircraft serve with VR-48 at Andrews AFB and two with VR-51, in Hawaii. The Marine Corps also operates a single C-20G. The contract for the USAF's C-20Hs actually preceded that for the Navy's C-20Gs, although they were delivered later, in 1994 and 1996. The USAF had originally expressed an interest in one C-20H plus two options, but only one of these was exercised. The second came off the production line as a GIV-SP. The first C-20H later underwent the ASC 190 modification to bring it up to GIV-SP standard, with the increased maximum take-off weight. This aircraft was also fitted with extra communications gear. The Navy's C-20Gs represent an important growth in capability for the C-20, as they are operated primarily as priority cargo transports, and all are fitted with a cargo door.

The cabin can be configured for up to 26 seats or three cargo pallets, and extra emergency exits have been provided to allow the aircraft to operate at configurations higher than 19 seats. A Marine crew comprises pilot, co-pilot, crew chief and loadmaster.

In 1990, a version of the Gulfstream IV was offered to the USAF by Gulfstream, in an unsolicited proposal for an Open Skies reconnaissance aircraft. Given the confusing and unofficial designation 'C-20F', this aircraft was essentially an SRA-4 variant which could be configured with camera, radar and IR sensor systems. An artist's impression of this 'C-20F' showed an aircraft with a large SAR radome under the forward fuselage. A modified C-135 was instead chosen as the USA's Open Skies platform.

C-20 roles and missions

In its primary role as a dedicated VIP transport, the C-20 serves the US Air Force, the US Navy (and by association the Marines) and the US Coast Guard (which uses its C-20B as a personal transport for its commandant). The Secretary of Transportation uses the FAA

package consisting of four C-32As (Boeing 757-200s) and two Gulfstream Vs (C-37As).

Aspiring C-20 pilots with the 89th must have a minimum of 2,500 hours and instructor pilot/examiner status before they can attempt to undergo the unit's rigorous selection and screening process. About 30 pilots and co-pilots are currently rated on the C-20, with another 10 or 12 attached staff officers. The standard tour for an 89th pilot is now four years, although it used to be longer. Each C-20 pilot can expect to notch up 30 or 40 flight hours per month.

The OSA mission

OSA encompasses the transportation of high-priority passengers and cargo with time-sensitive requirements. Because that sounds like, and is, something that could often be done by commercial carriers – with whom the US military does not want to be perceived as competing – the multi-service OSA fleet is officially justified in part because it also provides readiness training in the form of pilot proficiency (all services) and pilot seasoning (US Air Force only). The latter is regarded as extremely important by the USAF, which has long assigned selected junior pilots to C-21 Learjets and C-20s to give career-enhancing experience. Not the smallest part of this experience is the opportunity to rub shoulders with generals and other important people. (Among C-20s in USAF service, only those at Ramstein AFB, Germany are considered OSA assets; the aircraft with the 89th Airlift Wing do not receive OSA tasking.)

The worldwide fleet of several hundred OSA aircraft of 11 types (including 13 C-20 Gulfstreams of the US Air Force, Army, and Marine Corps) includes over 200 in the continental US (including 10 Gulfstreams) scheduled by the JOSAC (Joint Operational Support Airlift Center) at Scott AFB, Illinois. Although OSA has been recognised as a distinct mission since World War II, scheduling of OSA missions was centralised only in 1995 when the JOSAC opened at US Transportation Command headquarters at Scott.

OSA is easily understood when the Marine Corps' sole C-20G is tasked on short notice to carry Navy scientists and equipment from a facility outside Washington to another in Idaho where submarine research is conducted, or when an Army C-20E gets the job of flying top commanders from Hawaii to Alaska for a conference. It becomes more difficult to grasp the operational support concept when we see that each service continues to have its own terms and rules covering the mission.

The Army's OSA assets (including two C-20Es and one C-20F, but not the sole C-20J) are technically Service Support Airlift aircraft, and their job is to provide priority transport for senior leaders and commanders, and secure transport for critical equipment.

The Navy has some aircraft considered OSA assets only (C-12s, T-39s), plus a fleet of larger aircraft (C-9s, C-130s, C-20Gs) which support

The USAF's 89th AW has long maintained one C-20C and one C-20B (as seen here) in a civilian-style 'biz jet' scheme. The legality of such a colour scheme, which has no national identifying marks whatsoever (in contravention of international agreement), is open to question.

C-20C war readiness aircraft

Above and below: The role of the USAF's three C-20Cs is little-publicised and not fully understood outside the small official circle of those 'who need to know'. All C-20Cs are attached to the 89th AW, Andrews AFB. They are tasked with transporting the President, or other important decision makers in the US military chain of command, to safety in time of war (primarily aboard the E-4B airborne command post). C-20Cs are rarely seen in their home country but always travel in support of foreign visits by such VVIPs and will be based at nearby airfields, not capable of accommodating the much larger E-4Bs. At least one aircraft (86-0403) wears an unobtrusive 'plain Jane' colour scheme to allow it to pass more easily through sensitive locations.

the NUFEA (Navy Unique Fleet Essential Aircraft) Requirement. The latter, flown mostly by Reservists, are earmarked for unpredictable, quick-reaction, high-priority airlift of people, cargo and mail in support of aircraft-carrier and other fleet movements. Although some functions remain at the NALO (Naval Air Logistics Office) in New Orleans, Louisiana, Navy OSA scheduling became the responsibility of the JOSAC in December 1996, and the NUFEA mission was included in the Navy's OSA mission soon afterward.

The Marine Corps considers its OSA aircraft to be Base and Command Support assets. The Marine Corps' sole C-20G is tasked by JOSAC. (The Corps commandant's aircraft, a C-20D, belongs to the Navy and is not an OSA asset).

The secretive C-20C

The final OSA partner, the USAF, has about 100 support aircraft but only three of its Gulfstreams (the C-20As at Ramstein) are in the OSA category. Its three C-20Cs, operated by

the 89th Airlift Wing's 99th Airlift Squadron – and crewed by the same personnel who fly SAM C-20Bs and Hs – are nominally based at Andrews AFB but are never seen 'out-of-doors' except when actually flying. Although they appear on the USAF inventory, they are never acknowledged in official documents. These aircraft are frequently attributed, in other sources, to the US Army, but this is incorrect. However, when asked about the C-20C, USAF officials will say, "Our position is that we do not have any aircraft called a C-20C" (an Air Force Materiel Command programme manager at Wright-Patterson AFB, Ohio), or "No comment" (a communications specialist at Andrews), or "You will have to ask somebody else" (a pilot). Nor is Gulfstream prepared to comment on these aircraft or their operations.

Behind the caginess and secrecy is a programme to assure the survival of US government leaders in the midst of a nuclear attack, possibly known by the acronym CGOP (Continuity of Government Operations

Gulfstream II, III and IV in worldwide military/government service

Dates in tabular entries are approximate 'in service' dates, as opposed to GAC's official 'greenie' delivery dates – unless otherwise indicated.

ALGERIA

Government of Algeria
7T-VPR GIV-SP 1288 October 1996
7T-VPS GIV-SP 1291 November 1996
GIV-SPs operated in civilian markings on VIP duties. Between July 1983 and April 1984 Algeria took delivery of three GIIIs; 7T-VRB (s/n 368), 7T-VRC (s/n 396), 7T-VRD (s/n 399). Aircraft wore 'Democratic and Popular Republic of Algeria' titles. GIIIs traded in for GIV-SPs in 1996. GII 7T-VHB (s/n 230) delivered to Algerian government in July 1979 but was shot down by Iraqi fighters on 3 May 1982. Aircraft crashed inside Iranian territory.

ANGOLA

Government of Angola
D2-ECB GIII 474 April 1987
Delivered 'green' May 1986.

BAHRAIN

Amiri Royal Flight
A9C-BB GIII 393 December 1983
A9C-BG GII(TT) 202 February 1978
A9C-BB delivered from GAC in June 1983.

BOTSWANA

Botswana Defence Force Air Wing
OK1/Z12 GIV 1173 September 1991
The GIV-SP replaced a BAe 125-800B. It is operated by Z12 Squadron, Molepolole.

BRUNEI

V8-007 GIV 1109
(delivered by GAC August 1989)
V8-008 GIV 1176 August 1992
(delivered by GAC November 1991)
V8-009 GIV 1202
(acquired by Jordan 1998, q.v.)
V8-SR1 GIV 1150 December 1991
(delivered by GAC October 1990)
V8-009 formerly V8-MSB. V8-007 formerly V8-SR1. V8-SR1 formerly V8-009. Aircraft registered to Amedeo Corp but flown by Sultanate of Brunei, Royal (government) Flight. Confusion exists over whether aircraft 'registrations' use leter 'O' forms or numerical '0' forms (numeral is correct).

CAMEROUN

Presidence Republique du Cameroun
TJ-AAW GIII 486 July 1987
(GAC delivery June 1986)
GII TJ-AAK (s/n 093) operated between 1971 and 1986.

CHAD

TT-AAI GII 240 June 1991
This aircraft formerly 5A-DDR, Government of Libya. Delivered to Libya in 1979.

CHILE

Fuerza Aérea de Chile
911 C-20B (GIII) 465 May 1996
Formerly 86-0200, USAF. Transferred on 20 May 1996.

DENMARK

Kongelige Danske Flyvevåben (Royal Danish Air Force)
F-249 GIII (SMA) 249 16 April 1982
F-313 GIII (SMA) 313 23 February 1982
F-330 GIII (SMA) 330 19 June 1982
F-400 GIII 401
21 December 1996 to 3 December 1997
Multi-mission aircraft operated by Eskadrille 721, Værløse, on fisheries/coastal patrol and SAR duties. F-249 is the first GIII (f/f 2 December 1979). F-330 was lost in a crash on 3 August 1996. Replaced by 401, on lease until December 1997. GII N5102 (s/n 085) was leased to RDAF for training, prior to the delivery of the GIIIs, between 1 February and 1 August 1981. GIIIs to be augmented and possibly replaced by Challenger 604s.

DUBAI (UAE)

Government of Dubai
A6-HEH GIII 356 June 1983
(GAC delivery June 1982)
A6-HHH GIV 1011
(GAC delivery December 1987)
Operated by Dubai Air Wing (Royal Flight)/ Government of Dubai. GIII A6-CKZ (s/n 317) previously in service.

EGYPT

Al Quwwat al Jawwiya il Misriya (Arab Republic of Egypt Air Force).
SU-BGM GIV 1048
(GAC delivery May 1989)
SU-BGU GIII 439 April 1985
(GAC delivery September 1984)
SU-BGV GIII 442 April 1985
(GAC delivery October 1984)
GIV-SP 1329
GIV-SP 1332
Operated on VIP duties by the Cairo East AB-based Transport Regiment. Aircraft wear 'Arab Republic of Egypt' titles. S/ns of new GIV-SPs reflect airframes scheduled for delivery, but these may yet change.

GABON

Forces Aériennes Gabonaises (Gabonese air forces)
TR-KHC GIII 326 February 1982
Operated by the GLAM (Groupement de Liaisions Aériennes Ministerelles/ ministerial liasions group), Libreville (Base Aérienne 01). Used as a Presidential transport. Gabon previously operated GII(TT) TR-KHB (s/n 127), w/o February 1980.

INDIA

Indian Air Force/Bharatiya Vayu Sena
VT-ENR GIII 420 May 1987
K-2961 GIII 495? June 1986
K-2962 GIII 494? June 1986
India operates three GIIIs, only one of which (VT-ENR) is a VIP transport model. This aircraft has reportedly been allocated an IAF serial (K-2980) but this has apparently never been worn and aircraft carries civil identity on its manufacturer's data plate. VT-ENR is the original SRA-1 demonstrator (with cargo door etc.). The two previously delivered GIIIs are much-modified photo-reconnaissance aircraft, frequently erroneously identified as SMAs or SRA-1s. The serials often quoted for these aircraft in several public sources (K-2981, K-2982) may also be incorrect. It is possible that the IAF has deliberately swapped and invented identities for these aircraft. Furthermore, some confusion exists as to the tie-up between s/ns and IAF serials of the two modified aircraft known to have been delivered. The serials noted above are understood to be those worn by the two aircraft prior to delivery. Both aircraft are believed to be operated under the auspices of the IAF's Air Research Centre, Research and Analysis Wing, based at Palam and Charbatia. This unit may also operate the two Sigint/Elint-configured Boeing 707s that entered IAF service in 1997.

INDONESIA

PK-NZK GIV-SP 1219
Owned by BPIS, the holding company of state-owned Aerospace firm IPTN. Operates on military/government duties. Indonesian government previously operated GIII PK-PJA (s/n 395) between 1983 and 1988.

IRELAND

Aer Chor na h-Eireann/Irish Air Corps
251 GIV 1160 December 1991
The GIV is flown by the Ministerial Air Transport Squadron (MATS), No. 1 Support Wing, based at Casement Aerodrome, Baldonnel. Prior to the delivery of the GIV the IAC operated a GIII (249, s/n 413) which served between January 1990 and 1991.

ITALY

Aeronautica Militare Italiana/ Italian Air Force
MM62022 GIII 451 September 1985
(GAC delivery December 1984)
MM62025 GIII 479 January 1987
(GAC delivery December 1986)
Operated by 306° Gruppo Transporto Speciali (TS), 31° Stormo TS 'Carmelo Raiti', based at Rome-Ciampino. GIIIs are earmarked for replacement by Dassault Falcon 900EX.

IVORY COAST

Force Aérienne de la Côte d'Ivoire/ Ivory Coast air force
TU-VAD GIV 1019
(GAC delivery January 1988)
TU-VAF GIII 462
(GAC delivery March 1988)
Operated by the Escadrille Presidentielle, based at Abidjan Airport. Operational status of TU-VAF questionable. A G.159 (TU-VAC, s/n 133) perviously served the Ivory Coast government. It was replaced by a GII (s/n 218), with the same registration, in 1978.

JAPAN

Japan Air Self Defence Force
75-3251/251 U-4 (GIV-MPA) 1270 January 1997
75-3252/252 U-4 (GIV-MPA) 1271 January 1997
85-3253/253 U-4 (GIV-MPA) 1303
95-3254/254? U-4 (GIV-MPA) 1326?
Four U-4s on firm order for the JASDF, with eventual requirement for nine. First two delivered to Marshall Aerospace (June 1996) for cargo door modification then to Okura for fitting of mission equipment. Handed over in January 1997 and entered service the following month. U-4s operated by the Headquarters Squadron, 2 Yuso Kokutai (air transport group), at Iruma AB. Will provide long-range, rapid-reaction transport in Japan, and elsewhere.

Japan Civil Aviation Bureau
JA001G GIV 1190 September 1993
JA002G GIV-SP 1244 November 1995
Both operated as flight checkers for navaid/airfield calibration, replacing a GII (s/n 141) and some of six-strong YS-11 fleet. Handed over in April 1992 and April 1994.

GII JA8431 (s/n 141, ex-JCAB) is now in use for atmospheric research tasks. Registered to ***Mitsubishi Heavy Industry Finance Co. Ltd.*** Aircraft previously carried sensor pods mounted on forward fuselage but these have been replaced by an underfuselage pannier.

JORDAN

Government of Jordan
GIII JY-HAH 467 December 1986
(GAC delivery March 1986)
GIV JY-RAY 1202
Aircraft civil registered, but operated by Royal Flight of Royal Jordanian Air Force, based at Amman/Marka. JY-HAH wears a surrogate civillian scheme (resembling Royal Jordanian Airlines) with 'Hashemite Kingdom of Jordan' titles. GIV seen in London (in full Royal Jordanian colours) on 29 January 1998. Aircraft not acquired through GAC, but was previously V8-009.

KUWAIT

9K-AJA GIV 1157 December 1991
(GAC delivery January 1991)
9K-AJB GIV 1159 December 1991
(GAC delivery March 1991)
9K-AJC GIV 1161 January 1992
(GAC delivery March 1991)
All aircraft operated in livery of Kuwait Airways but used on government VIP duties. GIVs replaced two GIIIs (9K-AEG, s/n 408 and 9K-AEH, s/n 419) stolen by Iraqi ➡

Program). Other sources use the acronyms COG (Continuity of Government) and PSSS (Presidential Successor Support System). This effort is responsible for everything from an alternate underground facility for Congress in Greenbriar, West Virginia (abandoned after it was publicly revealed a few years ago) to an alternate National Military Command Center near Camp David, Maryland. The US clearly has a programme to get its leaders out of Washington in a crisis and the C-20C has a role in that programme.

In the strategy book of the nuclear warfighter, the tactic of 'decapitation' is an important one. It was a credible Cold War tactic for either superpower to attempt to destroy enough of the opposition's command and control infrastructure – in particular those individuals able to order the use of nuclear weapons – in the hope of preventing immediate full-scale retaliation. In the ensuing confusion and delay, perhaps whatever nuclear forces that remained unused could be destroyed in a second strike, or perhaps an uneven 'peace' extracted. The US response to such a threat relied heavily on protecting its decision makers onboard an E-4B NAOC (National Airborne Operations Center). Even today, an E-4B always accompanies the President or other important members of the military chain of command when they leave the USA. A C-20C always escorts the E-4 and is clearly tasked with transporting top-level personnel to the E-4 and safety, in time of crisis. The C-20C may even have a limited command and control facility itself. All C-20 pilots serving with the 89th AW are believed to be cleared to fly the C-20C, and may do so routinely. The C-20C does not have an EFIS cockpit fit, but instead is fitted with conventional electro-mechanical flight instruments – which offer a greater degree of EMP resistance.

The all-new C-37

The next Gulfstream to enter USAF service will be a Gulfstream V – but it will not be a C-20. The USAF has had an ongoing requirement to replace some of its older SAM aircraft which have had illustrious careers but are now becoming increasingly uneconomic to operate. This 'on and off' project crystallised into the VC-X competition which set out to find six 'large aircraft', in the class of the Boeing 767 or McDonnell Douglas MD-11, to replace the Boeing VC-137s. The plan received a Congressional veto, largely due to fears of the negative 'ramp image' such a sizeable number of new 'airliners' would cause. The USAF was redirected to find four large and two small aircraft instead. Again, worries about the impact of the Boeing 767 as a SAM type led to the selection of the Boeing 757 (C-32A), which many observers now believe to be too small and too short-legged to adequately carry out the missions required of it. For the 'small' element of VC-X, Gulfstream was pitted against the Dassault Falcon 900, Canadair (Bombardier) Global Express and the Boeing 737 Business Jet. The terms of VC-X called for both the supply of a new airframe and the supply of logistics support – by one contractor. On 28 April 1997 Gulfstream was awarded a $68.9 million contract to supply two Gulfstream V ultra-long-range jets, which will

Above and above right: Several US government agencies use Gulfstreams, including NASA (GIII, above) and NOAA (storm-chasing GIV-SP).

Right: This Gulfstream III is operated by the Ivory Coast air force as a presidential/VIP transport, alongside a Gulfstream IV.

be designated C-37. As the C-37 will be treading, to some degree, on the toes of existing C-20s it was considered awkward to have a C-20 seen to be 'replacing' a C-20, so a new designation was selected. In addition to supplying two GVs (with an option on an additional four), Gulfstream Aerospace will also support a 10-year contractor logistics support contract, with technical representatives stationed at Andrews, operating a 24-hour Contractor-Operated Supply Store. This deal is a one-year contract, with nine yearly options.

Gulfstream V

Gulfstream first announced its next-generation Gulfstream V in 1991 and committed to go-ahead with the design at the 1992 Farnborough air show. The GV was to be the first in a new breed of ultra-long range business jets capable of carrying four crew and eight passengers over 6,500 nm (12038 km; 7,480 miles), at Mach 0.80. A new engine was introduced in the shape of the BMW/Rolls Royce BR710 and while the basic outline of the airframe remained the same as its predecessors, the GV has several notable differences. The fuselage has been stretched by 7 ft (2.13 m) when compared to the GIV, resulting in an overall length of 96 ft 5 in (29.39 m). The wing is 15 ft 8 in (4.81 m) longer than the GIV's, it has been reprofiled to improve efficiency and the tail surfaces have also all been enlarged. The cockpit has been fitted with a Honeywell SPZ-8500 fully-digital flight management system utilising six colour LCD screens, and a Honeywell/GEC-Marconi HUD is being developed. The prototype GV made its maiden flight on 28 November 1995.

While the Gulfstream V has already chalked up a prestigious military order in the shape of the USAF's C-37s, Gulfstream's attention is now fixed on an even bigger prize – UK

In worldwide military service, Gulfstreams outnumber all other competitors in their natural role as VIP transports. Two examples, of many, are this Fuerza Aérea Mexicana Gulfstream III (below) and Arab Republic of Egypt Air Force Gulfstream IV (below right).

Ministry of Defence Staff Requirement SR(Land/Air) 925 ASTOR. Building on long-established relationships with several UK companies, Gulfstream Aerospace has teamed with Lockheed Martin UK Government Systems to bid for the joint British Army and Royal Air Force ASTOR (Airborne STand-Off Radar) competition. Based on a modified Gulfstream V airframe, the TeamASTOR bid is aimed at supplying an affordable, effective, long-range, all-weather 24-hour battlefield surveillance platform.

ASTOR for the UK

ASTOR has its roots in two different projects, both of which had been underway for many years. In the early 1980s the UK MoD launched the CASTOR (Corps Airborne STand-Off Radar) programme which tied together two essentially different systems. The British Army was developing a moving-target indicator (MTI) radar (CASTOR-I) which was originally intended to be helicopter-mounted. This Thorn-EMI I-band radar (Thorn-EMI replaced Ferranti on this contract) was fitted in the nose of a modified PBN BN-2T Turbine Islander and downlinked to ground stations. The CASTOR Islander first flew on 12 May 1982 and was intended to enter service in 1988. At the same time Thorn-EMI (Racal) was developing a synthetic aperture radar (SAR), based on the Searchwater, for the RAF. This system (CASTOR-C) was flown on a modified Canberra B.Mk 2. An MTI radar can detect and track moving vehicles in its search area, while an SAR system can deliver almost photo-graphic-quality images of an area (day or night, in all weathers), to provide essential targeting or intelligence information. Thorn-EMI/Racal

made the important technical step forward of proving that effective MTI and SAR functions could be combined in a single radar. Work on this new radar design continued from 1988 until 1991. In 1992 IBM Federal Systems (now Lockheed Martin UK Government Systems) established an ASTOR group, which teamed with Thorn-EMI in 1993. A request for quotations for an initial project definition phase was issued in February 1994. Out of seven candidates, IBM won one of the two project definition contracts awarded in February 1995 (Raytheon won the second). This project definition ended in July 1996 and was followed by a firm price offer in September. The ASTOR project was cleared by the EAC in March 1997, during the final weeks of the (then) Conservative government when it was agreed to downselect to Lockheed Martin UK and Raytheon and discount all other options such as J-STARS, U-2 or UAVs.

ASTOR has been described as 'a gatherer of near real-time intelligence', not a command post or a 'cut-down J-STARS'. The requirement for the radar is believed to call for a maximum range of 250/300 km (155/186 miles). To reach the specified 'grazing angle' the aircraft must be capable of cruising at 50,000 ft (15240 m). The radar must function in both SAR and MTI modes over a wide area (with a maximum resolution of 3 m/10 ft) and in 'spotlight' high-resolution SAR mode for specific fixed targets (with a maximum resolution of 0.5 m/1.6 ft). In MTI mode the radar must be able to detect targets moving at between 10 km/h (6.2 mph) and 270 km/h (167 mph) – such as helicopters. The system must be compatible with other platforms such as the USAF's U-2 and E-8, Italian CRESO, French HORIZON and the emerging NATO data communications standard.

forces during the 1990 invasion of Kuwait, but later destroyed in Baghdad by Coalition bombing in February 1991. Two GIIs 9K-AEB (s/n 244) and 9K-AEC (s/n 248) operated between 1980 and 1985.

LIBYA

Government of Libya
5A-DDS GII 242 January 1980
This aircraft was delivered in full Libyan Arab Airlines colours, but is operated by the Libyan Arab Republic Air Force. A second GII (5A-DDR, s/n 240) was delivered to Libya in December 1979. This aircraft is now believed to be in service in Chad (q.v.)

MALAYSIA

9M-ISJ GIV 1106
(GAC delivery July 1989)
Operated by the Government (Sultan Iskandar) of Jahore provence – hence the registration.

MEXICO

Fuerza Aérea Mexicana
TP-06 (XC-UJN) GIII 352 March 1990
TP-07 (XC-UJO) GIII 386 July 1990
Aircraft operated by the Presidential transport division of the Escuadrón Aéreo de Transporte Pesado (heavy air transport squadron), based at Mexico City (BAM No. 11, Benito Juarez IAP). GII TP-04 (s/n 161) no longer in service.

Procuraduria General de la Republica
XC-AA70 GII 18 June 1992

MOROCCO

Al Quwwat Al Jawwiya Al Malakiya Marakishiya (Royal Moroccan Air Force)
CNA-NL GII(TT) 182 September 1976
CNA-NU GIII 365 January 1989
Aircraft operated by air force VIP unit, based at Rabat-Sale Air Base. Air force aircraft allocated civil registrations, but in a corrupted form using first three letters of complete registration instead of national prefix (CN-) and separate sequence.

NETHERLANDS

Koninklijke Luchtmacht
V-11 GIV 1009
(GAC delivery December 1995)
Operated by 334 Squadron as a VIP transport, based at Eindhoven.

NIGERIA

Federal Government of Nigeria
5N-AGV GII 177 October 1976
5N-FGP GIV 1126 November 1990
(GAC delivery March 1990)
Nigeria previously operated a G.159 (5N-AAI) between 1961 and 1967.

OMAN

Omani Royal Flight
A40-AB GIV 1168 February 1992
(GAC delivery June 1991)
A40-AC GIV 1196 December 1992
(GAC delivery June 1992)
Operated in civil marks by the Omani Royal Flight, under the auspices of the Royal Air Force of Oman. Aircraft based at Muscat-Seeb International Airport. Sultan of Oman previously operated GII(TT) A40-AA (s/n 183) and GII A40-HA (s/n 214).

PANAMA

Servicio Aéreo Nacional de Panama
HP-1A GII 78 September 1995
Panamanian air force reconstituted as much reduced National Air Service after US invasion of 1989. GII based at Tocumen, as Presidential transport.

RUSSIA

Russian Air Force Flight Test Center
62 GII 62
In 1993 GII s/n 62 (N7PQ) and aircraft s/n 021 were delivered to Russia via a US company (CARC) based in Kansas City. On arrival in Russia aircraft could not be registered as the type was not certified by Russian authorities. Aircraft s/n 021 returned to the USA (now N8PQ). S/n 062 was 'adopted' by an arm of the Zhukhovskii-based Gromov Flight Test unit, and allocated a Russian air force 'serial' but is believed be operated (by military crews?) on a quasi-commercial basis for a Russian oil company. The GII is still not officially certified in Russia, unlike GIII and GIV.

SAUDI ARABIA

Royal Saudi Air Force (Al Quwwat Al Jawwiya Al Malakiya As Sa'udiya)
HZ-103 GIII 453 January 1986
HZ-108 GIII 353 December 1983
HZ-103 was previously '103' (registration HZ-109 allocated, but not taken up). HZ-108 was previously HZ-BSA (for Prince Bandar). Both aircraft allocated to No. 1 Squadron, King Faisal Air Base, Riyadh.

RSAF Medical Services
HZ-MS3 GIII 385 March 1983
HZ-MS4 GII 103 January 1985
HZ-MSD GII 256 September 1980
Operates specially configured medevac aircraft for senior members of Saudi Royal family, in conjunction with Saudi Arabian Airlines (formerly Saudia).

Royal Saudi Air Defence Command
HZ-ADC GIV 1037
HZ-ADC was previously a GII (s/n 187) between 1977 and 1988.

Saudi Special Flight Services
HZ-AFH GII 171 May 1976
HZ-AFI GII(TT) 201 December 1977
HZ-AFJ GII(TT) 203 December 1977
HZ-AFK GII(TT) 239 June 1979
HZ-AFN GIII 364 September 1982
HZ-AFR GIII 410 July 1984
HZ-RC3 GIII 331 July 1982
HZ-AFU GIV 1031 July 1990
HZ-AFV GIV 1035 September 1989
HZ-AFW GIV 1038 August 1991
HZ-AFX GIV 1143 March 1991
HZ-AFY GIV 1166 September 1991
HZ-MFL GIV 1128 February 1991
HZ-AFY was previously HZ-SAR. HZ-RC3 is operated on behalf of the Saudi Royal Commission (and is registered to the Directorate of General Jubail & Yanbu Projects). Special Flight Services is a division of Saudi Arabian Airlines. Aircraft are based at Jeddah and provide worldwide VIP transport for government officials. Associated division of Saudi Arabian Airlines operates VIP fleet of quasi-civilian aircraft in close association with RSAF and Armed Forces Medical Services (q.v.).

Presidency of Civil Aviation
HZ-PCA GII 179 December 1979
Previously HZ-CAD

SWEDEN

Svenska Flygvapnet/Swedish air force
102001/021 Tp 102A 1014 October 1992
102002/022 S 102B 1215 August 1995
102003/023 S 102B 1216 October 1995
Single Tp 102A VIP transport attached to the Sambandsflygrupp (liaison flight), F16 Wing, based at Uppsala. In practice, aircraft is based at Broma airport, Stockholm. Two heavily-modified S 102Bs acquired as Elint/Sigint reconnaissance aircraft, and are operated in this role by Malflygdivisionen 85, at Malmen. Tp 102A is a Gulfstream IV. S 102B are Gulfstream IV-SPs.

TURKEY

Turk Hava Kuvvetleri (Turkish air force)
12-003 GIV 1163 March 1992
(GAC delivery October 1991)
Aircraft operated by 224 'Dogan' (hawk) Filo (squadron), Hava Ulasim Genel Komutanligi (air transport general command), based at Etimesgut. 224 Filo is attached to 12 Hava Ulasim Ussu (12 air transport base), Erkilet, but reports directly to air force HQ.

Basbakanlik The Office of the Prime Minister
TC-ATA GIV 1043
(GAC delivery August 1988)
TC-GAP GIV 1027
(GAC delivery May 1988)
In 1987 a GIII (TC-GAP s/n 487) was also operated. Prior to this two US-registered GIIs were operated on lease.

UGANDA

Ugandan Air Force
5X-UOI GIII 345 December 1993
Operated by Entebbe-based Transport Unit on government/VIP duties. 5X-UOI replaced GII(TT) 5X-UPF (s/n 133).

UNITED STATES OF AMERICA

US Department of Commerce
N49RF GIV-SP 1246 December 1994
Operated by ***National Oceanographic and Oceanic Administration*** (NOAA) as a 'hurricane hunter' for storm/weather research. Aircraft is based at MacDill AFB, Florida and flies in support of National Hurricane Operations Plan synoptic surveillance mission. Modified by E-Systems with Main Aircraft Data System and Hurricane Analysis and Processing System, comprising new radar, GPS-equipped dropsonde and eight operator's stations in cabin. Has near-real time satcom capability. Entered service with NOAA in July 1996.

Federal Aviation Administration
N1 GIV 1071 May 1989
VIP transport for senior members of Administration. Registration reserved for 'flagship' transport of FAA.

Massachussetts Institute of Technology (MIT), AFMC
N105TB GII 031
Currently operated by MIT's Lincoln Laboratories establishment (since 1993) on classified research work, for AFMC's Electronic Systems Center, Hanscom AFB. The aircraft is listed as registered to AFMC. Fitted with underwing equipment test pods and has a modified nose with additional sensor/antenna pods under the redesigned radome. Previously registered as N200CC. Lincoln Labs formerly operated two GIs.

National Aeronautics and Space Administration (NASA)
N1NA GIII 309 January 1990
N944NA GII(STA) 144 May 1983
N945NA GII(STA) 118 February 1987
N946NA GII(STA) 146 September 1976
N947NA GII(STA) 147 September 1976
N948NA GII 222 May 1991
Flagship GIII 'NASA One' is attached to NASA's Office of Aeronautics and based at Langley Research Center, Virginia. GII(STA) aircraft are attached to NASA's Office of Space Flight, and based at Lyndon B. Johnson Space Center, Ellington ANGB. N945NA was previously propfan testbed N650PF. N946NA first flew in STA configuration on 29 September 1975 and was delivered to NASA on 15 September 1976. N947NA first flew as STA on 1 March 1976 and was delivered to NASA on 13 September 1976. N948NA is operated as a transport, and based at the Johnson Space Center.

US Coast Guard
01 C-20B 477 June 1994
Acquired from the USAF (86-0205) on 31 June 1994, replacing GII (VC-11A) 01. This aircraft (s/n 023), was delivered in July 1968 and sold in May 1995, to Tyler Jet Aircraft Sales, Inc., Texas (N7TJ). USCG also operates GI 02 (s/n 091), as a VC-4A.

VENEZUELA

Fuerza Aérea Venezuela
0004 GII 124 June 1981
0005 GIII 400 January 1984
Gulfstreams are flown by dedicated VIP unit Escuadrón 41, Base Area 'Generalisimo Francisco de Miranda', La Carlota, Caracas. Esc 41 also operates GI 8565 (s/n 194).

Bids for the ASTOR competition included a version of the U-2S from Lockheed-Martin and the E-8 J-STARS, from Northrop Grumman. Despite intense pressure (most notably on behalf of the E-8 bid) both these approaches were rejected in favour of two teams, led by Raytheon E-Systems and Lockheed-Martin. Both groups unveiled their ASTOR competitors at the 1996 Farnborough air show. Lockheed Martin selected the Gulfstream V, while the Raytheon E-Systems bid is based on the Bombardier (Canadair) Global Express airframe, which was chosen without the team requesting detailed information on the Gulfstream V. The Raytheon bid incorporates a modified Hughes Aircraft ASARS-2 radar, as fitted to the U-2S. Raytheon will be partnered by GEC-Marconi, Thomson-CSF and Short Brothers, amongst others. The engineering for the Global Express modifications, and at least the first major airframe modification, will all be undertaken at E-Systems, Greenville, Texas.

TeamASTOR members

The prime systems integrator for the Gulfstream V-based bid will be Lockheed Martin UK (until 1996 Loral UK Government Systems, and previously IBM Federal Systems). Marshall Aerospace, at Cambridge, will take delivery of 'green' Gulfstream V airframes from Savannah and undertake all necessary engineering modifications – and all test and development work will be done in the UK. Racal's Radar Systems Division will be the UK design authority for ASTOR's dual mode radar. Logica is the communications system 'architect' and will supply all communications equipment. GEC-Marconi Defence Systems is a significant subcontractor to TeamASTOR and will supply the aircraft's Defensive Aids Subsystem (DAS) along with contractorised logistical support (as is already being given to the RAF Tornado force). Both ASTOR teams completed their project definition studies in July 1997 and submitted their 'best and final' offers to the UK MoD in February 1998.

Five ASTOR platforms will be acquired, along with an estimated eight reconfigurable ground stations (two for headquarters use and six for tactical deployment). TeamASTOR chose the Gulfstream V in preference to the Global Express (G-X) because of its proven performance and simple, robust design. The GV was 12-18 months ahead in certification terms while the G-X was, and still is (at time of writing), in flight test. The airframe also permits a good radar 'view'. The wingbox of the GV is much further back than the G-X and this allows the radar antenna to be substantially longer – a crucial consideration for MTI performance. Tunnel testing to fine tune the final airframe configuration was conducted at Lockheed's Marietta facility. This configuration has been modified on several occasions, the most notable change being the repositioning of the satcom saddle antenna on the spine, to alleviate buffet.

The Gulfstream V-based ASTOR design will have a flight crew of two and a mission crew of three. Two image analysts (one for SAR, one for MTI) will work with a mission controller, who will manage the mission workload and undertake some analysis tasks. The Racal Radar Defence System multi-mode SAR/MTI radar is based on Searchwater 2000 technology and is a

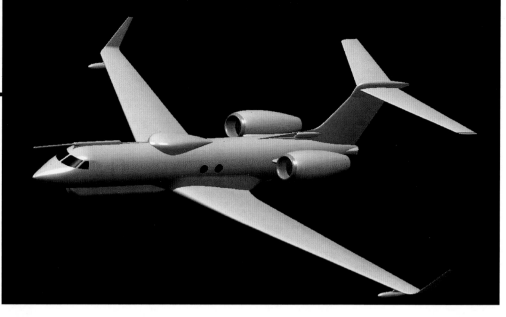

Lockheed Martin UK leads the TeamASTOR bid for the British ASTOR airborne stand-off radar competition. TeamASTOR's bid is based on the Gulfstream V airframe, which has also been selected by Northrop Grumman to carry a repackaged J-STARS system.

single-sided, electronically-scanned, phased-array (using antenna modules supplied by Texas Instruments). SAR processing hardware/software is the responsibility of Lockheed Martin, who will also develop the common datalink. ASTOR requires three datalinks: a two-way, narrow-band 'Quickfire' link for MTI target hand-over; a JTIDS/Link 16 system to relay the 'air picture' to/from AWACs, or to other ASTORs coming on station; the wide-band common datalink, capable of sending SAR imagery to two ground stations, simultaneously, or to J-STARS. Datalinking will allow the ASTOR to operate 'on tether', but the aircraft will also have an important 'off tether' role where the onboard operators/analysts are more important. In a crisis ASTOR might rapidly deploy to operate 'off tether' until ground stations could catch up. Team ASTOR's Gulfstream V will also be fitted with dual HF radios and three VHF/UHF radios, and SHF satcom system (perhaps the same system as selected for Nimrod 2000). The DAS system will comprise a radar warning receiver, missile approach warning system, towed radar decoy and chaff/flare launchers. Both pilots will have a DAS display. There will be no wing hardpoints available to the DAS so the radar decoy (a GEC-Marconi Ariel) will presumably be fitted in a housing on the tail of the aircraft.

An important role in the UK

Gulfstream has a long association with the UK aerospace industry. All 1,000+ aircraft delivered over the past 40 years have been powered by Rolls-Royce engines, and Marshall Aerospace has been a service and modification centre for Gulfstreams for 38 years. In fact, it could be argued that since Raytheon transferred the Hawker production line to Wichita in 1995, the Gulfstream IV-SP has had the highest UK-built content of any business aircraft available.

A contract award for the ASTOR winner (worth £750 million as announced by the MoD) is expected by September 1998, at the latest, and the system is scheduled to enter service in 2003. The Royal Navy is expected to take an active stake in the programme in the near future and the RAF is likely to build up a

'stand-off intelligence gathering triad' around the new aircraft, that will also include the Nimrod R.Mk 1 and E-3D Sentry. This will echo the moves already being made by Sweden in its S 102B/S 100B teaming. A successful introduction of ASTOR by the UK will also position the chosen system to fulfill the NATO AGS (Airborne Ground Surveillance) requirement – for which the E-8 J-STARS was rejected in November 1997. A decision on the preferred AGS system is expected in April 1998. The ASTORs are expected to be based at RAF Waddington, with an additional permanent ground station at RAF St Mawgan. A joint RAF/Army ASTOR unit of "some considerable size" will be established and the final aircraft is scheduled for delivery in 2005.

In November 1997 Northrop Grumman were allowed to re-enter the ASTOR competition with the J-STARS system, in a move seen by many as politically-driven by intense US government pressure. On 16 January 1998 the surprise news emerged that Northrop Grumman had decided to mate a repackaged J-STARS radar fit with the Gulfstream V airframe, for ASTOR. The original J-STARS bid was based on the E-8/Boeing 707 airframe, and was rejected. It is not clear what effect this new move may have on the specifics of the Lockheed Martin-led TeamASTOR bid – particularly as Lockheed Martin are currently attempting to merge with Northrop Grumman.

Looking to the future

Gulfstream Aerospace Corporation delivered its 1,000th aircraft in late 1997. For the first time in its history, Gulfstream is now a 'two aircraft company', with GIV-SP and GV production continuing side-by-side. If anything, demand for the GIV has increased in recent

years. As the GV comes on line, Gulfstream begins the transition from building 26 aircraft of one type per year, to 60 of two types per year, by 1999. This may prove to be a tall order – both aircraft are built on different jigs with about 20 per cent commonality. 'Green' (not outfitted) prices for each aircraft, in 1997, stood at $24.5 million for a GIV and $29.5 million for a GV. GAC has completed a new 200,000-sq ft (18580-m²) service centre at Savannah to allow accommodation of up to 12 GVs alongside GIV-SPs. The production facility has also been enlarged. Several new military customers are currently negotiating with GAC for VIP and special missions aircraft. Gulfstream also has high hopes that a positive decision in favour of TeamASTOR will favour a similar bid for the NATO AGS. In 1996 GAC delivered 27 aircraft and this total climbed to (approximately) 50 in 1997 – a huge total in a market where every single sale is hard-fought and hard-won. By the end of December 1997, in service Gulfstream Vs had amassed 1,781 hours, 781 flights and of these 777 were dispatched on time (99.5 per cent). None of the four missed flights involved a customer aircraft. Demand for the Gulfstream IV-SP is higher than ever and GAC has drawn up plans for an SRA-5 special missions variant. 1998 will see the introduction of the USAF's C-37s and the ever increasing likelihood of more orders from military customers who recognise the Gulfstream's unique talents.

Robert Hewson

with additional material by **Robert F. Dorr**

The Gulfstream family has grown from modest beginnings (as an elegant turboprop) into a capable family of long-range, high-altitude special mission aircraft, that are now far more than simple transports.

Sikorsky H-53
In the United States Marine Corps

Sikorsky's ubiquitous H-53 family plays an essential part in the US Marine Corps' inventory. The versatile CH-53D and the bulkier but more capable CH-53E are the Corps' primary heavylift helicopters – and invaluable power projection assets. They are partnered by small numbers of RH-53Ds and MH-53Es. At present 15 front- and second-line Marine units fly the H-53 and will continue to do so for many years to come.

It was the US Marine Corps who brought Sikorsky's mighty Sea Stallion to life. Although the CH-53 later became justifiably famous in the hands of the US Air Force – during the final years of the Vietnam War it operated as the 'Super Jolly Green Giant' rescue helicopter – it would never have existed without the Marines, who initiated its design and development. By the early 1960s the Marine Corps had recognised the benefits of a heavylift helicopter to rapidly move personnel and equipment from ship to shore. The pioneer in this role was Sikorsky's HR2S-1 (CH-37C), the 'cross-eyed monster'. However, this helicopter was an outdated, temperamental design that was becoming less and less able to meet the demands made of it. In October 1960 the Marines submitted a requirement for a new helicopter, which lead to the HH(X) competition of March 1962. Several novel solutions were proposed, but in July 1962 Sikorsky's twin-engined S-65 design was selected; it was built as the YCH-53A (see *World Air Power Journal* Volume 4).

The aircraft first flew in October 1964 and the first CH-53A found its way to the Marines in September 1965. After 141 A-model CH-53s had been built at Sikorsky's plant in Stratford, Connecticut, 126 of the more powerful CH-53D model followed (first flown in 1969). By February 1972 a mine-sweeping version of the CH-53D, the RH-53D, had flown, and the first aircraft entered service with HM-12 in mid-1973. By then a radically-new development of the Sea Stallion was on the horizon. The CH-53E boasted three T-64-GE-415 turboshafts, a seven-bladed main rotor, a longer fuselage and new tail unit. The first prototype YCH-53E flew on 1 March 1974. The first (pre-) production CH-53E flew on 8 December 1980 and the Marine CH-53E unit (HMH-464) reached IOC in February 1981. A dedicated mine-sweeping version, the MH-53E, followed in December 1981. While several Air Force versions of the CH-53 were developed, most notably today's MH-53J Pave Low III, the aircraft remains at heart a naval helicopter, and in practice it is the Marines who need it most.

Today's CH-53s

The primary mission of the CH-53 is to move cargo (carried internally and externally) and equipment. Secondary is the transferring and movement of troops ashore in an amphibious assault. The CH-53E has an incredible lifting ability, as one CH-53 pilot observed: "it has the capability to lift the weight of 10 TH-57C Sea Rangers together." The US Marines operate four versions – the RH-53D, the MH-53E, the CH-53D and the CH-53E. The CH-53D has a pair of General Electric

T64-GE-413 engines (rated at 3,925 shp/2924 kW each) and the RH-53D has T64-GE-415s (rated at 4,380 shp/3263 kW each). The more powerful CH-53E has three General Electric T64-GE-416 engines. In addition to the T64-GE-416, a minority of the Marine CH-53Es are equipped with T64-GE-416A engines. The 'Alpha' engines are products of orders placed by the Navy and can be found in MH-53Es also. The T64-GE-416As can be run hotter, in addition to producing a little more power. The trio of T64-GE-416s are rated at 4,380 shp (3267 kW) per individual engine continuous and at 13,141 shp (9803 kW) for 10 minutes. The engines have anti-ice systems and, since the aircraft has a dual digital automatic flight control system, it is rated as an all-weather machine. The 'Echos' are all around larger helicopters than the 'Deltas'. Their redesigned vertical tail is canted 20° to port, which helps counter the increased torque.

Sea Dragons

The most recent H-53 variant to join the Marines is the MH-53E Sea Dragon, which is primarily flown by the Navy. The USMC does the training for all its H-53 units, and New River-based HMT-302 has five of the special-purpose machines. The aircraft's speciality is AMCM (Airborne Mine CounterMeasures) and it can readily be identified by the extra-large sponsons on the fuselage. They were designed this way so that the MH-53E could carry significantly more fuel, allowing up to six hours on station without refuelling. The MH-53E has usurped the mission of the RH-53D, and the RH-53Ds left in the inventory (HMH-772) have been stripped of their gear and are now used in the same role as the CH-53Ds.

The CH-53 has many nicknames, one of which – the 'Hog' – reflects its large size and

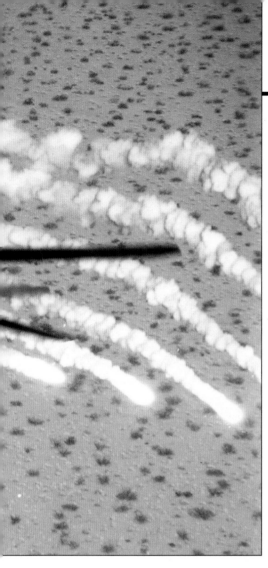

Above: This CH-53E is flown by HMH-464 'Condors', one of two USMC CH-53 units based at MCAS New River, North Carolina.

Left: The CH-53E is fitted with twin ALE-39B dispensers and can carry up to 60 flares. The Tracor-built ALE-39 can carry chaff, flares or radar decoys but is only loaded with IR flares when used with the CH-53. The CH-53D is not yet fitted with such a self-protection system.

pugnacious appearance (*i.e.*, big, dirty, oily and mean-looking). The 'Hog' tag has evolved into 'Pig' and 'Piggy'. Another size-derived nickname is 'Bigiron'. The most common nickname is 'Shitter': a trail of black smoke pours from the CH-53D/E's engines, the back end of the fuselage is covered with soot, and it tends to have leaky engines, hydraulic and transmission fluids. Since there are two models of CH-53 in the USMC inventory, the CH-53D is often referred to as the 'Delta' and CH-53E as the 'Echo'. CH-53Ds can also be 'Dumpsters', both because that is another 'd word' and the aircraft has a rectangular shape. CH-53D crews will also refer to their aircraft as the 'Corvette' because it is more manoeuvrable than the larger CH-53E.

The standard '53' has a crew of four: the HAC (Helicopter Aircraft Commander), the

co-pilot, the crew chief, and the aerial observer. The HAC can be found in either the left- or right-hand seat, although for aerial refuelling, boat landings or initial NVG he will always be in the right-hand seat. The crew chief sits in the forward right area of the cabin and the aerial observer (AO) in the forward left cabin, where they can easily swap positions. The CH-53 crew is noted to total three in most text books, but with the Marine Corps the AO is almost always present due to mission requirements and is onboard 99 per cent of the time. The crew chief is senior to the AO and is responsible for the cabin area.

Although large, the CH-53E is surprisingly fast, and has a (limited) maximum airspeed of 150 kt (172 mph; 277 km/h). The machine is capable of much faster airspeeds, but the 150-kt

limit helps minimise engine and airframe wear/stress. The CH-53D started out with a 170-kt (195-mph; 314-km/h) restriction, which was later reduced to 130 kt (150 mph; 240 km/h) to increase its airframe life. When CH-53Es were first introduced, they also had a 170-kt maximum, but the '53 Echo' can exceed 200 mph (231 km/h) if necessary. One problem with the CH-53E at high speeds is that the tail section is subject to high-frequency vibration, which is bad for the airframe and the long-term lives of various components. Other limits for the CH-53E are 35 kt (40 mph; 65 km/h) in sideways flight, 30 kt (34 mph; 55 km/h) in rearward flight, 150 kt (172 mph; 277 km/h) with external loads and 130 kt (150 mph; 240 km/h) for manoeuvring. The main gear is certified for the maximum airspeed (150 kt), although it is recommended that the gear not be dropped at speeds of more than 140 kt (160 mph; 258 km/h). In high winds, the CH-53 rotor engagement, pylon and blade-folding cannot be conducted when wind-

The Marines operate a mix of CH-53E Super Stallions and the smaller, twin-engined CH-53D Sea Stallion. The CH-53D lacks the refuelling probe of the larger aircraft. This CH-53D is a HMH-463 aircraft, while the 'E' is from HMH-361.

Above: A total of 126 CH-53Ds was delivered to the Marines, by 1972, replacing the CH-53A which entered service in 1966. Note the 0.50-cal machine gun mounted in the forward cabin door of this HMH-463 Stallion.

Left: The RH-53D was delivered as a dedicated mine-countermeasures (MCM) helicopter, but all remaining aircraft – such as this HMH-769 example – have now been converted to transports.

Below: The USMC's current MCM helicopter is the MH-53E Sea Dragon, based on the more powerful CH-53E. It is fitted with a 30,000-lb (13636-kg) tension tow boom, for towing both magnetic and electronic sweeping gear.

speed exceeds 45 kt (52 mph; 83 km/h). Flying a 360° turn in the hover within 15 seconds is also prohibited. The 'Hog' is restricted to a 60°, 45° or 30° angles of bank depending on aircraft weight, airspeed, altitude, external loads and other factors. These limits are for normal, peacetime operations but they can, and do, become secondary if circumstances demand it. Maximum g limits are +2g/-0.5g, and empty (with no fuel) the CH-53E tips the scale at 36,000 lb (16363 kg). With a full load of fuel and crew of four, the CH-53E weighs around 53,000 lb (24090 kg).

Self-defence systems

The CH-53D, RH-53D and CH-53E all carry the AN/ALE-39 flare/chaff dispensers. Known as 'buckets', two (one per side) are attached to the rear fuselage and can hold 30 cartridges (or 'expendables') each. The CH-53D can carry an AN/ALQ-157(V)2 IRCM set (IR jammers). The 'Echo' currently is not equipped to carry the system but this option is being explored. The CH-53D/E can carry two XM-218 0.50-in machine-guns for area suppression – another good reason for having a crew of four. A pair of lighter and faster-firing 7.62-mm M-60 machine-guns can be carried *in lieu* of the 0.50-in guns, but rarely are because the latter have more punch and better range.

The maximum gross 'weight on wheels' weight is 69,750 lb (31704 kg). Such a figure will seldom be reached since the cubic area of

the cabin will almost always be filled before the weight limitation is achieved. If an external load is added, the CH-53E's (theoretical) maximum gross weight climbs to 73,500 lb (33409 kg). The CH-53E is capable of lifting loads up to 36,000 lb (16363 kg) – the maximum load for the hook. The 'Delta' has a single-point hook attach system, but when the 'Echo' was designed a dual-point hook was added to allow greater stability and higher transit speeds when

hauling an 'external'. The CH-53E still retains the capability of carrying external loads via a single- or dual-point system.

A rarely used hydraulic utility/rescue hoist is mounted over the crew door. In the event that a CH-53E were to rescue a pilot using the hoist, the helicopter would have to hover at a minimum of 80-100 ft (128-160 m) above the ground to minimise the rotor wash. The hoist can lift up to 600 lb (272 kg) and has 245 ft (75 m)

of usable cable. The basic CH-53E is not a rescue aircraft and would only be used in an extreme emergency – which is not to say such a mission would never happen. However, landing in an LZ for a rescue would be the method of choice. The hoist can be used for HIFR (Helicopter In-Flight Refueling) operations from a ship that is not capable of CH-53 landings, such as an 'Aegis'-class guided missile frigate. In this scenario, the CH-53 would hover over the aft area of the ship, a refuelling hose would be attached to the winch and hauled into the aircraft, and the helicopter would hover while taking on fuel. This is not the most efficient method for refuelling, since the fuel burn rate is high when in a hover, but it can be a lifesaver.

The fuel tanks of the 'Echo' hold 2,277 US gal (8620 litres) of JP-4 (Jet B), JP-5 (Jet A-1), or JP-8. There are three internal fuel tanks, two holding 300 US gal (1135 litres) each and one 377 US gal (1427 litres), and the external auxiliary tanks carrying 650 US gal (2460 litres) each. The auxiliary tanks are only removed for maintenance but can be jettisoned in an emergency. Endurance of the CH-53E can be as long as 4.5 hours if required. It carries about 15,000 lb (6818 kg) of fuel and the burn rate is around 3,300-3,600 lb (1496-1633 kg) per hour, depending on aircraft weight and power

Marine H-53s still operate in a variety of colour schemes – not least the transport fleet of CH-53D/Es (and RH-53Ds) which wear a variety of overall green, green/grey camouflage and low-visibility grey finishes.

settings. The CH-53E can carry a trio of FAVs (Fast Attack Vehicles), or Jeeps with one of a 0.50-in gun, a Mk 19 grenade launcher or a TOW missile launcher mounted on top.

Designed for deployments aboard naval vessels, both the CH-53D and E have an automatic blade-folding system which is also used when the helicopter is tied down on land in high winds, or in the 'barn' (hangar) for certain maintenance procedures, or when the helicopter is being airlifted by C-5. When the hydraulic system is activated using the APP (Auxiliary Power Plant), it automatically aligns the rotors before the folding commences. A panel in the cockpit (left-hand pilot's side) has the switches for both the pylon- and blade-folding mechanisms. As soon as a CH-53 lands on a ship, the blades are quickly folded to maximise precious space. When folding is taking place, the crew chief watches from outside to verify that the system is functioning properly.

Offloading the troops

When carrying troops, the preferred method for rapid egress is to land in an LZ and open the ramp. Unlike the CH-53D with its very small 'hell hole' (the internal hatch opening in the centre of the cabin floor), the CH-53E allows troops to quickly 'fast rope' down through its larger hell hole. The troops wear gloves to brake their descent down the rope. This fast roping is essential for moving troops to building tops, small ships, or off-shore oil platforms. Because of the substantial rotor wash, CH-53s

When compared to the CH-53D, the CH-53E's extended fuselage, larger tail and three-engined configuration are all belied by its sleeker shape. There are currently nine USMC units equipped with the 'Echo' and this aircraft is attached to HMH-465 'Warhorses', at MCAS Tustin.

do not perform the SPIE (Special Patrolling Insertion Extraction) rigging mission. CH-53s also carry specialist PJs (parachute jumpers). Normal parachute operations are conducted at altitudes of 1,500 ft (457 m) or higher. A static line is used so all chutes are automatically deployed. On one pass, up to 24 Marines can jump. Another method is the HALO (High Altitude Low Opening) jump, which often is used by Special Forces personnel such as SEALS, Force Recon, or Army Special Forces. They jump at about 10,000 ft (3048 m) and free-fall, opening their chutes at a predetermined altitude; this gives them the element of surprise.

Today almost all CH-53Es are NVG-compatible, with the exception of a few aircraft attached to the training unit, HMT-302. NVGs are sensitive to red and white light, which causes a 'blooming out' effect, overloading the tubes and blinding the pilot. Thus, the NVG-configured CH-53s have NVG-friendly blue/green instrument panels and cabin lights.

New to the CH-53E community is the addition of a FLIR system. The system, known as the HNVS (Helicopter Night Vision System), can be used in conjunction with NVGs. The Hughes-manufactured HNVS AN/AAQ-16 is

This HMH-461 CH-53E is delivering rubber fuel bladders to a Marine exercise area. The 'Echo' can carry up to 36,000 lb (16300 kg) on its cargo hook. It might not be able to travel far with such a huge load, but the capability is invaluable.

permanently affixed to the forward left fuselage. A long support member attaches to the bottom of the fuselage and the black-coloured turret FLIR unit (TFU) is secured to the distal end, opposite the refuelling probe, on the right side of the aircraft. One component of the HNVS is the AN/AAQ-16 PDU (Panel Display Unit), found in the cockpit. The PDU necessitates a new instrument panel with relocated 'FLIR friendly' instruments and gauges. In addition to the TFU and PDU, there also is a joystick (or Multi-Function Control Unit/MFCU) in the cockpit that controls the rotation of the TFU.

Marine Corps CH-53 squadrons often are tasked with doing business in adverse weather or at night, using NVGs (ANVIS-6). Although NVGs make night operations possible, they are limited in low-light conditions such as overcast skies or blowing sand, and even in an excess of ambient light (caused by flares, gunfire explosions or bright city lighting, for example). Though FLIR systems have their own limitations, for the most part they complement NVGs and each system compensates for the other's weaknesses. The HNVS is used to detect obstacles, to ID checkpoints, and to locate landing zones. The

HNVS has been deemed 'very effective' by CH-53E crews that have flown with it, but at this time there are no plans to add it to the ageing CH-53D.

When the HNVS system is added to the CH-53Es, an embedded GPS is also installed in the cockpit. A new ARC-210 radio soon follows. The ARC-210 replaces the ARC-182 and both are UHF/VHF/FM capable. The ARC-210 is state-of-the-art technology, is more user friendly, and updates the radio system to today's standards. Some CH-53Es have the GPS or radio added prior to an HNVS upgrade.

Pilot seats with increased crash resistance are being added as well, and are rated for 10*g*. The new seats feature a five-point harness (compared to the previous four points), are known as VLEA (variable-load energy absorber) and are crash-attenuating. The pilot simply dials in his weight and the seat 'strokes' with the proper resistance on impact, acting as a shock absorber.

Flying the 'Bigiron'

When asked about flying the CH-53E, most 'Bigiron' pilots make the point that the CH-53E is one of very few helicopters – and virtually the only Western design – to offer true heavylift, with a payload up to 36,000 lb (16363 kg). In the words of one senior pilot, "I am impressed how easy it is to forget that you are flying a 100-ft (160-m) aircraft that weighs 53,000 lb (24090 kg) empty. The 'Bigiron' handles with such ease and precision that it is easy to lose sight of how massive it actually is. (We can) support ground combat elements and move most of their equipment, such as LAVs, M-198s, HMMWVs ('Hummers'), other aircraft, and engineering equipment. Long-range raids, with our inflight-refuelling ability, give us a true over-the-horizon capability to project power deep into hostile territory.

"(Compared to the 'Delta') the 'Echo' has a lot more power, a larger rotor disk, an extra rotor blade, and a third engine. The CH-53E generates a lot more torque, which is why the 'Echo' has the canted tail, a true engineering marvel. When flying the 53E, a dual computer AFCS system linked to the controls lets you feel as you manoeuvre the aircraft. It will keep you from manoeuvring in a manner that will lead to overstressing the airframe. The 53D has the older AFCS (Automatic Flight Control System) which is more seat-of-the-pants flying. Unlike the CH-53D, the CH-53E has such great power that typically there is not a need to monitor it closely. When deployed to areas that are higher and/or hotter, the need to monitor the power becomes more important due to a decrease in power available. The CH-53D crews need to be much more concerned with monitoring power with their less powerful machines. When I transitioned from the CH-53D to the CH-53E, I was really impressed with how much extra power it had.

Hauling a 'Hummer', this CH-53E is passing over a secure weapons storage compound, near Twentynine Palms. Twentynine Palms has a rough airstrip and ground facilities that replicate a deployed forward-operating location.

*Above: This **HMH-461 CH-53E** is landing at Twentynine Palms, the large **USMC** airfield and desert manoeuvre area, in California. Twentynine Palms is about 150 miles (241 km) east of Riverside, California and hosts a series of combined arms exercises ('CAX') each year.*

*Right: All who fly the **CH-53** are impressed by the spritely handling qualities of the big helicopter. It is only fatigue/airframe life considerations that limit the **CH-53E's** indulgence in the extreme bank angles (up to 90°) of which the seven-bladed titanium rotor system is easily capable.*

"The 53 'Echo' has a fantastic lifting capability, terrific speed, and can easily carry up to 36 combat troops. Our speed enhances our survivability and we can even outrun our escorts, such as AH-1Ws, if need be. Our dual-point external capability is superior to the single point system. When carrying externals a higher airspeed can cause the load to swing, which can cause a dangerous situation if not watched. The dual-point system eliminates the chance of the load spinning and minimises the pendulum effect. The heavier the load, the easier it is to carry due to the stability of the weight. The lighter the load the trickier it gets because the load is affected by the airspeed and moves around a lot more. If a load is large the combination of wind effect and drag can actually turn the helicopter. Usually we do not have to fly very fast when carrying externals. In the event that a load becomes dangerous or unmanageable (very rare), 'pickle-pickle-pickle' is quickly called by the HAC and the load is dropped instantaneously. For a dual-point external, when one hook releases the other automatically releases as well, for safety.

"Static electricity is generated by all helicopters. The amount of static electricity is dependent on the size of the helicopter. The 'Delta' can give a pretty good shock to those not careful. The 'Echo' (potentially) can give an even more powerful shock due to its size and the static electricity generated. The Marines on the ground receiving the external load grab the hook using a grounding rod, which allows others to then touch the hook.

"Both the CH-53D and E are very manoeuvrable aircraft, and if need be we could do a 90° angle of bank. When I trained in the 'Deltas' in the early 1980s we did an evasive manoeuvres syllabus and then we went through the ACM (Air Combat Manoeuvres) syllabus. Now we train for defensive manoeuvres to avoid detection.

'Normally when landing or taking off, we do not like to exceed 40 kt (45 mph; 74 km/h) ground speed. We usually do a hover take-off since that is a good way to do a power check and make sure the numbers match. The service ceiling is around 18,000 ft (5487 m), but to reach that we would have to go on oxygen and normally we do not have a need to exceed 10,000 ft (3048 m).

"For take-off, we typically taxi out, bring the aircraft to a hover, check the weight and power numbers to ensure everything looks good, then push the nose over to generate forward airspeed, pull a little more power through translational lift, and off we go. We usually cruise in the CH-53E at speeds around 120-130 kt (138 mph; 222 km/h). The gear has a limiting speed of 150 kt (172 mph; 277 km/h), which isn't a factor since we do not exceed 150 kt anyway.

Each flying hour requires a lot of maintenance hours, and all CH-53 flight crews give credit to the ground crews that keep them flying. When asked about the CH-53E, one QA officer said, "My job is to make sure maintenance practices are done by the book and done safely. This means the work must be accomplished properly and without shortcuts. The CH-53E is the most labour-intensive aircraft in the USMC inventory and we have to spend about 25 maintenance hours per one flight hour. The 'Bigiron' has excellent reliability and likes to be flown often.

"Our squadron does not have any 'hangar queens'; we have 19 CH-53Es, some being ex-Navy birds. In performing my QA job, I enjoy learning things about the CH-53E that you normally wouldn't learn as a pilot. I spend a lot of time with maintenance people, mechanics, and tech reps. We have eight FLIR-equipped machines now and eventually all be upgraded. In this modification, the GPS is added and the HF radio must be moved. With the addition of the GPS, we can eliminate the older Omega nav system. The production CH-53E HNVS/FLIR system was first introduced to HMH-464 at the end of 1994. In July 1995 HMH-461 received its first GPS and late in 1996 we (HMH-461) received our first HNVS system.

"The TBO (time between overhaul) for the engines is at 2,400 hours and parts are replaced on an as-needed basis. A CH-53E engine can be changed in two hours, and maintenance access is very good, with access panels and quick disconnects. The airframes are not rated in hours since SDLMs replace the worn components. A typical 'Echo' in our unit has around 3,000 hours on it."

CH-53E pilots routinely practise inflight refuelling. The IFR (Inflight Refuelling Probe) probe is 10.52 ft (3.20 m) long when retracted and pneumatically extends to 21.96 ft (6.69 m) for refuelling. The probe utilises engine bleed air to pressurise the pneumatics, and takes one minute to fully extend and two minutes to retract. When shore-based, the CH-53Es leave their probes on at all times, other than during maintenance.

Deploying to the boat

When the 'Hogs' deploy aboard ships, the probes are sometimes removed, allowing the helicopter to be manoeuvred on the boat deck and to ride the elevators without potentially damaging the probe. The probe would be reinstalled for missions that require IFR. The CH-53Ds are not capable of inflight refuelling, but their sister RH-53D is. Some USMC KC-130s are NVG-compatible and others are not. An NVG-compatible Hercules will secure all of its incompatible navigation lights (by pulling the circuit breakers) and use other NVG-compatible (IR) lights. The non-NVG compatible Hercules can black out the aircraft lights and tape over their refuelling pod lights temporarily.

When asked about inflight refuelling in the CH-53E, one pilot said, "It doesn't matter what type of C-130 we refuel from (HC-130/KC-130/MC-130), they are all the same from our prospective. The one exception is the USMCR KC-130T, which is fully NVG-compatible. The other C-130s can be made NVG-compatible using some adhesive tape and pulling a few circuit breakers. Our typical helicopter aerial refuelling speeds are around 115-120 kt (132-138 mph; 212-222 km/h), and altitude ranges from 500-10,000 ft (152-3048 m). We like to use both JP-5 and JP-8, but tend to keep away from the more volatile JP-4, especially when on the boat.

IFR operations

"During normal training ops for aerial refuelling we will take on around 3,000-5,000 lb (1360-2268 kg) of fuel. When refuelling from a C-130, the length of the hose from the refuelling pod is 56 ft to 76 ft (17 m to 23 m). The drogue diameter is 46 in (1.18 m) and the centre portion is 27 in (11 cm). The best case transfer rate is 600 US gal (2271 litres) per minute and worst case is 150 US gal (568 litres). If we take 5,000 lb of fuel at a transfer rate of 600 US gal, it would take just over eight minutes to accomplish the offload. We have a check list that we go through prior to tanking. We close our engine air particle separators to ensure they deflect any fuel that could spray into the engines. Then we check the refuelling probe for function and also make sure all the windows are closed. The concern is that if there happens to be a fuel leak somewhere, it is possible that the fumes could get to you after a while.

"When tanking, the KC-130 normally joins up on us. We start by doing a head-to-head pass and then the KC-130 will turn in behind us. We work with our transponders and the TACAN's air-to-air mode to locate each other.

Clearly visible on this CH-53E is the black turret for the Hughes AN/AAQ-16 FLIR, or Helicopter Night Vision System (HNVS) now being retrofitted to the entire CH-53E fleet. All front-line CH-53Es are also NVG-compatible.

As it comes slowly abeam, we do a lead change and the Herc assumes the aerial refuelling commander role. Then we will fall into a pre-contact stabilised position, similar to a left echelon. We will start out on the left side and fly off points on the C-130s wing.

"Our refuelling speeds are around 115 to 120 kt, and their low speed drogue has a 120-kt maximum speed restriction. Some KC-130 pilots have commented that when they are that slow with a CH-53E on the drogue, they can actually feel the rotor wash boundary on the tail of the 'Herc'. The CH-53 is close to the Hercules while refuelling. Typical altitudes are 1,000-8,000 ft (304-2438 m) for us to refuel, but we can refuel at 500 ft if we had to."

The USMC's CH-53s will notionally be replaced by the V-22 Osprey, but the date for this is still uncertain, and far in the future. All of the Marine CH-53D assets have been moved to MCB Hawaii, Hawaii. The 'Deltas' are now tasked with a medium-lift mission, but the HMH squadron designations will remain. The vital heavylift mission is now solely the responsibility of the 'Echo'. The changes were made to reflect actual usage in Hawaii, particularly since the CH-46Es that previously performed the medium-lift have all gone stateside or to Okinawa. With the entire 'Delta' community at one base, spare parts, training and logistics are more convenient. No retirement date has been set for the CH-53D and none has even been proposed for the CH-53E.

Ted Carlson

The Marines' CH-53 fleet is destined to be replaced by the V-22 Osprey, which has been described as the 'USMC's number one aviation priority'. However, no timetable for this replacement has been set and the CH-53 will serve the Marines for another 10 years, or more.

Current US Marine Corps CH-53 Units

Squadron	Tailcode	Type	Base
HMH-361 'Flying Tigers'	YN	CH-53E	MCAS Tustin, California
HMH-362 'Ugly Angels'	YL	CH-53D	MCB Hawaii, Hawaii
HMH-363 'Red Lions'	YZ	CH-53D	MCB Hawaii, Hawaii
HMH-366 'Hammer Heads'	HH	CH-53D	MCB Hawaii, Hawaii
HMH-461 'Ironhorse'	CJ	CH-53E	MCAS New River, North Carolina
HMH-462 'Heavy Haulers'	YF	CH-53E	MCAS Tustin, California
HMH-463 'Pegasus'	YH	CH-53D	MCB Hawaii, Hawaii
HMH-464 'Condors'	EN	CH-53E	New River, North Carolina
HMH-465 'Warhorses'	YJ	CH-53E	MCAS Tustin, California
HMH-466 'Wolfpack'	YK	CH-53E	MCAS Tustin, California
HMH-769 'Roadhogs'	MS(R)	CH-53E	MCAS El Toro, California
HMH-772 'Flying Armadillos'	MT(R)	RH-53D/CH-53E	Willow Grove, Pennsylvania
HMT-301 'Windwalkers'	SU	CH-53D	MCB Hawaii HI (trng)
HMT-302 'Phoenix'	UT	CH-53E/MH-53E	MCAS New River, NC (trng)
HMX-1 'Night Hawks'	(MX)	CH-53E	MCAS Quantico, Virginia

Note: 'MX' is the assigned HMX-1 tailcode but is not now worn. Tustin CH-53Es are moving to MCAS El Toro, then to NAS Miramar, but there are concerns in the local community of mixing a large number of helicopters with a large number of F/A-18s at Miramar. There is also a possibility that the CH-53Es and CH-46Es could be moved elsewhere (to be determined).

Tupolev Tu-22 'Blinder' and Tu-22M 'Backfire'

Andrei Tupolev's instantly recognisable 'Blinder' and 'Backfire' bombers were two of the greatest Cold War symbols – on both sides of the Iron Curtain. The Tu-22 'Blinder' was an impressive achievement and had a surprisingly long service career. Surprising, as the aircraft faced bitter opposition in its early days from those in Moscow who believed the manned bomber was dead and the Tu-22 was not needed. Surprising also as the aircraft was hated by its crews and had an accident-ridden career. Nevertheless, the 'Blinder' paved the way for the Tu-22M 'Backfire', which was a very capable strike/attack aircraft, much feared by NATO planners. The 'Backfire' became one of the most controversial aircraft of its time, as the USSR and the USA argued endlessly about its capabilities during the SALT negotiations. Though the 'Backfire' also had its problems, the latest version – the Tu-22M3 'Backfire-C' – has largely solved these and is an important asset in today's cash-strapped Russian air force.

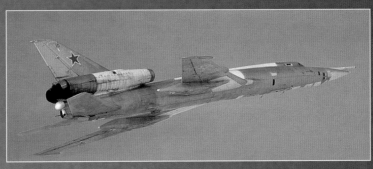

Right: Over its 35-year career Tupolev's Tu-22 has been developed into a series of mission-specific versions: the Tu-22B bomber, Tu-22R reconnaissance aircraft (as seen here), Tu-22K missile carrier, Tu-22P escort jammer and Tu-22U trainer.

Main picture and left: The 'Blinder' led to the swing-wing 'Backfire' which has evolved into the latest Tupolev Tu-22M3 'Backfire-C' version, optimised for low-level missions.

Tupolev Tu-22 'Blinder' and Tu-22M 'Backfire'

Above: Andrei Nikolaevich Tupolev was 70 years old when the Tu-22 (Project 105) made its maiden flight in 1958. As head of his Design Bureau, Tupolev oversaw the Tu-22 project, but the design team was led by chief designer Dmitri Markov. Tupolev's Design Bureau was famous for its bomber and large aircraft designs, whose lineage stretched back to the ANT-4/TB-1 of 1925. The four-engined ANT-6/TB-3 bomber of 1930 was one of the largest aircraft of its day. The five-engined ANT-16/TB-4 (1933) and eight-engined ANT-20 (1934) transports could carry 36 and 72 passengers, respectively. The ANT-25 set extraordinary long distance records, flying from Moscow non-stop to Washington state, in 1937. The Tu-2 (ANT-58) was the backbone of the Russian bomber force during the Great Patriotic War. After 1945, Tupolev developed his infamous B-29 copy, the Tu-4 'Bull', which led to the swept wing jet-propelled Tu-16 'Badger'. Other prototype jet bombers followed. The needle-nosed Tu-22 was thus not Tupolev's first jet bomber, but it was certainly his most adventurous.

The Tupolev Tu-22 'Blinder' and Tu-22M 'Backfire' represented a class of medium bombers that had largely disappeared in the United States Air Force by the 1960s. Although they were designed for strategic missions with nuclear weapons, they were not intended for intercontinental strike. Instead, they were intended for two distinctly different missions – continental strikes against strategic targets in Europe and Asia, and strikes against US Navy carrier battle groups.

The Tu-22 emerged during the most frigid years of the Cold War, the mid-1950s. Even in the wake of Stalin's death in 1953, and the end of the Korean War, relations between the superpowers remained tense. Complicating the confrontation were the enormous changes occurring in the very nature of modern warfare. The advent of nuclear weapons was at the heart of a revolution in military affairs that redefined the nature of military power. The Soviet Union had exploded its first atomic bomb, the RDS-1, in August 1949, and four years later exploded its first thermonuclear bomb, the RDS-6S. In spite of the power of these weapons and their American counterparts, there were serious problems with delivery. The United States had true intercontinental bombers – the B-36 and the new B-52 – but still depended on a significant number of medium bombers, the B-47 based in Europe, for any potential nuclear war with the Soviet Union. Britain also possessed a substantial strategic bomber force with its V-bombers. In addition, the US Navy provided the West with yet another possible means of delivery of nuclear weapons against the Soviet Union: its aircraft-carriers.

Early Tupolev bombers

In the face of these formidable forces, the Soviet Union possessed no reliable means of delivering its nuclear weapons, even within continental ranges against targets in Europe such as American and British bomber bases. As Soviet fighter regiments in Korea in 1950-51 had made clear, the World War II generation of piston-engined bombers, such as the B-29, were no match for modern jet fighters. At the time, the best-equipped regiments of the Soviet Long Range Aviation force were equipped with copies of the obsolete B-29, the Tupolev Tu-4. The Tu-4 was virtually worthless in the intercontinental delivery role due to its range limits and the lack of a significant refuelling

force. Harebrained schemes abounded to capture forward US bases for the Tu-4 in Greenland and in the Aleutians using a proposed new class of amphibious submarines, but they were more an indication of Soviet desperation than a realistic military option, and were not seriously pursued.

Shortly after World War II, Stalin established three secret organisations under the watchful eye of the sinister Lavrentiy Beria, head of the Soviet secret police. The First Chief Directorate was assigned the development of the Soviet atomic bomb, a programme which succeeded much sooner than American intelligence had anticipated. The Second Chief Directorate, under Dmitri Ustinov, was assigned the task of developing the platforms to deliver the nuclear weapons. The Third Chief Directorate was assigned the task of defending Moscow and other key cities against Anglo-American bomber attack.

The Second Chief Directorate sponsored at least four categories of weapons for the nuclear delivery task. Its most conventional programmes were two categories of bombers: an effort to develop medium bombers to strike Anglo-American bomber bases in Europe and Asia as well as US Navy carriers; and intercontinental bombers to strike the United States. The third programme was a revolutionary effort to develop nuclear armed ballistic missiles, first with ranges to strike targets in Europe, and eventually with the range to reach the United States. The fourth programme was to develop strategic cruise missiles to strike the USA and other objectives. This element remains the most secret to this day, as its projects, including the Lavochkin V-350 Burya, the Myasishchev RSS-40 Buran, the Ilyushin P-20 and the Tupolev Tu-121 Object S, were all failures.

One of the first successes of this effort was the Tupolev Tu-16 'Badger' medium bomber which began to enter serial production in 1954. This very durable aircraft would serve as the backbone of the Soviet Long Range Aviation regiments for many years, first carrying free-fall bombs, and later carrying stand-off missiles. However, in the mid-1950s, speed still remained the bomber's primary defence against fighters. Although the first crude air-to-air and surface-to-

air missiles had begun to appear, the bomber's primary opponent was the interceptor. A bomber's speed and high-altitude performance could drastically undermine the interceptor's chances of catching and engaging a bomber. Although the Tu-16 offered far superior performance to the Tu-4 in this regard, the subsonic 'Badger' emerged at a time when Britain and the United States were on the verge of fielding supersonic interceptors. It would grow increasingly vulnerable to its primary threat, so a supersonic medium bomber was needed.

Initial design efforts

Tupolev's Tu-22 was a response to the rapidly changing nature of strategic aerial warfare in the mid-1950s, intended as a supersonic replacement for the Tu-16 bomber much as the American B-58 Hustler was intended to replace the subsonic B-47 Stratojet. There is little evidence that any serious thought was given to competitive alternatives from Ilyushin or Myasishchev for this requirement. The early studies by the Tupolev OKB-156 design bureau in 1950-53 were not directed at a specific aircraft requirement, but rather at a variety of large supersonic aircraft that might have several roles, including as tactical strike aircraft, long-

range interceptors, medium and heavy bombers. This work began to coalesce in 1954 when the Tu-16 design was shifted into production. The supersonic aircraft programme received official government authorisation on 10 August 1954, in a decree from the Council of Ministers.

Wind tunnel studies were conducted at TsAGI in Zhukhovskii to determine the optimum configuration. Eventually, three preliminary design studies emerged: the Samolet 98 (Aircraft 98) tactical strike aircraft, the Samolet 103 medium bomber, and the Samolet 108 intercontinental missile carrier. Samolet 103 was the requirement that would result in the Tu-22, and was also known as Project Yu. The original conception of the Samolet 103 was an inexpensive evolutionary outgrowth of the Tu-16 with four Dobrynin VD-5 or VD-7 turbojet engines buried in the wingroot, stacked vertically two to a side. This design was far from satisfactory. In 1954 a design team under S. M. Yeger began to examine a more refined alternative, the Samolet 105, placing the twin jet engines in pods on either side of the tail. The fuselage and wing design was closer in conception to the Samolet 98 tactical strike aircraft than the Tu-16. Preliminary design was completed by the end of 1955, and detail design of sub-assemblies began.

Tupolev's Samolet 105, and the birth of the Tu-22 'Blinder'

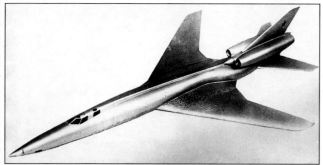

This Tupolev model (above) shows the original configuration of the Samolet (aircraft) 105, with its thicker wing and minus the undercarriage housings in the wing. The definitive Samolet 105A (below) had a reconfigured wing. An improved Mach 2-capable Samolet 106 design (right) was proposed, powered by Kuznetsov NK-6 engines housed in a common nacelle with a vertical 'shock wedge'. A T-tailed 106A with underwing engines was also proposed. Neither design proceeded.

Above and below: The 105 prototype was completed in December 1957 and is seen here before its 1958 flight tests. Among the detail differences between it and production aircraft are the nose windows for the navigator and the main undercarriage design, which retracted into the wing.

The prototype of the Samolet 105 was completed in December 1957 at the experimental plant of the design bureau near Moscow, and transferred to Zhukhovskii for flight trials. Debate over the defensive armament for the aircraft was protracted. The initial conception was for a pair of aft-mounted TKB-494 cannon, and the second for a pair of twin 23-mm cannon mounted above.

The trials of Samolet 105

The 105 design was far more complicated than any previous Tupolev aircraft, and the first flight did not occur until 21 June 1958. As in other bomber designs of the day, the lack of maturity of contemporary jet engines was a continual handicap, and many alternative engines were considered. In addition, wind tunnel tests at TsAGI in Zhukhovskii were revealing the nature of area rule for supersonic flight. By the time the first prototype had flown, the new Kuznetsov NK-6 engines were completing their design phase. As a result, in April 1958 a Council of Ministers decree authorised a major redesign, completing the second prototype in the Samolet 105A configuration with the NK-6 engines and a fuselage redesigned with area rule. In the end, the NK-6 was not ready in time, and the Samolet 105A was built with the VD-7M engine instead. A

thinner wingroot on the aircraft led to the adoption of separate nacelles for the undercarriage, as on the Tu-16. Other changes in the 105A included yet another alteration of the defensive armament, this time to the DK-20 tail gun barbette system with the R-23 (261P) cannon, directed by a PRS-3 Argon-2 radar and a TP-1 remote television, for the gunner in the cabin. Two prototypes were built, one for flight trials and the other for static tests. The well known Tupolev engineer D. S. Markov assumed the role of chief designer in 1959.

The first test flight of the Samolet 105A took place on 7 September 1959. Flight trials proved so promising that the Samolet 105A was authorised to enter production at State Aviation Plant No. 22 in Kazan in 1959, replacing the Tu-16 on the assembly lines there. The programme was stalled on 21 December 1959 when the prototype was lost on its seventh test flight due to control surface flutter. Test pilot Yu. T. Alasheyev stayed with the aircraft in an attempt to save it, joined by the navigator, whose K-22 ejection seat had failed. Both crewmen were lost, but the radio operator ejected (at a speed of 1380 km/h; 857 mph) and was able to inform the investigation committee of what had occurred. In spite of the accident, production of the Samolet 105A continued at Kazan.

Tupolev Tu-22 'Blinder' and Tu-22M 'Backfire'

The first three series production Tu-22 bombers emerged from the Kazan plant in July-August 1960 and were sent to Zhukhovskii for further trials. They were in the Tu-22B configuration, which carried an armament of free-fall bombs. The first flight of a production Tu-22B took place on 22 September 1960, and early flights revealed more problems, including a tendency to pitch up. After the design bureau adjusted the control system, another flight was undertaken on 17 November 1960. This time, there was a fracture of an engine oil pipe, leading to the loss of power in one engine. The pilot, V. R. Kovalev, belly-landed the aircraft, splitting the nose off from the rest of the aircraft in the process and trapping the crew. However, they were rescued in spite of the fire which engulfed the rest of the bomber. An automatic pitch-damping feature was introduced, as well as other flight control improvements to compensate for effects caused by wing twisting. Subsequent flight trials revealed aileron reversal problems at high speeds, which led to a decision to limit flight speeds to Mach 1.4 and to introduce a flaperon system. Some of these upgrades were not ready until 1965, after the aircraft had already entered service.

Tu-22 enters service

The Samolet 105A aircraft was designated Tu-22 in Soviet air force service. The aircraft was first unveiled to the public on Aviation Day 1961, over Moscow. NATO

originally codenamed it 'Bullshot', then 'Beauty' and finally 'Blinder'. In the Soviet air force, it was popularly nicknamed 'Shilo' (awl) by its aircrew for its metallic, pointed shape.

The first batch of aircraft was primarily composed of Tu-22Bs armed with free-fall bombs. The payload depended on the mission but could consist of 24 FAB-500 500-kg (1,102-lb) bombs or one of the massive FAB-9000 9-tonne (9.14-ton) blockbusters. It is doubtful that the aircraft was ever intended to actually carry the FAB-9000 bomb; this often stood in as a surrogate for large thermonuclear bombs in design studies.

The original Soviet air force plan called for the concurrent production of two variants of the Tu-22: the Tu-22B bomber, and the Tu-22R reconnaissance aircraft. Initial series production in 1961 was planned to be 12 Tu-22B bombers and 30 Tu-22R reconnaissance aircraft, trimmed back to seven and five, respectively. In the end, only 15 Tu-22B bombers were built, for reasons that will become apparent below.

The Tu-22B bombers produced were very trouble prone and they were used primarily for training. They were accepted for service in September 1962 and deployed with the 43rd Combat Training Centre (43 TsBP i PLS) in Dyagilevo near Ryazan. After a year of training, they were transferred to the 203rd Heavy Bomber Aviation Regiment of the 46th Air Army of the Long Range Aviation, commanded by Colonel A. Gamala, at Baranovichi.

All versions of the Tu-22 (this is a Tu-22K) were equipped with a twin cruciform braking chute. It was this variant which was first publicly seen, in 1961. The Tu-22B failed to adequately fulfil its intended role as a bomber – a role increasingly under threat from SAMs. The Tu-22K was, therefore, the first truly combat-capable 'Blinder'.

Below and below left: Few of the 15 Tu-22B bombers built ever entered service. Most were so trouble prone that they were quickly retired – the Tu-22Bs acquired by Libya and Iraq were rebuilt Tu-22Rs. The aircraft seen below left is preserved at the Monino museum, and has an early-model gun barbette plus VD-7M engine exhausts.

The Tu-22B bomber was followed into trials by the Project YuR, the Tu-22R ('Blinder-C'), which was essentially similar to the bomber version, but with film camera equipment in the nose and in the weapons bay. There have been stories that this version was sponsored by the KGB for use in gathering strategic intelligence over Europe and Asia; however, by the early 1960s, satellites had arrived, and the aircraft's missions were oriented towards traditional military reconnaissance tasks, especially for the navy. The Tu-22R also retained free-fall bombing capability, and carried the optical bomb sight and weapons control system of the Tu-22B bomber.

The camera array in the Tu-22R depended on the mission and could include the AFA-40, AFA-41/20, AFA-42/20, AFA-42/75, AFA-42/100 and NAFA MK-75. In addition to the camera systems, it was fitted with the usual Rubin-1A surface-search radar, as well as the Romb electronic intelligence (Elint) system. For self-defence, the Tu-22R was fitted with KDS-16 dispensers at the rear of the undercarriage nacelles. The aircraft could also be adapted as an escort jammer, substituting the APP-22 palette in the bomb bay in lieu of reconnaissance equipment. A total of 127 of this type was built, making it the most common 'Blinder' model manufactured.

Tupolev Tu-22R 'Blinder-C'

Left: Wearing flight test photo calibration markings on its nose, this Tu-22R (2019012) was one of the very early production reconnaissance aircraft.

Above and below: Several attempts were made to improve the Tu-22's airfield performance. RD36-35 lift engines were fitted in the wheel wells of this Tu-22R (above). The same engines had previously been planned to provide boundary-layer control in the unbuilt Tu-22RTK. Rocket-assisted take-off trials using four SPRD-63 rockets were also conducted (below). They reduced take-off run from 2300 m (7,546 ft) to 1000 m (3,281 ft).

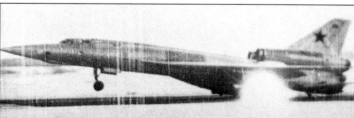

Above: The Tu-22RD (D=dalniy/long-range) was fitted with a refuelling probe. All aircraft were later refitted with VD-7MR engines.

Left: This Tu-22R of the 13th Heavy Bomber Aviation Division, based at Poltava, Ukraine, is fitted with the tail gun, later replaced by an ECM system.

Left: This early production Tu-22R, without a refuelling probe, is seen here departing on a training mission in November 1970. Not all Tu-22Rs were converted to Tu-22RD standard.

Above: This Tu-22RD of the 121st DBAP (Long-Range Aviation Regiment) was based at Machulishche, Byelorussia in the late 1980s. It has received the RWR upgrade (note the antenna housing beneath the navigator's window).

The first Tu-22R aircraft were issued in 1962 to the 290th OGDRAP (Separate Guards Long Range Reconnaissance Regiment) of the 46th Air Army at Zyabrovka near Gomel and the navy's 15th DRAP (Long Range Reconnaissance Regiment) at Chkalovskii near Kaliningrad with the Baltic Fleet. In 1965, two additional regiments were raised, the 199th OGDRAP in Nezhin northeast of Kiev with the 46th Air Army, and another naval DRAP at Saki attached to the Black Sea Fleet. In the case of the navy regiments, the Tu-22R replaced older Ilyushin Il-28R aircraft. As a result, the production run of the Tu-22R was split roughly equally between the regiments of the air force and navy. At peak strength in 1969-70, the two navy regiments had a total of 62 Tu-22R reconnaissance aircraft, a number which continued to decline until the mid-1980s when the type began to be withdrawn in favour of the Sukhoi Su-24MR. In total, the navy received about 80 of the 311 Tu-22 aircraft that were manufactured.

The Tu-22R was the first 'Blinder' to introduce a refuelling system into the series, in 1962, consisting of a nose-mounted refuelling probe system called *shtir-konus* (probe-and-drogue) in Russian. As a result of Tu-22R experiments with the refuelling system, all other Tu-22 aircraft were fitted with this system after 1965. Aircraft so-equipped had the suffix D (*dalni*/long range) added to their designation (*e.g.*, Tu-22RD, Tu-22KD). The refuelling capability of the Tu-22 led to a programme to convert obsolete Tu-16A bombers into Tu-16N tankers to support them, using the fuelling system first developed for the 3MS-2 'Bison' tankers.

Hunchback 'Blinder-D' and Tu-22K

The Tu-22R was followed into service by the hunch-backed Tu-22U trainer ('Blinder-D'), which was found necessary due to the radically different handling characteristics of the Tu-22 compared to its predecessor, the Tu-16. The state of the art in flight simulation was not particularly high at this time, and the standard KTS-22 simulator gave the new pilot only the roughest approximation of the handling characteristics of this very demanding aircraft. In the Tu-22U, a raised cabin for an instructor pilot was located above the station formerly occupied by the weapons officer. This version lacked the tail gun barbette, and fuel tankage was decreased. A prototype was completed at the end of 1960, and the type was accepted for service in 1962. The first production Tu-22U was deployed with the 46th Air Army in 1963 and a total of 46 Tu-22Us was eventually manufactured.

The Tu-22B bomber was quickly dropped from production after only 15 had been completed, due to a variety of factors. On the one hand, by 1960 it was appreciated that air defence had improved immeasurably since the aircraft had been conceived in the early 1950s. In many missions,

the primary threat would be radar-directed surface-to-air missiles (SAM), not interceptor aircraft. The Tu-22 was designed to operate at high altitudes, and low-altitude tactics to skirt under enemy radar were not considered to be realistic, given the design limits of the aircraft and the lack of a terrain-following radar. As an alternative, the Soviet air force decided to use stand-off tactics, firing a supersonic air-to-surface missile from outside the lethal envelope of enemy SAMs.

This led to the decision to develop a missile carrier version of the Tu-22, the Tu-22K ('Blinder-B'), an approach reinforced by the personal opinions of Soviet leader Nikita Kruschchev. Since the success of Sputnik in October 1957, and later Soviet space spectaculars,

In this view of a Tu-22RDM landing at Engels air base, the ventral housing for the Shompol sideways-looking radar is obvious. Between 1981 and 1982, a small number of RDs were modified to RDM standard. The existing camera fit was replaced by the SLAR and other IR sensors. Two AFA-42/100 cameras replaced a fuel tank and SPS-151 ECM and ASO-21 flare dispensers were also added.

Left: These Tu-22RDs were attached to the naval 'Blinder' regiment based at Saki, on the Crimean peninsula, that supported operations by the Black Sea fleet. The most obvious difference between these aircraft and the Tu-22KD cruise missile carriers comes in the nose configuration: the Tu-22KD's radome is bulged and extends over the tip of the nose.

Below: The added-on antenna housings of a late-model 'Blinder-C' are clearly visible in this view of a Ryazan-based Tu-22RD.

Not all Tu-22Rs ever made it to RD standard. This quartet of unmodified Tu-22Rs was destined for scrapping, in 1995, at the hands of the 6213 BLAT (base for the liquidation of aviation technology), Engels AB.

December 1959 as the premier arm of the Soviet armed forces, and its first divisions were armed with R-12 and R-14 intermediate-range ballistic missiles – aimed at many of the same targets as were intended for the Tu-22. Two of the Long Range Aviation's proudest medium bomber units, the 43rd Air Army at Vinnitsa and the 50th Air Army at Smolensk, were disbanded in September 1960 and their personnel transferred to the new missile divisions. Kruschchev threatened to convert additional medium bomber divisions.

Naval role for the 'Blinder-B' and Kh-22

The design of a missile-firing version of the Tu-22 was absolutely essential to its survival in the halls of the Kremlin, as well as its survival in the new air defence environment. The one factor in favour of the Tu-22's survival was that it could be employed in maritime strikes against US naval carrier battle groups. This was a role for which ballistic missiles were ill-suited, although there were little-known Soviet experiments at this time for such missions. Kruschchev was very concerned about the nuclear power projection capabilities of the carriers, and so was expected to tolerate the continued production of the Tu-22 if modified. As a result, the Tu-22K was designated a missile carrier (*raketonosets*), and the term 'bomber' disappeared from the vocabulary of the Soviet air force for many years.

The Tu-22K ('Blinder-B') missile carrier was the most delayed of the 'Blinder' sub-types. It was armed with the K-22 (Kompleks-22) weapon system with its associated new supersonic, rocket-propelled, stand-off missile, the Kh-22 (AS-4 'Kitchen'). The delay in the Tu-22K's introduction into service was due to problems with both the missile and its integration into the aircraft. The aircraft had not originally been designed to accommodate such a large missile, and even when carried semi-submerged in the belly, it significantly altered the aircraft's flight characteristics.

The Kh-22 missile was powered by an Isayev liquid-fuel, two-chamber R201-300 rocket. The fuel was inhibited red fuming nitric acid (IRFNA) oxidant and hydrazine propellant. On launch, the missile was controlled by a preprogrammed APK-22A autopilot with a radio altimeter with Doppler input. During the cruise phase, the gyrostabilised autopilot also controlled the missile, unlike previous Soviet cruise missiles which tended to rely on command guidance, due to the shortcomings and cost of contemporary inertial guidance packages. There were at least two attack modes, depending on the target. For low-altitude attack to minimise radar detection, the missile climbed to 12000 m (39,370 ft) and made a shallow Mach 1.2 dive towards the target, under 500 m (1,640 ft) for the last portion of the flight. Against naval targets or certain land targets, the missile climbed to about 27000 m (88,580 ft) and made a steep Mach 2.5 dive. The anti-ship missile relied on contact fusing for the warhead detonation, while the nuclear warheads could be airburst, based on the guidance system. Tests found that even with a conventional warhead, the Kh-22 would blow a hole 20 m (65 ft) square in the side of a ship, to a depth of 12 m (39 ft). System range was dependent on the altitude and speed at which it was launched. When

Kruschchev had become a great fan of missile technology. He was also intent on imposing substantial reforms on the Soviet military in the hopes of reducing the economic burden of defence. These views melded into a strongly-held belief that missile-armed systems were the wave of the future, and that smaller numbers of missile-armed aircraft, warships, and armoured vehicles would replace much larger inventories of more traditional weapons. Kruschchev viewed strategic bombers as an archaic concept, and prematurely terminated the Tupolev Tu-95M and Myasishchev 3M production programmes in favour of intercontinental ballistic missiles. To Kruschchev, bombers were the epitome of old-fashioned, costly and ineffective weapons.

In the early 1960s, there was a very real fear among Soviet air force leaders that the new Tu-22 bomber was the next item on the Kremlin's chopping block. Kruschchev had formed the new RVSN (Strategic Missile Force) in

Above and right: Both of these Tu-22RD 'Blinder-Cs' retain the DM-20 remotely-controlled tail gun position. Twin AM-23 guns (with 250 rounds per gun) were linked to the PRS-3A Argon-2 ranging radar, housed in the white radome immediately above the gun turret. Above the engines is the TSP-1 TV gunsight for close-in firing.

Tupolev Tu-22K 'Blinder-B'

Above: This prototype Tu-22K carrying a Kh-22 missile provided the first glimpse of either, at the 1961 Tushino Aviation Day. Only a partial refuelling system was fitted.

Below: The PN radar of the Tu-22K provides the distinctive nose configuration of this variant. Most 'Blinder-Bs' were built as Tu-22KDs.

Above: This early-production Tu-22K is carrying the nuclear-tipped version of the the Kh-22, the Kh-22N – as evidenced by the black dielectric panel of the PSI guidance system under the nose. The Kh-22N has a 350-kT warhead (estimated).

Right: The tarpaulin-covered ejection seats of this Tu-22KD are extended for maintenance.

This Tu-22KD, in full afterburner, is not carrying its missile payload so the folding panels ahead of the bomb bay can be clearly seen.

Above: The bogies of the Tu-22's main undercarriage folded on retraction, allowing them to slot compactly into the podded undercarriage housings on the wing trailing edge.

Right: This 'Blinder-C' (Bort number 08) is a Tu-22KPD fitted with the Kurs ESM system to detect NATO surveillance radars.

released from 14000 m (45,930 ft) at 1720 km/h (1,070 mph), it could reach targets 550 km (340 miles) distant; at a release altitude of 10000 m (32,810 ft) and a cruise speed of 950 km/h (590 mph), it could reach 400 km (250 miles).

Initial tests of the K-22 system were conducted from a modified Tu-16 'Badger' medium bomber, designated Tu-16K-22. Missile fabrication for the Kh-22 programme was undertaken at state aviation plant No. 256 and the first test missiles were available in 1962. The first example of the

Tu-22K was completed in early 1961 and it, along with a model of the Kh-22, took part in the annual Tushino show.

The Tu-22K was fitted with the Leninets design bureau's PN radar (NATO 'Down Beat'), a modification of the widely-used Rubin-1A radar. Flight tests of the Tu-22K with the Kh-22 missile were conducted at the GNIKI VVS (Gosudarstvenniy nauchno-ispatitelniy Krasnozanmenniy institut VVS: State Red Banner Research Experimental Institute of the Air Force) in Akhtubinsk. The test

Above and top: During the late 1980s, a number of Tu-22KDs were rebuilt with an ECM system replacing the tail gun. This comprised the SPS-151, SPS-152 or SPS-153 system, in a streamlined fairing.

The Tu-22 had an accident-ridden early history and bad luck plagued it afterwards. In one incident, on 2 April 1976, a Guards unit aircraft was dropping FOTAB-250-215 bombs over the Karagaysky range. One of the six bombs exploded in the bomb bay, breaking the aircraft in half – although several of the crew managed to escape. However, during follow-on trials at the Akhtubinsk test centre – with the same bomb load – another Tu-22 was destroyed and the bomb was withdrawn from the inventory. This Tu-22KD is an aircraft of the 121st TBAP, previously based at Machulishche, in Belarus.

programme was plagued by problems, including fuselage deformation due to stress, fuel leaks, and onboard fires. It was found that during supersonic flight, the skin of the aircraft became overheated, deformed and passed some of the heat to the control booster rods. This led to erratic aircraft control. In addition, the new aircraft had problems with the autopilot, resulting in the loss of one test crew. A second crew was lost due to an engine fire. The Kh-22 missile was accepted for service use in 1964 before the Tu-22 aircraft trials were completed, as it was also intended to arm a new missile-carrying version of the Tu-95 'Bear' bomber. The state commission overseeing the Tu-22K aircraft test programme declared it to be a failure, but Andrei Tupolev himself was able to use his considerable political influence to avoid the programme being cancelled.

Production of the Tu-22K and the associated missile took place before the state acceptance trials were successfully concluded, and aircraft were issued to bomber regiments in 1965 while tests were continuing. The missile/aircraft

combination proved to be a hazard in service, due to unresolved problems with the basic Tu-22 aircraft, and the unreliability of the PN radar. A modification programme continued for several years, with no fewer than eight major modification programmes to bring the aircraft and missile complex up to acceptable standards.

The Tu-22K was finally accepted for service in 1967, about two years after it had actually been deployed. A total of 76 Tu-22K missile carriers was built at state aviation plant No. 22 in Kazan, including the improved Tu-22KD with the upgraded engines. This total was significantly below original plans, largely due to the protracted difficulties with the aircraft. Although intended to replace the Tu-16 in both air force and navy service, insufficient numbers were built to replace the air force 'Badgers'. Only a handful of Tu-22K missile carriers were delivered to the Soviet navy for trials, and no naval missile-carrier regiments were formed with the Tu-22K, the Tu-16K remaining in service instead. US intelligence estimated that about 700 Kh-22 missiles were built from 1961 to 1972, when initial production finally ended.

Although not officially accepted for service use, the first Tu-22Ks were issued to air force bomber regiments in 1965. Three regiments of Tu-22K became operational in 1965: the 121st DBAP (Long Range Aviation Regiment) at Machulishche near Minsk, the 203rd DBAP at Baranovichi, and the 341st DBAP at Ozernoye near Zhitomir, all attached to the 15th Heavy Bomber Division of the 46th Air Army of the Long Range Aviation. The Tu-22K appeared in service after the coup against Kruschchev in 1964, and there was some reconsideration of its mission as a result. Two combat roles for the Long Range Aviation's 15th Heavy Bomber Division predominated: nuclear strike missions against major strategic targets in NATO's Central Front or Southern Front, and a secondary role against NATO warships in the North Sea and Mediterranean. There have been reports that another air force 'Blinder' regiment operated in the Pacific area from Zavatinsk with the 30th Air Army.

Tu-22P: electronic snooper

The final major sub-series of the 'Shilo' was the Tu-22P ('Blinder-E'), designed as an electronics intelligence variant. This version employed the REB-K Elint system mounted in the bomb-bay area with a prominent ventral air scoop,

and sometimes had the aft defensive machine-gun barbette replaced with an SPS-100A Rezeda-A jammer station, although some Tu-22P carried the normal gun barbette. The role of the Tu-22P was to determine the location of targets – usually US Navy carrier battle groups – based on their radar and radio emissions. The Tu-22P also evolved into the role of stand-off-jammer, accompanying the Tu-22K strike aircraft and providing jamming support. A total of 47 Tu-22P-1s and Tu-22P-2s was built, the two versions varying in the precise configuration of the electronics package. As was the case with the other Tu-22 variants, the aircraft was upgraded with the RD-7M-2 engines and refuelling probe from 1965, and redesignated Tu-22PD. Eventually, the electronic warfare package was gradually improved, leading to the Tu-22P-4, Tu-22P-6 and Tu-22P-7 variants. The Tu-22PD was usually issued on the basis of one squadron per regiment of Tu-22K missile carriers, to provide EW support.

Tu-22 operational career

Although an aesthetically pleasing design, the Tu-22 was one of the least popular designs of its generation, and widely dreaded by the Long Range Aviation crews. It was dubbed 'unflyable' by some bomber pilots. The situation was by far the worst in the 1960s, due to uncorrected technical problems, and led to a number of instances of the crews refusing to fly the aircraft type. This was exacerbated when the Tu-22K missile carrier was pushed into service prematurely, with a resultant high accident rate. It was also due to inherent design flaws in the aircraft, which made it difficult to operate and difficult to fly, and a continual string of upgrade and modification programmes intended to fix

the lingering problems. Furthermore, the aircraft used downward-firing K-22 ejection seats, making ejection during take-off and landing impossible. This was an especially unhappy arrangement given the hazards of landing the Tu-22.

One of the most dangerous features of the Tu-22 was its high recommended landing speed of 310 km/h (192 mph) and a minimum speed of 290 km/h (180 mph), about 100 km/h (62 mph) higher than on the Tu-16, which made transition between the two aircraft especially troublesome. In the event that the speed dropped below the minimum, the aircraft had a tendency to pitch up and smash into the ground tail first. Once the aircraft safely touched down, the crew's troubles were not over. The undercarriage was spongy and tended to bounce. Inadequate shock absorption led to occasional undercarriage collapses, usually the nose-wheel. The Tu-22K had a high fatality rate during accidents due to the special hazard posed by the fully fuelled Kh-22 missile under its belly. Undercarriage failures would lead to spectacular explosions.

The pilot's perspective

The Tu-22, unlike its predecessor the Tu-16, had only a single pilot in order to reduce the frontal cross-section. Unfortunately, this was coupled with notoriously heavy flight controls. A pilot recalled that the aircraft was very tiring to fly even with both hands on the controls, and that even with the frequent use of the autopilot, no more than two missions a day could be flown because of pilot fatigue. The ergonomics of the crew stations were very poor. The pilot's seat was located slightly off-centre, to the left, to avoid the obstruction caused by the centre windscreen frame. However, when the pilot compensated for a cross-

The Tu-22K was not a success, although it was certainly more capable than the Tu-22B. The Kh-22 stand-off missile, its primary weapon, had a patchy development history and, even though the test programme ended with some successful launches, the Soviet state evaluation committee determined that the weapon was not an effective operational system. The PN radar guidance system was also flawed. Despite this, full Tu-22K production proceeded, as did Kh-22 deployment. The delays involved meant that the Tu-22K followed the Tu-22R into production and service, and so it was not until 1965 that the Soviet air force had any combat-capable 'Blinders' – albeit of limited effectiveness. It took another two years for the Tu-22K/Kh-22 combination to become operational. The Tu-22K was notoriously unpopular amongst crews, and there are several well-documented cases of pilots refusing to fly the aircraft. Over the course of its operational life the Tu-22K underwent eight major modifications, chiefly to its control systems, in an attempt to produce a better aircraft.

One of the rarest of Tu-22 sub-variants is the Tu-22KPD, the dedicated anti-radar/EW version, armed with the Kh-22P missile and fitted with the Kurs-N system. The only outward sign of this is a small twin-pronged 'pitchfork' antenna mounted above the nose, behind the radome, to starboard. It is just visible on the aircraft in the extreme right-hand side of this photograph.

Tupolev Tu-22 'Blinder' in detail

Tupolev Tu-22 'Blinder' production

1957	1958	1959	1960	1961	1962	1963	1964	1965	1966	1967	1968	1969
1	1	5	20	0	33	36	49	35	40	50	27	16

Tu-22K 'Blinder-C' technical data

(Tu-22KD data in parentheses)

Bureau designation:	Samolet 105A, Izd. YuK
Soviet air force designation:	Tu-22K
NATO designation:	'Blinder-C'
Powerplant:	two RD-7M2 (replacing VD-7M from 1965), each rated at 11000-kg (107.9-kN, 24,250-lb) thrust static and 16500-kg (161.9-kN, 36,376-lb) in reheat
Crew:	Three
Length:	41.6 m/42.6 m with refuelling probe (136.48 ft/139.76 ft)
Wingspan:	23.6 m (77.43 ft)
Height:	10.0 m (32.8 ft)
Maximum weight:	84000 kg (185,185 lb)
Maximum take-off-weight:	94000 kg (207,230 lb), with four RATO
Normal weight:	85000 kg (187,390 lb)
Fuel weight:	42500 kg (93,695 lb)
Maximum bomb load:	24000 kg (847,547 lb)
Effective range:	4900 km (3,045 miles)
Range, with one refuelling:	7150 km (4,443 miles)
Practical combat radius:	1300-2200 km (808-1,367 miles)
Maximum speed:	1510 km/h (938 mph)
Navigation/attack radar:	Rubin-1 (PN)
Optical bomb sight:	PSB-11
Defensive radar:	PRS-3 Argon II
Defensive weapons:	2x R-23 23-mm cannon
Active jamming system:	SPS-161 or SPS-162

Above and below: The Tu-22 was fitted with three K-22 downward-firing ejection seats (a Tu-22UB is seen above). Note the different configuration of the seats on the Tu-22KD below. The first seat is for the navigator, who sits in front of and below the pilot. The rear seat is occupied by the communications/navigation officer.

Above: The Tu-22RDM is fitted with the Shompol SLAR in its converted bomb bay.

Above right: The Tu-22R retained the bomb bay of the Tu-22B. Note also the pop-out emergency generator.

Right: Tu-22 crews can only access the aircraft by being raised and lowered on their seats.

Above and left: The height of the Tu-22's engines from the ground presents considerable problems to its maintainers. Note the RD-7M engines fitted to the Tu-22RD above.

Right: By the mid-1980s, the Soviet air force had recognised the inadequacy of the tail gun and began refitting 'Blinder' with an ECM system instead. On the Tu-22RDM, this usually comprised the SPS-151 system.

Handling qualities

The Tu-22 did not have a reputation as a pilot's aircraft and could be very difficult and dangerous to fly. Remarking on its heavy controls, test pilot Alexey Nikonov once said, "two flights per day, without the autopilot, are enough for anyone." The Tu-22 could not be allowed to slow below 290 km/h (180 mph) on approach, without risking an uncontrollable pitch-up and stall. One such spectacular landing accident was captured for the opening sequence of the Soviet safety film 'Kindness to a roaring animal'.

Refuelling the Tu-22

Aerial refuelling was one of the most difficult operations for an inexperienced crew. Refuelling with the Tu-16 tanker took place at altitudes of 5000-8000 m (16,400-26,245 ft) and at a speed of 600 km/h (373 mph). The Tu-22 pilot would position his aircraft about 50 m (165 ft) to the right of the Tu-16, and gradually decelerate until behind the tanker. The bomber would then accelerate forward to connect the nose probe to the trailing drogue. The Tu-22 flight controls were not delicate, and many inexperienced pilots found themselves closing in on the drogue much too quickly and being forced to abandon the link-up with a fast descent to the right. Some less experienced pilots needed almost 45 minutes to secure a link-up. During the 1970s, the 199th OGDRAP at Nezhin developed a simpler technique to position the aircraft a few metres behind the drogue, and then use engine control alone to effect the link-up.

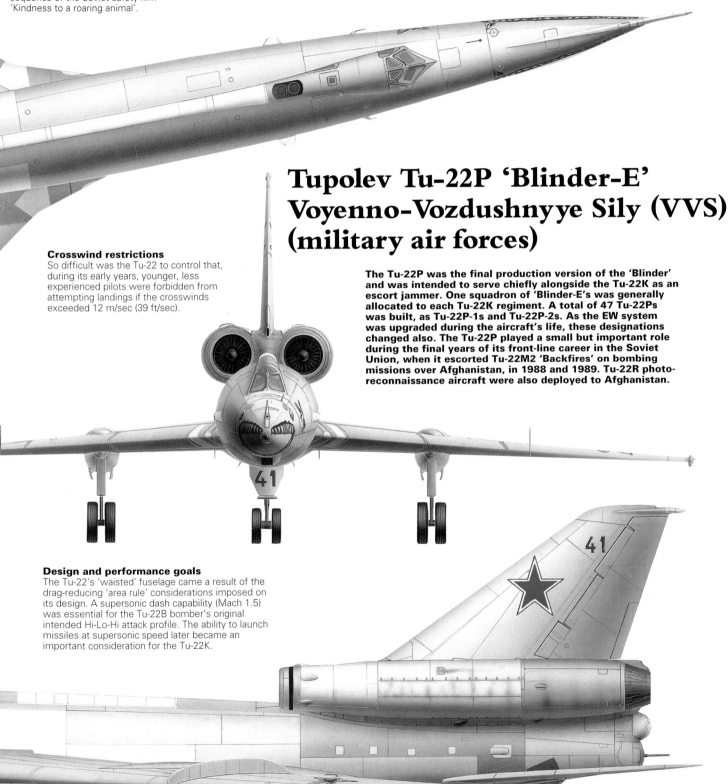

Tupolev Tu-22P 'Blinder-E' Voyenno-Vozdushnyye Sily (VVS) (military air forces)

Crosswind restrictions

So difficult was the Tu-22 to control that, during its early years, younger, less experienced pilots were forbidden from attempting landings if the crosswinds exceeded 12 m/sec (39 ft/sec).

The Tu-22P was the final production version of the 'Blinder' and was intended to serve chiefly alongside the Tu-22K as an escort jammer. One squadron of 'Blinder-E's was generally allocated to each Tu-22K regiment. A total of 47 Tu-22Ps was built, as Tu-22P-1s and Tu-22P-2s. As the EW system was upgraded during the aircraft's life, these designations changed also. The Tu-22P played a small but important role during the final years of its front-line career in the Soviet Union, when it escorted Tu-22M2 'Backfires' on bombing missions over Afghanistan, in 1988 and 1989. Tu-22R photo-reconnaissance aircraft were also deployed to Afghanistan.

Design and performance goals

The Tu-22's 'waisted' fuselage came a result of the drag-reducing 'area rule' considerations imposed on its design. A supersonic dash capability (Mach 1.5) was essential for the Tu-22B bomber's original intended Hi-Lo-Hi attack profile. The ability to launch missiles at supersonic speed later became an important consideration for the Tu-22K.

Kh-15 (AS-16 'Kickback') development

This small, solid-fuel missile was developed in parallel with the much larger Kh-45 Molniya, as the Kh-2000. Like the American AGM-69 SRAM, the Kh-2000 was intended to be launched outside the range of hostile air defences to destroy key radar or missile sites. Because of the missile's small size, a bomber could carry a large number of them to help penetrate the defences, so the missile was sometimes dubbed a penetration aid, or 'penaid'. The missile could also be used to attack primary targets if necessary, but the Kh-45 Molniya was the preferred solution for primary targets. The Kh-2000 programme was re-examined in the mid-1970s as a result of the Pleyada study, to arm the new Tu-160 intercontinental bomber. In 1976-77 the programme was revived at the MKB Raduga design bureau under the internal designation of Izdeliye 115, and later as Kh-15. The configuration of the missile was modified at this time to permit it to be fired from new internal revolver launchers, and to be used for both anti-radar and anti-ship missions to satisfy the Chetkost-P requirement. Kh-15 was virtually unknown in the West until 1988, when the US Secretary of Defense William Perry visited the Soviet base at Kubinka, to see the Tu-160 'Blackjack' bomber. 'Kickback' can be carried by the Tu-95MS 'Bear-H', Tu-160 and Tu-22M3. The Tu-22M3 can carry six Kh-15s on an internal rotary launcher.

'Backfire' undercarriage design

The Tu-22M was designed to operate from a Class 1 field (2.7 km/ 1.8 miles of hard concrete) or from unpaved runways, so its landing gear was designed to handle its considerable weight by reducing the ground pressure on the individual tyres. Unlike earlier Tupolev designs, or even the Tu-22M0, the standard production aircraft dispensed with the usual podded fairing for the undercarriage, and have them mounted instead in the centre of the SChK central wing element, with the wheels contained within the lower fuselage. The undercarriage includes three axles and six wheels per side, with the centre pair extending slightly outside the front and rear pair. The undercarriage was designed with special attention for robustness after the unfavourable experience with the Tu-22 'Blinder' undercarriage. Interestingly enough, one of the few elements carried over from the Tu-22 'Blinder' is the front undercarriage assembly, although it, too, was strengthened and improved.

Kh-22 (AS-4 'Kitchen') development

The Kh-22 missile received its designation from its primary intended carrier, the Tu-22. The 'Kh' designations for Soviet air-to-surface missiles stemmed from the first such Soviet weapon, the Chelomey 10Kh of 1944. The Cyrillic letter Kh resembles the Roman 'X' and was patterned after the British and American practice of applying X designations to experimental weapons. Work on the Kh-22 was authorised on 17 June 1958 by a Council of Ministers decree. It was designed by Berezniak's OKB-2-155 design bureau in Dubna, which by this time had split off from the Mikoyan fighter design bureau with which it had originally been associated. This organisation is better known today as the MKB Raduga (MKB/machine-industry design bureau). The configuration of the Kh-22 was pioneered by the earlier Beriev K-12 missile system, which used a conventional aircraft-style fuselage and a liquid-propellant rocket engine. The missile was designed from the outset for three missions: the Kh-22 for precision anti-ship missions with a conventional warhead; the Kh-22P for precision missions against key enemy air defence sites with a nuclear warhead; and the Kh-22N area attack weapon with a nuclear warhead. The precision attack versions used an active radar seeker, while the area attack versions relied on inertial navigation and command guidance. In 1957/58 testbeds for the guidance system were mounted on analog aircraft derived from the MiG-19S fighter, designated SM-K/1 and SM-K/2.

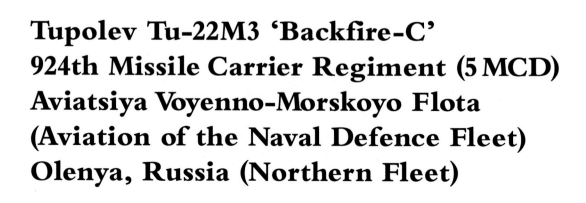

Tupolev Tu-22M3 'Backfire-C'
924th Missile Carrier Regiment (5 MCD)
Aviatsiya Voyenno-Morskoyo Flota
(Aviation of the Naval Defence Fleet)
Olenya, Russia (Northern Fleet)

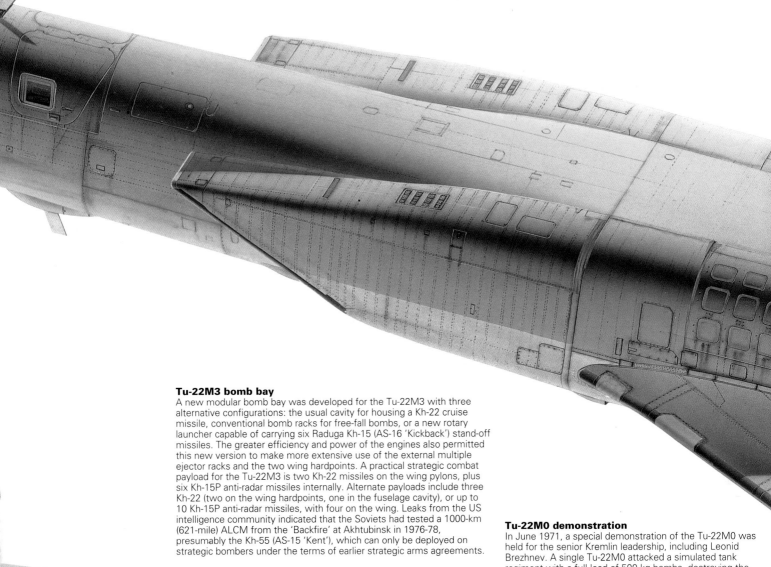

Tu-22M3 cockpit design
The cabin of the Tu-22M was designed in the wake of strenuous criticism of the earlier Tu-22 'Blinder' cockpit. The original designs had considerably larger clear openings than the production aircraft, but they had to be reduced due to the amount of light they let into the cockpit, which interfered with viewing the radar scope and other instruments. The cockpit layout is conventional, with the pilot and co-pilot sitting in front, and the navigation and weapons officer behind. Aircraft climate control is handled by the KSKV system.

Tu-22M3 bomb bay
A new modular bomb bay was developed for the Tu-22M3 with three alternative configurations: the usual cavity for housing a Kh-22 cruise missile, conventional bomb racks for free-fall bombs, or a new rotary launcher capable of carrying six Raduga Kh-15 (AS-16 'Kickback') stand-off missiles. The greater efficiency and power of the engines also permitted this new version to make more extensive use of the external multiple ejector racks and the two wing hardpoints. A practical strategic combat payload for the Tu-22M3 is two Kh-22 missiles on the wing pylons, plus six Kh-15P anti-radar missiles internally. Alternate payloads include three Kh-22 (two on the wing hardpoints, one in the fuselage cavity), or up to 10 Kh-15P anti-radar missiles, with four on the wing. Leaks from the US intelligence community indicated that the Soviets had tested a 1000-km (621-mile) ALCM from the 'Backfire' at Akhtubinsk in 1976-78, presumably the Kh-55 (AS-15 'Kent'), which can only be deployed on strategic bombers under the terms of earlier strategic arms agreements.

Tu-22M0 demonstration
In June 1971, a special demonstration of the Tu-22M0 was held for the senior Kremlin leadership, including Leonid Brezhnev. A single Tu-22M0 attacked a simulated tank regiment with a full load of 500-kg bombs, destroying the vehicles but hurling shrapnel into the reviewing box.
A second attack to demonstrate the accuracy of the new weapons control system placed a single bomb on a railroad car, completely destroying it. Brezhnev was very enthusiastic about the aircraft after the demonstration, and its approval for production was assured. This was important, since the production of the Tu-22 was coming to a premature end and the Kazan plant's bomber line would otherwise become idle.

Tu-22M3 weapons
The basic system weapon of the Tu-22M is the Kh-22M (AS-4 'Kitchen') guided missile. A single missile can be carried suspended in the bomb bay with the BD-45F internal pylon, and up to two more can be carried externally under the wings using the BD-45K pylon. The Tu-22M3 can also carry a new revolver launcher with six Kh-15 (AS-16 'Kickback') missiles internally and an additional four externally. The full range of Soviet/Russian conventional and nuclear bombs can be carried, including the FAB-250, FAB-500, FAB-1500 and FAB-3000 high-explosive fragmentation bombs. The Tu-22M is the only aircraft to carry the little-known UPAE-1500 guided bomb. The Tu-22M can carry up to 12 tonnes (11.8 tons) of bombs internally, suspended on the KD3-22RD, KD-3-22M or KD4-105AD systems (depending on type), and had hardpoints for up to four external MBD3-U9-68 multiple ejector racks, which can increase the maximum combat load to 21 tonnes (20.7 tons). A typical conventional load would consist of 69 FAB-250s and 42 FAB-500s. An alternative with heavy bombs would be eight FAB-1500s and two FAB-3000s.

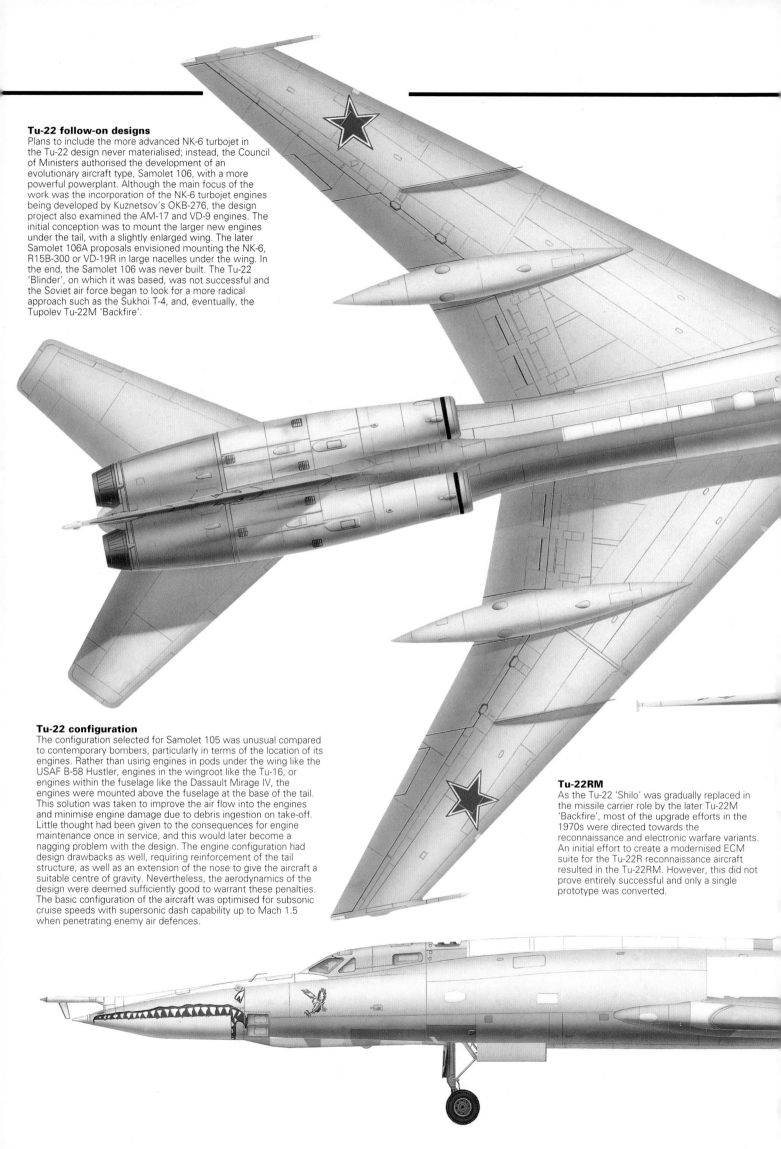

Tu-22 follow-on designs

Plans to include the more advanced NK-6 turbojet in the Tu-22 design never materialised; instead, the Council of Ministers authorised the development of an evolutionary aircraft type, Samolet 106, with a more powerful powerplant. Although the main focus of the work was the incorporation of the NK-6 turbojet engines being developed by Kuznetsov's OKB-276, the design project also examined the AM-17 and VD-9 engines. The initial conception was to mount the larger new engines under the tail, with a slightly enlarged wing. The later Samolet 106A proposals envisioned mounting the NK-6, R15B-300 or VD-19R in large nacelles under the wing. In the end, the Samolet 106 was never built. The Tu-22 'Blinder', on which it was based, was not successful and the Soviet air force began to look for a more radical approach such as the Sukhoi T-4, and, eventually, the Tupolev Tu-22M 'Backfire'.

Tu-22 configuration

The configuration selected for Samolet 105 was unusual compared to contemporary bombers, particularly in terms of the location of its engines. Rather than using engines in pods under the wing like the USAF B-58 Hustler, engines in the wingroot like the Tu-16, or engines within the fuselage like the Dassault Mirage IV, the engines were mounted above the fuselage at the base of the tail. This solution was taken to improve the air flow into the engines and minimise engine damage due to debris ingestion on take-off. Little thought had been given to the consequences for engine maintenance once in service, and this would later become a nagging problem with the design. The engine configuration had design drawbacks as well, requiring reinforcement of the tail structure, as well as an extension of the nose to give the aircraft a suitable centre of gravity. Nevertheless, the aerodynamics of the design were deemed sufficiently good to warrant these penalties. The basic configuration of the aircraft was optimised for subsonic cruise speeds with supersonic dash capability up to Mach 1.5 when penetrating enemy air defences.

Tu-22RM

As the Tu-22 'Shilo' was gradually replaced in the missile carrier role by the later Tu-22M 'Backfire', most of the upgrade efforts in the 1970s were directed towards the reconnaissance and electronic warfare variants. An initial effort to create a modernised ECM suite for the Tu-22R reconnaissance aircraft resulted in the Tu-22RM. However, this did not prove entirely successful and only a single prototype was converted.

'Backfire' wing design

The variable-geometry configuration was selected for aerodynamic efficiency at a wide range of altitudes and speed, including low-altitude subsonic flight and high-altitude supersonic dashes. The wing design consists of two elements; the SChK or central wing element which contains the main spar and wing hinges, and two PChK moving wing sections. The loads from the PChK wing panels are absorbed by massive hinge joints which are themselves reinforced by the centre fuselage bulkheads and main wing spars. The wing can be locked at 20°, 30°, 40°, 50° and 60° on the Tu-22M2, while on the Tu-22M3 the angles are 20°, 30°, 50° and 65°. The wing was designed to minimise the movement of the centre of wing pressure and centre of gravity during the wing sweep to about 2 per cent, to maintain stability. The wing angles are employed in the expected fashion, with the 20° angle used during take-off and landing, the 30° angle for climb and sustained cruise at subsonic speeds, the 50° setting for low-altitude flight at transonic speeds, and the 60° (or 65°) setting for supersonic dashes. The wings are operated by two RA-57 hydraulic power units synchronised by a hinged shaft around the weapons bay, which also provides a redundant avenue of power if one of the wing swing power units fails. Management of the wing angle is handled either manually or automatically via the ABSU-145M flight control system. The wing panels have differential spoilers rather than ailerons, and the panels are fitted with double-slotted flaps and leading-edge slats. The wing control surfaces are activated by an RP60 hydromechanical motor for the slats and a MVD-25D25 for the flaps. The Tu-22M has fuel tanks in both the SChK centre-section and in the PChK wing sections, connected with sealed hinged joints, plus tanks in the fuselage and dorsal fin.

Structural design

The fuselage design consists of the forward crew stations, a central weapons bay, a rear engine compartment, and a pair of air intakes and tunnels working their way around the weapons bay to the engines. The side-mounted air intakes and large wing centre-section created problems at high angles of attack by creating airflow problems over the tail and rudder. They were solved by increasing the dorsal fin in front of the rudder, with the dorsal fin being used to store additional equipment and fuel cells. During initial operation of the Tu-22M1, pressure losses were discovered in the long engine air ducts while on the ground and at lower air speeds. As a result, in the production Tu-22M2, an array of additional intake doors was added on the sides of the fuselage, a feature that can also be seen on the Tu-22M3. Numerous redesigns of the air intakes were made during Tu-22M evolution.

'Backfire' powerplant

The Tu-22M's Kuznetsov/NPO Trud NK-22 two-spool afterburning turbofan engines were mounted in the fuselage after the unfavourable experience with the high-mounted engines in the Tu-22 'Blinder'. They were derived from the NK-144 engines used on the Tu-144 supersonic transport and had the same thrust and fan diameter. These engines were replaced with the more powerful NK-25 engines in the Tu-22M3, offering 245 kN (55,115 lb) of thrust vs 216 kN (48,500 lb) in the earlier type. Static thrust for the NK-25 is 140 kN (31,525 lb). Both engines use the usual types of Russian aviation kerosene, including TS-1, T-1 and PT, with the fuel management handled by the automatic TATsZ-1V system; the Tu-22M3 used the KAZ-833. A TA-6 auxiliary power unit is mounted in the dorsal fin to provide electrical power to the aircraft on the ground and to power up the engines. The aircraft's electrical system is 27V and power supply is from six GS-18NO generators, with three per engine plus an emergency GS-12TO generator. For operations from fields under Class 1, the Tu-22M was fitted with both an arrester hook and a braking chute. A pair of PT-12024-69 parachutes is carried, each of 52m² (560 sq ft). The Tu-22M is fitted with four hardpoints under the fuselage for the installation of RATOG rocket boosters for operations out of unprepared fields, or for operations with heavy payloads.

Defensive tail gun

The Tu-22M's primary defensive weapon is the rear-mounted GSh-23 cannon. In the Tu-22M2 it was in a four-barrelled configuration as part of the UKU-9A-502 system, while on the Tu-22M3 it was reduced to a single gun with two barrels with the UK-9A-802, as part of the weight-saving effort. In the Tu-22M2 the ammunition supply is 1,200 rounds of PIKS infra-red decoy and PRLS chaff ammunition. The rear defensive machine-gun system is aimed using the PRS-4 radar or the supplementary TP-1 television sight.

Tu-22M technical data

	Tu-22M2	Tu-22M3
Air force designation:	Tu-22M2	Tu-22M3
Production designation:	izd. 45-02	izd. 45-03
NATO code name:	'Backfire-B'	'Backfire-C'
Crew:	four	four
Length:	41.46 m (136.02 ft)	42.46 m (139.30 ft)
Height:	11.05 m (36.35 ft)	11.05 m (36.25 ft)
Wingspan:	25-34.28 m (82.02-112.47 ft)	23.3-34.28 m (76.4-112.47 ft)
Radar cross-section:	20 m² (215.29 sq ft)	20-25 m² (215.29-269.11 sq ft)
Max. take-off weight:	122 tonnes (120.08 tons)	124 tonnes (122.05 tons) (126.4 tonnes/124.41 tons with RATO)
Fuel:		53550 kg (118,056 lb)
Max. payload:	24 tonnes (23.62 tons)	24 tonnes (23.62 tons)
Max. speed:	1800 km/h (1,119 mph)	2300 km/h (1,429 mph)
Cruising speed:	900 km/h (559 mph)	900 km/h (559 mph)
Practical combat range:	5100 km (3,169 miles)	6800 km (4,225 miles)
Service ceiling:	12600 m (41,340 ft)	13300 m (43,635 ft)
Powerplant:	Kuznetsov/Trud NK-22	Kuznetsov/Trud NK-25
Engine thrust w/afterburner:	196 kN (44,090 lb)	245 kN (55,115 lb) (140 kN/31,525 lb w/o)
Attack radar:	Leninets PN-A ('Downbeat')	Leninets PN-AD ('Downbeat')
Radar target acquisition range:	150-200 km (93-124 miles)	150-200 km (93-124 miles)
Defensive armament system:	UKU-9K-502	UK-9A-802
Defensive gun:	two GSh-23 23-mm	one GSh-23 23-mm
Defensive gun sight:	Krypton/TP-1-KM (TV)	Krypton/TP-1-KM (TV)
Defensive gun radar:	PRS-3 Argon-2 ('Bee Hind')	PRS-3 Argon-2 ('Bee Hind')
ECM system:	Ural (retrofit)	Ural
Threat warning:	Sirena-3	Sirena-3
HF radio:	R-846	R-846
VHF radio:	R-832M	R-832M
Radiocompass:	ARK-15	ARK-15
Radioaltimeter:	RV-18	RV-18

Tupolev Tu-22M2 'Backfire-B'

The 'Backfire-B' was the definitive production version of the Tu-22M, although it has been supplanted (if not completely replaced) by the more capable Tu-22M3 'Backfire-C'. Production lasted from 1972 to 1983 and a total of 211 was built, for air force and navy units. The best-known aspect of the aircraft is its refuelling probe, or the lack of it. In its early service days, the Tu-22M2 was fitted with a refuelling probe, but this was later removed (as a stipulation of the SALT treaty) in order to ensure that the 'Backfire' did not have true intercontinental range. In fact, the probes could be refitted in a matter of hours and the truth of the matter was that the Soviet Union simply did not have the air-to-air tanker assets to make such missions possible. Other points of note about the Tu-22M2 are its conventional splitter-plate intakes, and twin side-by-side tail guns.

Tupolev Tu-22M1 'Backfire-A'

The Tu-22M1 was the very unsuccessful initial production variant of the Tu-22M. Only nine aircraft were built between 1969 and 1971. The type entered limited service and was used for much early trials work, but all were soon retired in favour of the much improved Tu-22M2. All Tu-22M1s were fitted with a refuelling probe and had a bullet-shaped antenna for the Argon-2 tail gun ranging radar, unlike the cylindrical fairing of the Tu-22M2.

Tupolev Tu-22M0 'Backfire-A'

Tupolev's Samolet 145 design emerged as the Tu-22M0 prototype of 1969. Its impressive performance was more than enough to convince Brezhnev that the new bomber had merit. The most obvious difference between Tu-22M0 and Tu-22M1 was the former's large EW and brake chute housing at the base of the fin.

Tupolev Tu-22M 'Backfire' production

	1972	1973	1974	1975	1976	1977	1978	1979	1980	1981	1982	1983	1984	1985	1986
Tu-22M2	3	14	15	17	17	21	22	26	23	23	20	10			
Tu-22M3					1	1	3	5	7	7	10	20	30	28	30

	1987	1988	1989	1990	1991	1992	1993
Tu-22M3	28	27	25	20	17	6	3

A total of nine Tu-22M0 prototypes was manufactured in 1969-71 and nine Tu-22M1s in 1971-72

Above and right: The Tu-22M dispensed with the cumbersome entry system of the Tu-22 and uses conventional access doors on the upper fuselage. The Tu-22M has a crew of four: commander (left front), co-pilot (right front), communications officer (radio-telegrafist: left rear) and navigator (shturman: right rear). The typical crew uniform is the VKK-6MP flight suit, TZK-2M jacket and GSh-6A helmet, although the older VMSK-4 flight suit with ZSh-5A helmet can still be seen in use.

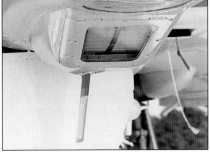

Left: The Tu-22M3 retains an optical bomb aiming capability, using a forward-pointing OPB-15T television sight, fitted behind the radome of the Leninets PN-A attack radar.

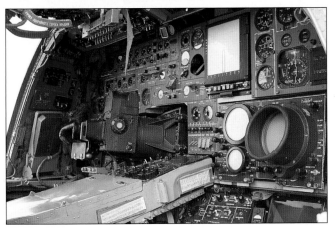

Above and left: The front and rear cockpits of the Tu-22M2 and M3 differ only in minor details (these views are of an M2). The crew all sit on KT-1 ejection seats, which are not 'zero-zero'. Very little modern avionics are in evidence and the instruments are almost all electro-mechanical 'clockwork' dials. Although the rear crewmen have no forward visibility, they do have a surprisingly large side window each, which contrasts sharply with the Tu-22.

Above and left: The Tu-22M3 is powered by NK-25 engines, replacing the earlier NK-22s. Coupled with its new intake design, this boosted maximum speed from Mach 1.65 to Mach 2.05.

Tupolev Tu-22 'Blinder' and Tu-22M 'Backfire'

Late-model Tu-22s, such as this 121st DBAP Tu-22KD, were powered by RD-7M2 turbojets, which replaced the earlier VD-7Ms from 1965 onwards. The Tu-22 could reach Mach 1.5 at high altitude. Every crew had to conduct two supersonic training runs each year, which involved manoeuvres (up to 60° turns) and weapons releases. On one occasion, a Tu-22R of 199 OGDRAP encountered unusual atmospheric conditions that carried its shockwave down to the ground from a height of 11000 m (36,089 ft), to the town of Sumy – breaking every window in the town centre.

From this vantage point it is easy to see how the Tu-22 gained its Soviet air force nickname of 'Shilo' (awl).

wind from the left, the frame blocked his view of the runway. The accident rate was significant enough that less-experienced pilots were not permitted to take-off if crosswinds exceeded 12 m (39 ft) per second.

The cockpit was poorly designed, leading to some crews developing their own pull strings and hooks to operate controls that were out of reach. The navigator was located in 'a black pit' deep in the fuselage, and the visibility from the weapons officer's stations was poor. This prompted a sarcastic refrain among Tu-22R crews along the lines of 'it is a marvelous reconnaissance aircraft in which the pilot who should see the runway can only see the sky, the navigator who should see the terrain in front can only see it below, and the weapons officer who should keep an eye out over the tail can only see the wing.'

The Tu-22 was no more popular with ground crews. The combat readiness rate of the aircraft was low, which was attributable in part to difficulties in servicing the aircraft due to its design, such as the high-mounted engines. The location of the engines high above the fuselage required the use of special servicing scaffolds, which were not always available in the numbers needed. In addition, the aircraft had a relatively low durability, with a design life of only seven years or 1,000 landing cycles. The Kh-22 missile was especially unpopular with the ground crews because of its toxic oxidant. The fumes of the IRFNA oxidant were so toxic if breathed that the crew had to wear 'slime suits' (rubberised chemical protective ensembles with full face masks) when handling the weapon. One of the few prized

features of the Tu-22 was the need for 450 litres (99 Imp gal) of pure grain alcohol for various hydraulic and de-icing systems – which the base personnel sometimes diverted for unofficial use. As a result, the Tu-22 was known as a '*spirtonosets*' ('booze carrier') by ground crews, a play on its official designation of *raketonosets* (missile carrier).

By the 1970s, many of the Tu-22's problems had been ironed out, and enough operational experience had been accumulated to reduce the accident rate. Nevertheless, the 'Blinder' was never a popular aircraft and continued to have one of the highest accident rates in the Soviet air force. Over 70 aircraft were lost in accidents through 1975, about 20 per cent of the total production, with an attendant high loss rate of crews. It was particularly unpopular compared the docile and dependable Tu-16 'Badger'. These losses were comparable to those suffered by the US Air Force's B-58 Hustler, although it should be pointed out that the Hustler was employed in the more demanding low-altitude environment, and had a higher operational tempo, giving it a lower loss-rate-per-sortie than the Tu-22.

Tu-22 mission profiles

The Long Range Aviation's 46th Air Army had two main missions: attack of high-priority NATO targets, and attack of aircraft-carrier groups of the US Sixth Fleet in the Mediterranean. For these missions, initial scouting was performed by the 46th Air Army's two Tu-22R 'Blinder' reconnaissance regiments, the 199th and 290th DRAP. The 199th DRAP operating out of Nezhin in Ukraine was assigned the task of operations over central Europe including Germany and Austria, as well as the southern region including Turkey, Greece, the Black Sea and the eastern Mediterranean. The 290th DRAP out of Zyabrovka was assigned strategic reconnaissance over the Baltic including Denmark, Scandinavia, and around 'the corner' beyond the Kola peninsula and down along the Norwegian coast. During peacetime, training missions for these two regiments were often conducted eastward along the Volga and towards the Caspian Sea. The Caspian Sea was also used for missile carrier training, with live missiles fired against hulks.

Seek and destroy the Sixth Fleet

In addition to acting as strategic scouts, these regiments would also serve as pathfinders during actual strike missions, especially strikes by the 15th Bomber Division against carrier battle groups. This was considered to be the 46th Air Army's most difficult and dangerous assignment. The strike mission would be cued by various intelligence assets, including land-based high-frequency direction-finding arrays (HF-DF, or 'Huff Duff'), intelligence trawlers shadowing the American warships, or other naval vessels like submarines. Although these systems could provide a rough indication of the location of the American carrier battle group, it would be necessary to determine the location with greater precision, and especially to distinguish the carrier from other ships in the battle group. This was the difficult assignment given to the Tu-22R crews. A typical mission against the Sixth Fleet in the Mediterranean would be preceded by a group of four Tu-22R reconnaissance aircraft, which would proceed to the target, usually over the friendly portions of the Balkans. If need be, some fighter escort could be provided part of the way. The carrier battle group would be approached initially at low altitude to avoid detection. As they neared the objective, a pair of Tu-22R reconnaissance aircraft would pull up while two more 'Blinders' proceeded into the heart of the carrier battle group. The pair that peeled off was assigned the mission of ECM activity against the fleet's surveillance radars, as well as acting as airborne relays for data from the penetrating pair. The penetrating pair was assigned the unenviable task of locating the precise position of the carrier within the group. This often required actual visual

detection, since it could be difficult to distinguish the carrier from its escorts with the Tu-22K's PN radar in surface search mode. Once the carrier was identified, this data was immediately radioed back to the Tu-22R relays, which passed it on to the Tu-22K attack element.

Carrier hunting

The Tu-22K missile carriers of the 15th Bomber Division would carry out the attack in groups of up to a regiment in size, *i.e.*, 24-30 Tu-22K missile carriers, and four to eight Tu-22P electronic escort jammers. The attack would be conducted at stand-off ranges from the fleet, theoretically as far away as 550 km (340 miles) if the launch aircraft was at 14000 m (45,930 ft) or 400 km (250 miles) if launched from an altitude of 10000 m (32,810 ft). The usual launch range was 250-270 km (155-170 miles), since the aircraft had to acquire the target on its PN radar. For long-range

stand-off, the missile's autopilot was pre-programmed to fly to a cruise altitude of 22500 m (73,820 ft) and then begin a sharp supersonic dive on the target at speeds of 1400-1720 km/h (870-1,070 mph), relying on its active radar seeker for terminal guidance. The active radar guidance was not needed if the missile was the nuclear-armed version.

While the Tu-22K missile carriers were conducting their stand-off missile attack, the Tu-22P escort jammers would be attempting to mask the attack with various forms of electronic jamming. This jamming would be directed against naval air defence radars to pre-empt the use of Standard air defence missiles against the attacking bombers and missiles, and against fleet defence aircraft.

The viability of these tactics was severely undermined in the early 1970s with the advent of the F-14 Tomcat fighter. The F-14 was specifically developed to deal with the threat posed by Soviet bomber-fired anti-ship missiles. Due to its

The clean-lines of the Tu-22 were ruined in the ungainly Tu-22U 'Blinder-D' trainer conversion (which originally had the NATO name 'Blinder-C'). This aircraft wears the regimental badge of 121 TBAP.

Tupolev Tu-22U 'Blinder-D'

Above: The absence of a second pilot's seat in the Tu-22 made a trainer essential. This is the prototype Tu-22U, without refuelling probe.

Right: A small initial production series of Tu-22Us was built with provision for probes, which were added later. Note the open bomb bay doors.

Above: The Tu-22U was not fitted with a tail gun and the instructor pilot sat where the gunner (navigator) used to be.

Right: The two small domes behind the second cockpit are for the BTs-63 astro-sextants, used for long-range navigation.

Above: This is a Tu-22U of 121 DBAP. A few 'Blinder-Cs' were allocated to each 'Blinder' unit, in addition to the central training unit at Ryazan.

Tupolev Tu-22 'Blinder' and Tu-22M 'Backfire'

The Tu-22U was the least evolutionary of the entire Tu-22 family. It neither received, nor required, any of the ECM or systems upgrades applied to the other variants and so it remained free of antennas, fairings and other blemishes. Most Tu-22Us were based at Dyagilevo near Ryazan, the main training base for Long-Range Aviation. The 43rd training centre (43 TsBP i PLS) was located there, as was the main school for the 46th Air Army, which operated the 'Blinders'. Tu-22U production (totalling 46) was completed by 1960, acceptance and evaluation by 1962 and the first aircraft were issued to units in 1963. In practice, this meant that all early 'Blinder' crews had made the difficult transition to the Tu-22 without access to a trainer and had only a vague idea about how their dangerous new aircraft would perform.

long range, the Tomcat could provide combat air patrols a significant range from the carrier, forcing the 'Blinder' (or 'Bear' or 'Badger') to come within the lethal envelope of its Phoenix missiles. The tactic was to discover the incoming Tu-22R scouts or other similar aircraft using the E-2C Hawkeye, then vector the F-14s into the area. This could prevent the detection of the carrier and foil the attack before it started. Should the attack proceed anyway, the Tomcats were then expected to deal with both the missile carriers, and the Kh-22 missile if it had been released before interception of the bomber. The Phoenix missile was designed to reach targets at very high altitude – up to 18000 m (59,000 ft). The Kh-22 could be intercepted either in the early phase of flight, or in the terminal phase, but its high-altitude cruise regime was beyond the interception envelope of the Phoenix, if unclassified data is to be believed.

Upgrading the 'Blinder'

In addition to the development of new versions of the Tu-22, a significant rebuild programme for the Tu-22 was instituted throughout much of the 1960s to cure lingering problems. Aileron reversal problems were finally cured in 1965 with the addition of aileron fences. Additional hydraulic boosters were added to the flight control system to ease the pilot's handling problems. Improvements were made to the wing-mounted landing gear due to problems that had led to wing damage on landing. A string of engine upgrades was undertaken; the Dobrinin VD-7M was replaced from 1965 with an improved derivative, the Kolesov RD-7M2 engine, which offered 162 kN (36,375 lb) of static thrust compared to 159 kN (35,273 lb).

Following the development of an inflight-refuelling system for the Tu-22R reconnaissance aircraft, the system was adapted to the missile carriers due to the shortfall in their intended range compared to the official requirement. This upgrade programme began in 1965, with the missile carriers having a 'D' suffix added, such as Tu-22KD.

Electronic warfare systems were gradually improved through the career of the 'Blinder'. The basic defensive complex consisted of two passive radar warning receivers: the Avtomat-2 tuned to interceptor bands, and the Avtomat-3 tuned to ground-based radar bands.

New electronic systems for the Tu-22

The widespread deployment of the MIM-14 Nike Hercules and MIM-23 HAWK air defence missiles by NATO in the late 1950s presented a serious threat to any Soviet bomber strikes against high-value targets. GOSNIIAS, the main government avionics institute, began a detailed study of this problem under the codename Ekho. In 1962, experiments were conducted with a modified version of the Tu-22K adapted to attack key air defence radar installations with a special anti-radar version of the Kh-22 missile, the Kh-22P. The modified 'Blinder' was designated Tu-22KP and was fitted with the Kurs-N and later the Kurs-NM electronic intelligence system, which passively scanned for the emissions of standard NATO air defence radars. This version could be distinguished by a prominent 'pitchfork' antenna array carried on the right side of the nose. Most were built in the Tu-22KPD config-uration with the standard refuelling system.

In the 1970s, some Tu-22R aircraft were upgraded with the Kub electronic intelligence system, with the antennas for the Elint system mounted in scabbed-on blisters on either side of the forward fuselage and in the wingroot. They were sometimes called Tu-22RK, but, since most were built with the refuelling probe, they were mostly designated Tu-22RDK. This was related to the system mounted on the MiG-25RBK reconnaissance aircraft.

In 1975, work began on another Tu-22R upgrade. A new reconnaissance package was developed, mounted in the bomb bay with a tub projecting under the fuselage for associated antennas and camera ports. The new centre package included M-202 Shompol side-looking radar, additional short focal-length cameras, and a new infra-red line scanner. The Shompol, developed by NPO Vega-M, was related to the type fitted to the MiG-25RBSh recon-naissance aircraft. The upgrade also included the addition of two AFA-42/100 cameras in place of one of the fuel tanks. Its ECM improvements included the incorporation of an SPS-151 jamming station (or the SPS-152 and SPS-153 Liutik jammers) and the addition of an ASO-2I chaff dispenser system. A small number were converted from Tu-22RD aircraft in 1981-82 as the Tu-22RDM.

A total of 311 Tu-22 and two prototypes was manufactured at Kazan through 1969, including 15 Tu-22Bs, 127 Tu-22Rs, 76 Tu-22Ks and 46 Tu-22Us.

Foreign exports and Libyan combat

In spite of its less than auspicious career in the Soviet air force, several air forces in the Middle East expressed interest in obtaining an aircraft more modern than the Tu-16. Sale of the new Tu-22M 'Backfire' was out of the question at the time, and the Tu-22 had been out of production for several years. After some discussion, the Ministry of Aviation Production decided to convert Tu-22R reconnaissance aircraft back to the Tu-22B configuration for export purposes. The total number converted is not certain, but Russian sources state it was over 20. In addition, a handful of Tu-22Us and Tu-22Rs were modified for export. One of the first requests was from Egypt, but this request was eventually turned down as its relations with the USSR cooled. Two export orders were approved: Libya and Iraq.

A Libyan squadron was the first to employ the Tu-22 in combat when, in 1979, Idi Amin of Uganda requested military support in his losing war with neighbouring Tanzania. On the night of 29-30 March 1979, a pair of Tu-22B bombers attacked the town of Mwanza in Tanzania, causing little damage. The Tu-22 bombers saw most of their combat action in the 1980s during the Libyan military campaigns in Chad. These air raids were seldom carried out by more than a pair of aircraft at a time, raising some questions about the availability of trained aircrews. In March 1980, civil war broke out again in Chad, with Colonel Muamar Khadaffi supporting Goukouni Oueddi's forces against those of defence minister Hissene Habre. On 9 October 1980, a small number of Tu-22B bombed Habre's forces

near N'djamena. The war eventually petered out and Khadaffi announced a union of Libya and Chad in January 1981. Habre managed to raise another insurgent army, and the civil war resumed in early 1982, with Habre's temporary victory. After a short interlude, the fighting broke out again in 1983, with Libya again supporting Goukouni against Habre. A number of bombing missions against Habre's forces from July to September 1983 used the Tu-22Bs, including raids on Fad, Faya-Largo and Umm-Shaluba.

International mediation brought the war to a close for three years until February 1986, when Goukoni's forces, with Libyan backing, attacked over the 'Red Line'. France decided to take a firmer line this time, and dispatched forces to assist Habre's forces. On 17 February 1986, a

This Tu-22U is seen connected to a a truck-mounted APA-50 electric 'start cart', as its crew prepare for a training sortie. All three crew K-22 ejection seats retract upwards into the fuselage. There are small emergency access hatches in the windscreen for the pilot and above the fuselage for the other crew.

Above and left: The Tu-22UD could be fitted with a complete refuelling probe, or the stubby housing for one above the nose. A Tu-22 typically refuelled from a Tu-16 tanker at heights between 5000 m (16,404 ft) and 8000 m (26,247 ft), and speeds of 600 km/h (373 mph). Air-to-air refuelling in the Tu-22 was a difficult and, in some cases, virtually impossible procedure. Reports tell of aircraft with inexperienced crews travelling 450 km (280 miles) together before achieving a successful hook-up.

Tupolev Tu-22P 'Blinder-E'

Above and left: The Tu-22P was the dedicated EW version of the 'Blinder'. Tu-22PDs of 341 TBAP saw action over Afghanistan, protecting bombers from Pakistani F-16s and SAMs. The dragon badge was adopted, in-theatre, in 1988.

Above: This view of the Tu-22P 'Blinder-E' escort jammer prototype shows the housings for the SPS-100A Rezeda-A ECM system. Some aircraft, however, retained the gun barbette. The Tu-22P also had antenna housings on the fuselage and in the wing root leading edge.

Right: Approximately 30 Tu-22P-1 and P-2 aircraft were built and each Tu-22K regiment was allocated a squadron of Tu-22Ps. The Tu-22P was designed to escort strike packages of missile carriers into and out of the target area. The baseline Tu-22Ps later evolved into Tu-22P-4/6/7s, with new equipment and antenna fits.

The air cooling scoop required by all its internal electronic equipment can be seen underneath this 'Blinder-E'. Also apparent are the problems faced by Tu-22 maintenance crews. The 'Blinder' sits high off the ground and none of its critical components – particularly the engines – is easily accessible.

single Tu-22B left Sebka air base, used terrain masking to approach N'djamena airport, and dropped three 500-kg (1,100-lb) bombs on it, hitting one of the main taxiways. Libyan forces were deployed in substantial numbers during this campaign, and the Tu-22B bombers were forward-deployed to Wadi-Dum air base to assist in supporting their operations. Bombing missions were carried out from October 1986 through March 1987. Habre's forces later captured Wadi-Dum, and found two derelict Tu-22B bombers there among other Libyan spoils. By August 1987, Habre's forces, supported by France, reached the disputed territory on the Chad-Libyan border. During the fighting near Aouza airbase on 8 August 1987, a Tu-22B was downed by a surface-to-air missile, apparently a Kub (SA-6) captured from the Libyans by Habre's troops. In response to a Chadian raid on the Maaten-es-Sara air base in Libya, on 5 September 1987, Khadaffi ordered a retaliatory raid on

N'djamena again. By this time, France had deployed an MIM-23 I-HAWK battery of the 402ᵉ Regiment Anti-Aérien. One Tu-22B was shot down, with the loss of its crew, and the other dumped its bombs and escaped.

The Tu-22Bs continued to launch pin-prick raids against Chadian forces at Wadi-Dum, Fada and Faya-Largo, until the ceasefire on 11 September 1987. Libya had been routed by the irregular Chadian forces, losing about $1.5 billion in equipment and a substantial number of troops.

While the war was going on against Chad, Libya became involved in border skirmishes with Sudan, which was supporting Chad in the conflict. As a result, Khadaffi ordered a Tu-22B bomber raid against Ondurman in March 1984, which caused civilian casualties. In April 1985, President Nimeiri was overthrown by forces friendly to Libya. As a result, the Libyan Tu-22B bombers were sent on several occasions in 1985 to support Sudanese forces in their campaigns against Christian insurgents in the southern regions of the country.

Iran-Iraq War

The second major conflict involving the Tu-22B bombers took place between Iran and Iraq in 1980. The Iraqi aircraft were heavily committed, and their range let them reach nearly any target in Iran. However, they faced much more serious opposition than their Libyan counterparts. When the war began on 19 September 1980, the Tu-22B bombers were committed to attacks against Teheran and Isfahan. During a 23 September 1980 raid on Teheran airport, the Iranians claim to have downed one Tu-22B bomber. After this initial onslaught, the Iraqi air force substantially reduced its operational tempo, returning only to carry out specific operations. In early October, the Tu-22B bombers returned in force, with fighter escort, to strike two automotive factories in Teheran. There have been reports that the Tu-22B bombers were occasionally allowed to operate from bases in Saudi Arabia and North Yemen, which served as a sanctuary from retaliatory Iranian strikes against their main operating base at Al-Walid.

The tempo of Tu-22 bomber strikes diminished when the Soviet Union imposed an arms embargo on Iraq. By 1984, Iraqi strength had been reduced to about eight Tu-22B

bombers, although it is not clear if the attrition was due to combat losses or accidents. The Tu-22B squadron continued to stage raids against key oil refineries and other military targets. Through 1982, Iran claims to have downed a further two Tu-22B bombers. In May 1985, the Iraqi air force resumed heavy air operations against Iranian cities, striking Teheran, Isfahan, and Shiraz with Tu-22 raids. This provoked the 'war of the cities' in which both sides pelted each other's cities with 'Scud' ballistic missiles. The Iraqi raids did not go uncontested and there were reports of at least one Tu-22B being damaged in an encounter with an Iranian F-4 Phantom, which severely damaged its stabiliser with an AIM-9 Sidewinder missile. Other aircraft suffered damage from MIM-23 HAWK missile batteries.

In March 1988, the Tu-22B bombers were used for the first time in maritime strikes during the 'tanker war'.

Tu-22Bs were credited with setting two supertankers on fire during a 19 March 1988 mission, the *Awai* and the *Sanandai*. By the end of the war in 1988, Iraq was reported to have only five Tu-22B bombers left in service. This suggests that as many as seven may have been lost in combat during the war.

Soviet 'Blinders' in combat

The Tu-22 was used in a limited support role during Soviet operations in Afghanistan. In October 1988, four Tu-22PDs of the 341st Heavy Bomber Regiment in Ozernoye were deployed to Mary-2 air base to provide electronic warfare support for Tu-22M3 'Backfire' bombers of the 185th Heavy Bomber Regiment from Poltava. The requirement for ECM support was prompted by the use of 'Backfires' near the Pakistani border, where there were

Sadly, this Tu-22PD 'Blinder-E', and its huge sharksmouth, is seen here withdrawn from service and awaiting its fate at the Engels dismantlement facility in 1995. It did not get broken up straight away, however, and survived at Engels for some years.

Tupolev Tu-22LL

A number of Tu-22s have served as trials aircraft for new engines and camera/reconnaissance systems. Of all these, the Tu-22LL stands out. In 1971, a single Tu-22R was converted at Tupolev factory N22 at Kazan (where all Tu-22 production was undertaken) to act as a high-speed equipment testbed. It was redesignated as the Tu-22LL (LL=letayuschchaya laboratoriya/flying laboratory). This Russian term is used indiscriminately and can be applied to an engine, avionics, equipment or weapons testbed or a research/survey aircraft. It is not known what functions the Tu-22LL and its modified (camera?) nose cone performed, but the aircraft ('Red 05') is still to be seen at the Russian flight test institute (LII), Zhukhovskii.

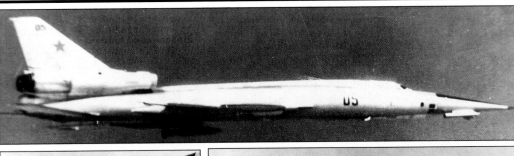

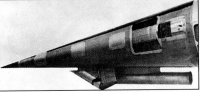

concerns that Pakistani F-16 fighters or radar-directed SAMs might be employed. After three months of operations, this unit was replaced by four Tu-22PD stand-off jammers from the 203rd Heavy Bomber Regiment from Bara-novichi in January 1989. They saw very little action as, by this time, bombing operations had shifted to the Salang pass area where there was no need for ECM support. As a result, the last Tu-22PDs were sent back to their bases in February. There had been plans to use Tu-22Rs of the 199th OGDRAP for photographic reconnaissance missions over Afghanistan in November 1988 from Mozdok, but they never took place.

Andrei Tupolev himself regarded the Tupolev Tu-22 as one of his "less fortunate creations." Its troubled history can be linked both to design problems and to the rapidly changing military environment in the later Kruschchev years. Although intended to take over the continental strike mission from the Tu-16, this never transpired. Much of the role was assumed by the Yangel design bureau's R-12 and R-14 (SS-4 and SS-5) intermediate-range missiles. In addi-tion, the high cost and troubled early career of the Tu-22 led to a scaling-back of production compared to earlier plans. In its primary combat role as a stand-off cruise missile launcher, the 'Blinder' was inferior to the Tu-16, which could carry two missiles to the Tu-22's one, had better range, and was more dependable. The Tu-16 remained in service many years beyond its presumed life-expectancy, in part to make up for the problems with the Tu-22. The Tu-22's primary role in its later career was long-range reconnaissance, which it performed well after its teething problems had been overcome in the mid-1970s.

At the moment, the Tu-22 is on the brink of retirement. Given its shaky start, it is surprising it lasted this long. All Russian 'Blinders' are waiting for disposal. Ukraine possesses a small number of aircraft, but their long-term prospects for continued operational use seem poor. 'Blinders' in Iraq and Libya are likewise on the verge of extinction, if for no other reason than a lack of spare parts.

The same fate probably awaits the Tu-22's predecessor, the hardy and dependable Tu-16.

Taking the Tu-22's place has been a far more durable and successful aircraft, the Tu-22M 'Backfire'. The simi-larity in designation of the two aircraft is slightly misleading, but was not aimed at spy agencies in NATO. It was prompted by a complex power struggle in the halls of Kremlin in the late 1960s over the future of Soviet heavy combat aircraft development.

Tupolev Tu-22M 'Backfire'

The Tupolev Tu-22M 'Backfire' bomber was one of the most controversial Soviet aircraft of the 1980s. Intended as a follow-on to the Tu-22 'Blinder', it represented such a significant leap in capabilities that some intelligence analysts in the United States thought it was an intercontinental strategic bomber rather than a mere medium bomber. This led to protracted arguments at the strategic arms limitation talks between the USA and USSR. Its origins and missions stemmed from unusually intense rivalries within the Soviet military industrial complex.

In 1959, the 3rd Directorate of the NII-VVS (Scientific Research Institute of the Air Force) developed the tactical-technical requirements document (TTT) for a new-generation supersonic strategic bomber. The requirement was clearly influenced by the US XB-70 project, and the Soviet docu-ment referred to the need for a "reconnaissance strike complex" reflecting the US conception of this aircraft. As in the American case, the requirement pushed the state of the art, requiring a high level of performance and consider-able advances in aircraft avionics including an automated astro-navigation system and fly-by-wire flight controls. The new design was intended to serve as a follow-on to the Tu-22 'Blinder'; it would have an effective combat radius of 2000 km (1,243 miles) and would carry two 1500-kg (3,310-lb) nuclear-armed Kh-45 Molniya stand-off missiles. The aircraft was designed to attack US Navy carrier battle groups, as well as key regional targets in Europe and the

Tupolev Tu-22 'Blinder' and Tu-22M 'Backfire'

chairman of the State Committee for Aviation Engineering (GKAT), who headed the Soviet aviation industry. The requirement was issued instead to three other bureaus, two of them fighter bureaus: Myasishchev's OKB-23, Sukhoi's OKB-51 and Yakovlev's OKB-115. Myasishchev's bureau had been working on a string of successor designs to its failed M-50 bomber (NATO's 'Bounder'), including the M-56 design. This bureau was quickly eliminated, quite literally, as Kruschchev's frustration over the bureau's past failures led to his decision to close the design bureau and turn over its assets to Chelomey's missile design bureau to assist with the new UR-100 (SS-11 Sego) missile programme.

Sukhoi was not as closely attuned to Kremlin politics as Tupolev, and threw the full weight of his bureau into the effort, coming up with the radical T-4 design. This sophisticated titanium aircraft was also called izdeliye 100 or T-100 due to its 100-tonne (98-ton) take-off weight. Yakovlev offered the Yak-33 design. Although not officially invited, Tupolev offered his Samolet 135 for the requirement, a 205-tonne (202-ton) design that strongly resembled the American XB-70 in configuration and grossly exceeded the design weight of the requirement. The designs were evaluated by a state commission in the spring of 1962, at which point it became apparent to Tupolev that the scales had been rigged and that his aircraft was far too large to compete with the Sukhoi or Yakovlev designs. As a result, Tupolev quickly came up with a substantially pared-down design, the Project 125, with a take-off weight of 130 tonnes (128 tons) and a cruising range of 6000 km (3,728 miles). However, the competition had been loaded in favour of his challengers, and Sukhoi's elegant T-4 design was selected to proceed.

The Sukhoi bureau was at first entrusted with the development of both the Molniya missile system and the aircraft itself. As the magnitude of the task became clear, the missile project was split off and delegated to the more experienced MKB Raduga design bureau in Dubna. The Molniya missile was to be powered by a solid rocket engine, with an effective range of 1500 km (932 miles), about three times

Pacific, but did not have the range for strategic strikes against the USA. The aircraft was required to have a top speed of Mach 3 and a cruising speed of Mach 2.8, a significant challenge given both structural airframe life and engine fuel economy issues.

The obvious choice to undertake the programme would have been Tupolev's OKB-156 design bureau, which had designed most post-war Soviet strategic bombers. However, Kruschchev was becoming disenchanted with Tupolev, in part due to his arrogant assumption that his bureau would be entrusted with all future bomber designs, as well as problems with the Tu-22 design that were becoming more evident. Nevertheless, Tupolev had continually bested all his rivals, emerging on top in contests with the experienced Ilyushin and the hapless Myasishchev. Kruschchev was also unhappy with Tupolev's design conservatism and reluctance to examine novel technologies.

Kruschchev made his views known to the Pyotr Dementyev,

Far left and below: By the late 1970s, the 15th Bomber Division's 'Blinders' were growing increasingly obsolete in one of their primary roles, that of attacking US Navy carrier battle groups. By this time, however, the 'Blinder' was being supplemented by the more modern Tu-22M 'Backfire', which was assigned the same mission. The first 'Backfires' entered service in 1971/1972, but it was not until 1976 that the first real operational variant, the Tu-22M2 'Backfire-B', was ready. The aircraft seen here are the latest model Tu-22M3 'Backfire-C'. In addition to the new bomber, a new family of Kh-22 missiles was introduced, the Kh-22M (AS-4 'Kitchen'), which incorporated features aimed at improving the probability of the missile 'leaking' through a carrier battle group's increasingly tough defences.

Tupolev T-22M0 and Tu-22M1 'Backfire-A'

Left: Wind tunnel tests at TSAGI revealed that the Tu-22M0 had several shortcomings, including its inadequate range. This tunnel model is a Tu-22M1, with bomb racks.

Below: Nine pre-production Tu-22M0s were built. This one survives at the Irkutsk military engineering academy.

Above: Redolent with Cold War intrigue, this photo shows one of the Tu-22M0s during test operations. Note the distinctive tail configuration and refuelling probe.

Right: Another preserved Tu-22M0 is now at the Kiev military aviation academy. Its probe was removed after SALT II.

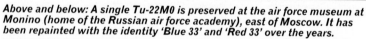

Above: This is how the 'Tu-26' was revealed by the US DoD in 1982.

Left: The large undercarriage fairings of the Tu-22M0 were dropped on production aircraft.

Below: This Tu-22M1 is carrying a single Kh-22 and is equipped with the OPB-15 optical bombsight ahead of the nose gear.

Above and below: A single Tu-22M0 is preserved at the air force museum at Monino (home of the Russian air force academy), east of Moscow. It has been repainted with the identity 'Blue 33' and 'Red 33' over the years.

the range of the contemporary Kh-22. The missile would be command-guided during the cruise phase, with an active terminal guidance system. There were also plans to develop a separating warhead section for the missile, to improve its survivability against SAMs. The missile would be lofted on a semi-ballistic trajectory and its warhead would separate upon re-entry into the upper atmosphere, with an active radar seeker on the re-entry vehicle providing terminal guidance. In some respects, this missile was similar to the Skybolt missile being developed at the time for the US Air Force and the RAF. The T-4 bomber would carry two Molniya missiles in internal bomb bays.

With preliminary design of the T-4 complete, Dementyev called Sukhoi to his office and crudely remarked, "the Negro has done his job, the Negro can leave." With his task of chastening Tupolev accomplished, Dementyev saw no further need to proceed with the T-4 programme. However, Sukhoi had became enamoured with the engineering challenge posed by the T-4 effort, and had won some support within the Military Industrial Committee (VPK) to continue the work, even if not fully funded. While Sukhoi was struggling through the early phase of the T-4's development, Kruschchev was ousted from power in the autumn of 1964.

Tupolev's lack of favour with Kruschchev rebounded to his benefit after the coup, and he enjoyed strong support from the new Brezhnev regime. In late 1964 Tupolev was able win approval to proceed with his new Samolet 145 design as a follow-on to the Tu-22. The project had the strong endorsement of the air force commander, General P. S. Kutakhov. Unhappy about the limitations of the new Tu-22 'Blinder', the Soviet air force wanted a more capable aircraft. The requirement for the new bomber included a range of at least 5000 km (3,106 miles), a speed of at least Mach 2 at high altitude, a speed near Mach 1 during low-altitude penetration missions, a payload of at least 20 tonnes (19.7 tons) to include missiles and bombs, and the ability to operate from forward air bases. The Samolet 145 had been conceived without government backing in 1962 as a lower-cost alternative to either the Tupolev Samolet 125 or the Sukhoi T-4. Development of the Samolet 145 was opposed by Kruschchev, who regarded manned aircraft as inferior to

The addition of a refuelling probe to the Tu-22M2 was the most controversial point in the history of the 'Backfire' and photos of such aircraft are rare. This photograph was taken by an SH-37 Viggen, in 1980.

Tupolev Tu-22M2 'Backfire-B'

Above and left: The Tu-22M2 was in flight test while SALT II negotiations were being conducted, but development aircraft were never fitted with refuelling probes. Note the early bullet-shaped fairing for the Argon-2 fire control radar above the tail guns.

Above: The most distinctive feature of the Tu-22M2 – the enlarged and revised air intakes feeding the NK-22 engines – is evident in this view of an aircraft on its take-off run.

Above: This Tu-22M2 has the revised, squared-off, PRS-3 Argon-2 radome and multiple ejector rack mounted on its ventral hardpoint.

Below: The complete deletion of the probe housing from some M2s led to a smoother nose profile.

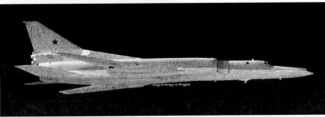

Above: A Tu-22M2 carrying a live Kh-22 missile – the type's primary armament for virtually all operational missions.

Right: This overhead view of a Tu-22M2 is one of those required for release under the terms of the CFE (Conventional Forces in Europe) arms reduction treaty. Like all its predecessors, the Tu-22M2 had a wing sweep range of 20° to 60°.

Right and below: By late 1969, Western intelligence agencies had determined that a 'new variant' of the Tu-22 existed and the first US satellite images of a Tu-22M on the ramp were taken over Kazan in July 1970. Russian hackles were raised when photos of the Tu-22M2 appeared – they had been taken at Poltava air base by a West German 'tourist'. It it was not until 1979 that the first good photographs, taken by the Swedish air force and others, began to appear. The photos seen here are both US Navy intercept shots, of Tu-22M2s, taken in 1989.

This Tu-22M2 is one of those operated by the training centre at Ryazan. The complete removal of the refuelling probe housing from the nose considerably alters the profile of the 'Backfire-B'. When the 'Backfire' became an issue during the SALT talks, its estimated maximum range, coupled with its refuelling capability became a hugely contentious issue. The CIA and independent US industry sources (chiefly McDonnell Douglas) maintained that Soviet figures were correct and the aircraft had a range of approximately 3,000-3,500 nm. The US Air Force and the DoD steadfastly attributed an unrefuelled range of 5,000-6,000 nm to the aircraft. The Soviet Union was permitted only 2,400 'strategic delivery systems' under the terms of the Ford-Brezhnev Vladivostok agreement that established the SALT II guidelines. Ultimately, the Soviet position that the 'Backfire' was a medium-range theatre bomber was accepted, but only with the removal of its refuelling capability.

missiles for nuclear strike missions. When resubmitted to the new Brezhnev administration, the aircraft was depicted as a mere upgrade of the existing and seriously flawed Tu-22 'Blinder'. If the Samolet 145 had not been offered as a safe and cheap alternative to the T-4, it also might have been armed with the highly sophisticated Molniya missile. Instead, it was to be equipped with the existing Kh-22 and K-22 weapon system that armed the Tu-22K bomber.

The selection of the older Kh-22 missile for the new bomber, rather than a new weapon such as the Kh-45, was tied to Tupolev's marketing strategy with Brezhnev and the Council of Ministers. The competitor for the requirement was the struggling Sukhoi T-4 programme, an entirely new and expensive aircraft. In contrast, Tupolev was offering his

Samolet 145 as a less expensive alternative, linked to the existing Tu-22. The internal bureau designation reflected that relationship; the Tu-22 had been Project Yu, the new design was Project YuM (later, more honestly, Project A). The Samolet 145 would use an upgraded version of the K-22 system, designated K-22M, based around the Leninets PN-A radar (NATO's 'Down Beat'), derived from the radar used in the earlier Tu-22K.

Samolet 145 wins out

Brezhnev's decision to permit Tupolev to proceed with Project 145 meant that in the late 1960s the Soviet air force was funding the development of two parallel intermediate-range bombers armed with two entirely different missile systems. In November 1967, the Council of Ministers decided to proceed with engineering-manufacturing development of the Samolet 145 instead of the T-4. The decision was based on several factors. To begin with, the Tu-22 'Blinder' had proved very disappointing in service and a new aircraft was needed to replace it on the production lines. The Tu-22 never came close to replacing the Tu-16, which was one of the original goals of the programme. Secondly, there was some concern about the cost of the T-4. It was pointedly nicknamed '100 tonnes of gold' due to the high cost of its titanium structure. The Samolet 145 appeared to be a more reasonable compromise in terms of performance and cost. Thirdly, the new Brezhnev administration was becoming increasingly concerned about the threat posed by China. Strikes against China posed a different set of requirements than those

against the more technologically advanced threat of NATO, and an aircraft with a hefty payload was more attractive than the elegant but more lightly armed T-4.

Although promoted as a mere upgrade of the Tu-22, the Samolet 145 was in fact an entirely new aircraft, sharing only a common weapon system. In the end, the only structural assemblies in common between the two aircraft were the front landing gear and the bomb bay doors. The construction of the first prototype was accomplished fairly quickly, with the first Tu-22M0 being delivered to the Flight Test Institute (LII) at Zhukhovskii in the summer of 1969, hardly two years after the project had officially been blessed. The first test flight took place on 30 August 1969. In order to hasten the testing, it was decided to build a somewhat larger pre-series batch than the normal five aircraft, 10 being planned. Trials revealed some problems in the design, but they were to be addressed in the early production aircraft. The problems included flexing and deformation problems with the wing fillet, excessive landing gear weight and complexity, and the lack of utility of the planned arrester hook. The prototype employed the Kuznetsov NK-144-22 engine, derived from the engine on the Tu-144 supersonic transport. It was not sufficiently fuel efficient, and the Tu-22M0 was below the range requirements at only 4140 km (2,573 miles). A total of nine of the pre-series Tu-22M0 was manufactured at Kazan in 1969-71. The final production aircraft incorporated some of the features intended for the series production aircraft, including the rear UKU-9K-502 defensive machine-gun position designed by I. Goropov's Vympel OKB-43 in place of an electronic warfare station and braking parachute housing of the original aircraft. The decision to add the defensive station was not applauded throughout the air force, and it came at a time of increasing doubts about the usefulness of such weapons as a defence against fighters. As a concession to critics, the role of the machine-gun position was changed. Instead of firing conventional ammunition, it sprayed out a stream of special PIKS anti-IR projectiles with a thermite fill, and PRLS anti-radar projectiles which dispensed small chaff dipoles.

Troubled Tu-22M1

The series production aircraft received the evolved NK-22 engine, which offered about 10 per cent more thrust. This engine was developed by the N. Kuznetsov design bureau and manufactured at the Trud Plant in Kuibyshev (now Samara). Production was scheduled to begin at the State Aviation Plant No. 22 in Kazan in 1971, after the conclusion of Tu-22 'Blinder' production there.

The initial production type was designated Tu-22M1. This production batch used a simplified landing gear retracting into the wingroot, and the wing span was increased. Design problems persisted with this version of the aircraft as well, and only nine Tu-22M1s were manufactured in 1971-72. Operational trials were conducted by the 185th Guards Heavy Bomber Aviation Regiment, 13th Guards Heavy Bomber Aviation Division in Poltava, Ukraine, commanded by the later head of the Russian Air Force, P. S. Denikin. There has never been a detailed explanation of the full extent of the problems with the Tu-22M1, but it was not accepted for series production. Russian accounts state that the Tu-22M1 was specifically intended for naval applications and that seven of the nine aircraft manufactured were deployed with naval regiments.

The improved design required additional work, and official service acceptance did not take place until 1976. It incorporated the modified ABSU-145M flight control and NK-45 flight navigation systems, plus improvements to the weapons system. The revised design can be identified by the change in the configuration of the air inlets, the intake

This page, clockwise from top left: The first clear photos of the 'Backfire-B' came in 1979 when 'Red 78' was photographed by the Swedes. 'Red 43' was next seen in 1980, again over the Baltic. Eventually the Tu-22M became a common sight – particularly in the northern European region. The Flygvapnet brought back the first clear images of the AS-4 'Kitchen' missile (Kh-22), carried by 'Red 76'. In this case (three photos) it is a silver training ('uchebniy') round of the Kh-22MA low-level nuclear-armed version. The missile-carrying Tu-22M2 is seen escorted by a Flygvapnet J 35F Draken. In 1980, two Danish air force RF 35 reconnaissance Drakens intercepted a gaggle of Tu-22M2s over the Baltic. The Drakens left the scene upon the arrival of Soviet MiG-23s sent to shepherd the 'Backfires'. The Tu-22s then went on to make the first observed (but only on radar) air-to-surface firings of the Kh-22 against shipping and ground targets (on the East German island of Rugen). The 'Backfires' were operating as part of exercise Brotherhood in Arms-80, supporting amphibious landings. The RNAF 331 Skv F-16A is seen escorting Tu-22M2 'Red 41' which is carrying a standard Kh-22 training round – containing all the missile avionics, but no fuel or warhead.

Tupolev Tu-22M3 'Backfire-C'

Above and left: The prototype Tu-22M had a refuelling probe stub which was removed from all subsequent M3s as part of the Soviet concessions to SALT II. The aircraft seen left is one of the pre-production batch.

Above: A clandestine photograph of an early Tu-22M3 'Backfire-C', seen landing at Zhukhovskii.

Left: The M3 routinely carries its missile armament under the wing, on BD-45K pylons, unlike earlier 'Backfires' or the 'Blinder'.

Below: A Tu-22M3, armed with a single Kh-22M, departs on a training mission.

Above: The boundary-layer intakes over the main engine intakes are visible in this overhead CFE view of a Tu-22M3.

Left: Free-fall bombs are rarely seen on the 'Backfire', particularly on the Tu-22M3.

Below: A Tu-22M3 in landing configuration.

and venting ports for an APU added in the dorsal fin, and reshaping of the dielectric cover over the Argon-3 aft-facing defensive radar. The standard production version was designated Tu-22M2 ('Backfire-B'), and it was nicknamed the 'Dvoika' (deuce) by its crews. Total production of the Tu-22M from 1972 to 1983 was 211 aircraft, all manufactured at the State Aviation Plant No. 22 in Kazan.

The standard payload of the Tu-22M2 was a single Kh-22 (AS-4 'Kitchen') in a recessed central bomb bay under the fuselage. For short-range missions, the Tu-22M2 could increase its payload at the expense of range, typically a pair of Kh-22N missiles, one under each wing pylon. As many as three Kh-22s could be carried simultaneously, at the expense of range, but this configuration appears to have been rarely used with this version of the aircraft.

The Tu-22M2 was received with enthusiasm by its crews, in contrast to the earlier Tu-22 'Blinder'. It had far better handling characteristics and cockpit ergonomics. In addition to their deployment with the Long Range Aviation branch of the air force, Tu-22M2s were also issued to Naval Aviation regiments of the Northern and Black Sea Fleets to replace the Tu-16K. In this role, they could be fitted to deliver aerial mines. Training for both branches was undertaken at the 43rd Flight Personnel Combat Training and Conversion Centre at Ryazan. Tu-22M2 regiments were organised around 18 bombers, although regimental strength was sometimes as high as 20. In addition, the accepted practice was to deploy at least a squadron of Tu-16P escort jammers with each Tu-22M2 regiment for electronic warfare support. Due to the high

cost of the aircraft, it was decided to develop a conversion trainer for crews, the Tupolev Tu-134UBL, based on the common twin-engined airliner.

Early service troubles

The reputation of the Tu-22M2 began to suffer as the aircraft aged. The design was quite complicated, which led to servicing problems. The mean-time-between-overhauls (MBTO) of the NK-22 engines on the initial aircraft was an appallingly low 50 hours, and led to a service-wide edict to limit turbine temperatures and, therefore, engine thrust. The ECM system had not been well integrated with the aircraft avionics, leading to interference problems which sometimes shut down the automated flight control system, forcing the crew to fly the aircraft manually. The Tu-22M2 was not well suited to low-level tactics, even though they were supposed to be its primary combat envelope. Rivets in the air intake would pop off, causing cracks in the fuselage and potentially leading to engine ingestion of parts and subsequent engine disintegration. A programme of strengthening the intake splitters alleviated some of these problems. The aircraft was ruefully referred to as the

'vsepogodniy defektonosets' (all-weather defect-carrier) a play on its official designation of *vsepogodniy raketnosets* (all-weather missile-carrier).

Range controversy

The international controversy over the role of the 'Backfire' bomber had already begun by 1975 when the bombers were first entering widespread service. At the time, negotiations were underway between the US and USSR on the SALT II (Strategic Arms Limitation Treaty) talks.

The Tu-22M3 was fitted with more powerful NK-25 engines, which necessitated revised (and very distinctive) forward-raked air intakes. It also had an improved and strengthened main wing, with an increased maximum sweep angle of 65°. The 'Backfire-C' was optimised for low-level operations, down to 50 m (164 ft), and intended for use in conjunction with A-50 'Mainstay' AWACS and MiG-31 or Su-27 escorts. The Tu-22M3 has never been seen by Western observers in such an operational setting, even though the first aircraft specifically intended for low-level missions entered service in 1983 (with the 185th Guards heavy bomber air regiment).

This is the Tu-22M3 exhibited at the 1992 Minsk-Machulishche military exhibition, held for visiting heads of state and defence ministers. It was the first 'public' showing of the 'Backfire-C'. Note the redesigned vertical cannon installation refitted to late-model 'Backfire-Cs'.

Weapons of the Tu-22M3 'Backfire-C'

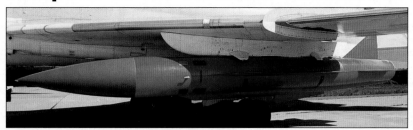

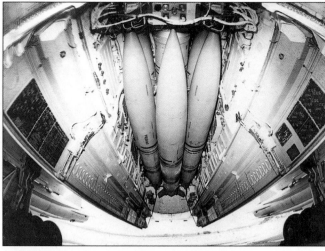

Above, left and below: The primary weapon of the 'Backfire', particularly in the anti-shipping and land attack role (against large targets), is the Kh-22 (AS-4 'Kitchen') missile. The Tu-22M3 can carry up to three Kh-22s (two underwing on BD-45K pylons) over a short range. Kh-22 was only carried recessed by the Tu-22M2. The missiles seen here are Kh-22M training rounds.

Above and left: The Tu-22M3 was modernised to carry the Raduga Kh-15 missile (AS-16 'Kickback') on a six-round internal rotary launcher.

Left, above and below: When first seen by Western observers, the Tu-22M's MBD3-U9-68 multiple ejector rack was identified as 'ECM equipment'. Up to four racks can be carried. The Tu-22M served as a bomber in the Afghan and Chechen conflicts. The aircraft seen here is carrying nine 250-kg FAB-250 HE fragmentation bombs.

The Tu-22M2 (above) was fitted with the UKU-9K-502 gun barbette, comprising two twin-barrelled GSh-23 23-mm cannon. The Tu-22M3 (left) adopted a single GSh-23 installation in a UK-9A-802 housing. The 'Backfire-C's guns are equipped to fire IR decoys and small chaff-dispensing projectiles.

The 'Backfire-A' was first spotted by US intelligence satellites in July 1970, and the 'Backfire-B' in May 1973. The US Air Force's intelligence branch took the hardest line on the 'Backfire', arguing as early as 1971 that the bomber was being developed for both the intercontinental and peripheral attack missions. 'Peripheral attack' was the US's phrase at the time for strategic missions not directed at the continental United States, but against objectives in Europe and Asia. The initial CIA assessment in 1970 was that the 'Backfire' had a maximum combat radius of 5550 km (3,450 miles) when flying a subsonic high-altitude mission with refuelling, similar to that of the 3M 'Bison' bomber. As more data on the 'Backfire' became available, CIA estimates of the aircraft's effective radius dropped, and by 1976 it was down to 3380 km (2,100 miles).

USAF versus the CIA

Other intelligence organisations, and the US Air Force in particular, strongly disagreed. The USAF argued that it was intended for intercontinental missions, while the CIA and Navy argued it was intended primarily for peripheral attack missions in Eurasia. Contemporary US Air Force intelligence assessments estimated that the 'Backfire-B' had an unrefuelled combat radius of 5650 km (3,510 miles) (10450-km/6,495-mile range), and with a single refuelling a combat radius of 7780 km (4,835 miles) (14350-km/8,915-mile range). The argument continued in earnest in the mid-1970s during the SALT deliberations, with the CIA and the

State Department leaning toward the lower estimates, and the Defense Intelligence Agency (DIA), Air Force and Army leaning toward the more alarmist estimates. The high Air Force assessments were in part due to overestimates of fuel stowage, which USAF and DIA analysts put at 68040 kg (150,000 lb) and the CIA at 49895 kg (110,000 lb). Recent Russian accounts indicate that for the Tu-22M3 the figure was 53525 kg (118,000 lb). Air Force estimates also posited a more fuel-efficient engine than was the case, estimating that at its maximum static thrust with afterburner of 55,500 lb (247 kN), it had a specific fuel consumption of 1.99 lb/hr/lb, while at its maximum thrust without afterburner of 33,000 lb (147 kN), its specific fuel consumption was 0.61 lb/hr/lb.

The 'Backfire' compromise

The Soviets argued equally vehemently that the 'Backfire' was not intended for the intercontinental role and therefore should not be classified as a 'heavy bomber' in SALT terminology. At first, the Soviet negotiators believed that the US position was simply a negotiating ploy due to the sharp disparity between the US assessment of the 'Backfire' and its stated performance. However, given Minister of Defence Marshal A. A. Grechko's hardline views on the arms control treaties, the Soviet Union was unwilling to release any significant documentation on 'Backfire' performance to the Americans. Indeed, Grechko even refused to give the Soviet negotiators the aircraft's true designation, using the NATO

name 'Backfire' instead. As a result, the service designation for the 'Backfire' was something of a mystery for many years, with Tu-26 being one of the more popular mistakes. The Soviet negotiators' failure to supply any data rendered any detailed discussion of the issue impossible.

In spite of opposition from the Soviet General Staff, the Kremlin finally decided to make a concession in the 'Backfire' controversy. During the course of negotiations on SALT II in Vienna in 1979, Leonid Brezhnev provided a formal letter to President Jimmy Carter. It stated that any significant increase in the range or payload of the 'Backfire' would be inconsistent with the terms of the treaty, and that production would be frozen at the current annual rate of 30. The Soviet side also agreed to remove the nose refuelling probe from the 'Backfire', to put to rest the contention that the bomber could reach intercontinental ranges if refuelled. In recognition that the aircraft could be easily retrofitted with the refuelling probes, assurances were given that the size of the Soviet tanker force would not be enlarged sufficiently to support the use of the 'Backfire' in an intercontinental role.

In 1985, the DIA conceded that the CIA's lower combat radius estimate of 4825 km (3000 miles) was substantially correct. Ironically, this concession came just as evidence began to emerge that the new 'Backfire-C' variant might have range advantages over the standard 'Backfire-B'.

Recent Russian accounts indicate that the combat range of the Tu-22M1 was 5000 km (3,106 miles) unrefuelled with a 3-tonne (2.9-ton) payload and that the Tu-22M2 was 5100 km (3,169 miles), and that combat radius was only 2200 km (1,367 miles) unrefuelled when carrying a single Kh-22. Range figures are highly contingent both on fuel/payload mixes and flight profiles, and Russian range data has seldom been accompanied by any explicit description of these criteria. However, the Russian and later American estimates may not be as divergent as they seem at first, since the US estimates considered an aircraft flying at economical cruise at high altitude with an internal load of bombs, while the Russian figures apparently refer to a more realistic combat mission consisting of a payload of a single Kh-22 missile with higher drag than internal bombs, and a hi-lo mission profile.

Mission profile

As in the case of the Tu-22 'Blinder', the Tu-22M 'Backfire' was used on two principal types of missions: attacks on strategic land targets, and attacks on US Navy carrier battle groups. In contrast to the 'Blinder', the majority of 'Backfires' were of the missile-carrying versions. Instead of only a single 'Blinder' missile-carrier division, there were five 'Backfire' missile-carrier divisions – three with the Long Range Aviation branch of the Air Force and two with the Navy – plus independent regiments in the Pacific. As a result, the operating environment of the 'Backfire' was considerably larger than in the case of the 'Blinder', including much of the North, Baltic, Black and Mediterranean Seas. 'Backfires' also operated in the Far East against the US Pacific Fleet and Japan.

The Tu-22M3's new NK-25 engines were test flown on a Tu-142 testbed, before being fitted to the Tu-22M2Ye trials aircraft, which integrated the fuel system and other related equipment. The Tu-22M3 made its maiden flight on 20 June 1977.

This Tu-22M3 was involved in weapons trials from Zhukhovskii air base, Moscow. Note the unusual serial presentation (9804) on the forward nosewheel door – most Tu-22s carry a service 'Bort' number on the tail. This 'Backfire-C' is carrying a heavy load of two Kh-22 (AS-4) missiles – both missiles are test versions of the Kh-22 anti-shipping variant with the full dielectric nosecone, indicating that the round is fitted with the active radar seeker.

Tupolev Tu-134UBK and Tu-134UBL

The Tu-134UBL is intended to train Tu-22M3 'Backfire-C' and Tu-160 'Blackjack' crews, who have never had a dedicated trainer, like the Tu-22U. The Tu-134 and Tu-22M have a similar thrust-to-weight ratio and comparable low-speed handling. The Tu-134UBL is a purpose-built aircraft, not a conversion, and is instantly recognisable by its long pointed nose, housing a ROZ-1 radar. Each aircraft has only nine cabin windows and all Russian air force aircraft are grey painted, with a red lightning bolt. By late 1983, 90 aircraft had been built. Tu-134UBLs serve with the pilot's schools at Orsk and Tambov. A single Tu-134UBL was converted to Tu-134UBK standard, in 1982, to train Tu-22M3 for anti-shipping missions. This aircraft has a small undernose fairing to house the re-located ROZ-1 radar, and the nosecone instead housed the bomber's PN-A attack radar. A fixed Kh-22 acquisition round was installed under the fuselage and the 'Backfire's OPB-15T electro-optical targetting system was also fitted. This aircraft was delivered to the naval conversion training centre in Nikolayev, on the Black Sea, and was taken over by the Ukrainian air force.

Top: The standard operational load for the Tu-22M3 is a single Kh-22 missile – to provide maximum range for the launch aircraft. The 'Backfire-C' can easily carry two Kh-22s, however, along with (theoretically) a full load of Kh-15 short-range attack missiles. Despite its age, and the many problems that plagued its early development, the Kh-22 remains an important weapon in the Russian inventory. It is the primary weapon of the 'Backfire' and the Tu-95 'Bear-G'. It is also believed to be in the Ukrainian, Belarussian and Kazakh inventories. When allegations of a Tu-22M sale to Iran surfaced in 1994, the most controversial aspect of the 'sale' was the suspected supply of Kh-22 and Kh-26 (AS-6 'Kingfish') missiles with the aircraft.

The 'Blinder' made its terminal approaches to the carrier battle group at relatively high altitudes, which made it easily detectable by both surface-based naval radars and airborne radars such as the E-2C Hawkeye. The Tu-22M 'Backfire' was designed to address this problem by using low-altitude approaches which reduced its vulnerability of detection. It was not nap-of-the-earth flying, but rather low-altitude flying. Most peacetime training missions were not carried out at such altitude since it placed greater stress on the airframe and increased the likelihood of training accidents. However, in wartime, most attack missions would have been conducted in a hi-lo-hi profile: high-altitude economical cruise into the target area to conserve fuel and extend range, low-altitude approach and egress when within radar range, and high-altitude return.

The tactics and force structure of the 'Backfire' regiments differed from the 'Blinder' regiments due to important changes in intelligence gathering. While a very large percentage of 'Blinders' had to be devoted to the naval reconnaissance mission, by the late 1970s this mission was being assumed by satellites. The reasons behind this are fairly apparent, as the description of the Tu-22R 'Blinder' tactics makes it quite clear that such missions would be almost suicidal with the advent of improved US Navy air defences, especially the F-14 Tomcat.

The first efforts to develop an MKRT (*sistem morskoy kosmicheskoy razvedki I tselkazaniya* – naval reconnaissance and targeting space system) had begun in the late 1950s

when the 'Blinder' was still on the drawing boards. The programme was a co-operative effort between the Chelomey OKB-52 missile design bureau (onboard targeting system, satellite bus); A. I. Savin's KB-1 MRP/OKB-41 design bureau (satellite); and I. Ya. Brukhanskiy's NII-17 GKRE design bureau (radar and electronic intelligence sensors). The MKRTs was much delayed due to the enormous technological challenge it presented. A small series of test satellites was launched from 1965 but the lack of a sufficiently high-energy power source continued to hinder the programme. A number of compact nuclear power sources were developed, from which the Topaz system from TsKB Mach in Leningrad was selected. The first successful element of this system, the new nuclear-powered US-A RORSAT (Radar Ocean Reconnaissance Satellite), was finally launched in October 1970. The US-A was fitted with a NII-17 active surveillance radar powered by the Topaz nuclear reactor, which gave it enough power to detect and track naval formations. Sufficient US-A satellites were launched for the system to be accepted into service in October 1975. The second element of the MKRTs system was the US-P naval EORSAT (Electronic Intelligence Ocean Reconnaissance Satellite), which began launches in 1975. The US-P was a new generation of Elint satellites fitted with passive electronic sensors to locate naval formations by their radar emissions and radio communications transmissions. The US-A and US-P satellites were the space-based elements of an extensive naval reconnaissance system codenamed Legenda (legend), which was finally accepted for service use in 1978. The satellites were managed by the GRU military intelligence arm of the Soviet General Staff for the regiments of the Long Range Aviation, and by the Department of Satellite Intelligence of the Naval Intelligence Directorate of the Main Navy Staff for the naval 'Backfire' regiments.

The Legenda system gradually replaced the fleet of Tu-22R 'Blinder' aircraft. Data from the system was analysed at primary command centres and transmitted to the 'Backfire' bombers via conventional radio or the Molniya satellite communication datalinks. The advent of the Legenda maritime reconnaissance satellites removed the need for large numbers of reconnaissance 'Backfires', and this hazardous task was conducted from the relative security of space, instead.

New versions of the Kh-22

With data on the location of the carrier battle group, the Tu-22M 'Backfire' squadrons would conduct their final approach to the target at low altitudes. This necessitated changes in the Kh-22 missile to enhance its survivability against US naval air defences. The new system was designated K-22M, and new missile variants as Kh-22M and Kh-22MA. The Kh-22M was intended to attack naval targets and high-radar-contrast land targets. It had two flight profiles: an aero-ballistic profile like the earlier Kh-22 intended to take the missile over the lethal envelope of the F-14 Tomcat, and a new low-altitude approach to reduce the missile's vulnerability to detection. The Kh-22MA was specifically designed for low-altitude attack at minimal approach heights. Both versions had improved electronic counter-countermeasures (ECCM) and datalinks for mid-course corrections from the launching 'Backfire'. The other major advantage of the 'Backfire' over the 'Blinder' was its ability to carry several Kh-22 missiles per mission. As a result, on short-range missions, a 'Backfire' regiment could fire about 50-75 missiles against the carrier battle group, saturating the battle group's defences even if many missile were shot down by Phoenixes from the F-14 Tomcat or other naval air defences.

The viability of 'Backfire' tactics was never proven, and a constant cat-and-mouse game continued between both sides in an attempt to determine each other's weaknesses.

After the fall of the Shah of Iran in 1979, the Soviet Union managed to obtain one or more F-14 Tomcat fighters and Phoenix missiles. This gave them a better appreciation of the strengths and limitations of this element of the defence, and provided the final evidence of the need for a more modern missile to arm the 'Backfire'.

Tu-22M3 'Backfire-C'

As production of the Tu-22M2 was underway, a comprehensive modernisation of the aircraft was initiated in the mid-1970s, under the internal designation Project AM. The shortcomings of the initial NK-22 jet engines prompted efforts to improve their service life and other features. The evolved engine type was designated NK-25. The new engines, as well as previous problems with the initial vertical variable compression air intakes, led to a new 'scoop' horizontal air intake design, which was trialled on a modified Tu-22M2Ye testbed. A variety of other improvements were incorporated at the same time. The maximum wing sweep was extended back to 65°, a feature so secret that crews were forbidden to leave the aircraft on the ground with the wings locked in this position for fear it would be photographed by US satellites. A vigorous weight trimming programme took 3 tonnes (2.9 tons) off the aircraft. Combined with the more powerful and fuel-efficient engines, the new version offered a 33 per cent extension in range (from 5100 to 6800 km/3,170 to 4,225 miles), and doubled the practical combat load from 3 to 6 tonnes (2.9 to 5.9 tons). The new propulsion system improved the

thrust-to-weight ratio from 0.33 on the Tu-22M2 to 0.4 on the Tu-22M3, and maximum speed at altitude increased from Mach 1.65 to Mach 2.05. The only deficit of the new design was a 20 per cent increase in radar cross-section at some view angles caused by the new intakes.

By the 1970s, the K-22 weapons system of the Tu-22M2 was obsolete. Its evolutionary improvements had petered out, and the missile had a lessening probability of success when faced with typical defences of the period, especially in the naval arena when facing Phoenix-armed Tomcats. The Kh-22 missile was nearing the end of its practical life. It had proved to be an enduring hazard in service due to its use of inhibited red fuming nitric acid (IRFNA) oxidiser, a chemical that was highly lethal if the fumes were inhaled, and was extremely prone to starting fires when in contact

The battered appearance of these naval aviation Tu-22M3s is an indication of the use that Russian forces are still getting from their 'Backfires'. Evident in this view are the row of (six) auxiliary inlet doors on the main engine intake and the rectangular APU intake on the main fin fillet.

Above: This 'Backfire-C' is one of the early developmental airframes, still in use with the LII flight test centre. The APU auxiliary inlet is open on this aircraft.

The Tu-22M3 has a pair of folding landing lights under the nose, and one under each air intake.

Tupolev Tu-22M3(R) 'Backfire'

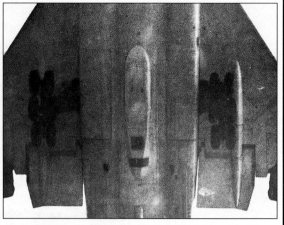

Though the role has been largely adopted by satellites, a small number of Tu-22M3s were modified to act as quick-reaction reconnaissance platforms for the Soviet/Russian navy. This version of the 'Backfire-C', the Tu-22M3(R), sometimes referred to as Tu-22MR, has a large sensor package built into the bomb bay. This equipment resembles that of the Tu-22RDM and so may include the Shompol side-looking radar, or a similar system. The Tu-22M3(R)'s primary role is believed to be as an Elint gatherer and it may be fitted with the Miass EW system. Approximately 12 Tu-22M3s were rebuilt to this configuration and there may be plans to convert some additional older Tu-22M2s to augment those in service.

The Tu-22M3 has been dubbed the 'Troika' (trio) by its crews. The earlier Tu-22M2 was the 'Dvoika' (deuce). The Tu-22M3 is notionally still in production at Kazan, although in reality no new aircraft have been delivered since 1993. As a result, export orders for the aircraft have assumed ever-increasing importance, and perhaps only substantial outside political pressure has halted sales to customers such as Iran and China.

with any type of hydrocarbon including normal fuels, oils and plastics. A solid-fuel missile was desired, like the Kh-45 that had been abandoned as a short-cut in the early 1970s.

A major study programme codenamed 'Pleyada' was launched by the GOSNIIAS air weapons institute in the early 1970s to examine future air-to-surface missiles for strategic aircraft. One of the conclusions of the study was that a missile was needed that could climb to very high altitudes to avoid the lethal envelope of the Phoenix. This study, and its follow-on codenamed 'Chetkost P', urged the services to concentrate on a smaller number of multi-role missile systems instead of the plague of separate sub-types being developed. Several different contenders for the Tu-22M3 armament system were considered, including designs from the Zvezda, Novator and Raduga design bureaux. The Raduga Kh-22 was retained as one option for the Tu-22M3, since there was an available inventory of the missiles, supplemented with a single new type.

The new weapon selected for the Tu-22M3 was MKB Raduga's Kh-15 (AS-16 'Kickback'). The origins of this weapon can be traced to 1967, when it was first called Kh-2000. The Kh-15 uses a solid fuel rocket engine which, after release, boosts it to altitudes up to 40000 m (131,000 ft), well over the operational envelope of the F-14's Phoenix missile. It then dives on its targets at speeds of up to Mach 5. The very high speeds and steep dive angle are intended to reduce its vulnerability to air defence missiles and air-to-air missiles such as the AIM-54 Phoenix, as well as reducing its vulnerability to ship-based defences such as the RIM-67 Standard missile. A missile with this flight profile is sometimes called an aero-ballistic missile due to its terminal flight profile. The basic strategic version of the missile is the nuclear-armed Kh-15P and its guidance system is purely inertial, with no terminal guidance. Due to its planned use on the navy Tu-22M3, a conventionally-armed anti-ship version, the Kh-15A (export designation:

Kh-15S) was developed with a millimetre-wave active radar seeker for the terminal phase of the dive.

The new Tu-22M3 version was accepted for service in 1983; it was called 'Backfire-C' by NATO. It was first deployed, again, with the 185th Guards Heavy Bomber Aviation Regiment. In service, it was nicknamed the 'Troika' (Trio). A total of 268 Tu-22M3s was manufactured when production ground to a halt for lack of funding in 1993.

Electronic warfare

The original ECM system for the Tu-22M2 was unsatisfactory, as mentioned earlier, due to integration problems, leading to a variety of exploratory studies on improvements. Among the alternatives considered was the SPS-55 Buket (Bouquet) system, already in use on Tu-16P escort jammer aircraft. Eventually, the Tu-22M3 was fitted with the new Ural system consisting of the SPS-171 and SPS-172 jammers, the AG-56 noise jammer, the L-082 Mak IR-missile warning systems and the Sirena-3 radar warning system. Although the Ural system doubled the ECM effectiveness of the aircraft compared to the earlier Tu-22M2, the electronic warfare system on the Tu-22M3 was still not considered to be entirely satisfactory. At least some Tu-22M2 were later upgraded with the Ural system.

In the mid-1980s a dedicated EW escort-jammer aircraft to accompany the Tu-22M3 was sought to replace the old and much slower Tu-16P aircraft used in Tu-22M2 regiments. Two options were developed. The Tu-22MP was a Tu-22M3 airframe fitted with the Miass electronic warfare system. The first prototype was completed at Kazan in 1986, followed by two more in 1992. It had not entered service at the time this article was written. This version can be distinguished by the use of a dielectric fairing at the base of the tail, a dielectric fairing on the side of the air intake tunnel, and a semi-recessed 'canoe' under the belly of the aircraft. The second option was a more sophisticated electronic warfare platform based on the Il-76 transport, called the Il-76PP. This system was developed by the G. M. Beriev design bureau in Taganrog on the basis of a modified Il-76MD transport. The electronic warfare complex used was the Dandish system, which required far more power than could be provided on a modified 'Backfire'. The prototype was tested at the main electronic warfare proving ground at Chernaya Rechka near Tashkent, but no series production took place. As a result, Tu-22M3 regiments were forced to retain earlier escort jammer aircraft, mainly older Tu-16P types.

Navy scout

The Soviet navy largely abandoned the use of aircraft such as the Tu-22R for strategic reconnaissance due to the advent of reconnaissance satellites in 1975-78. The navy still perceived a need for a modest number of aircraft, since it was found that a real-time intelligence source with the strike force was necessary to distinguish the carrier from other warships in the battle group. Attention turned –

obviously enough – to the Tu-22M. A single Tu-22M3 was modified to the Tu-22M3(R) (or Tu-22MR) configuration in 1984 and was accepted for navy use. A total of 12 was built, and their manufacture is included in the Tu-22M3 figures presented here. Details of the exact sensor fit on these aircraft is lacking, although the ventral tub bears some resemblance to the system on the Tu-22RDM with its Shompol SLAR. In 1994, it was decided to begin converting some older Tu-22M2s into reconnaissance versions, designated Tu-22M2R. As is evident from their small numbers, they do not begin to match the large number of Tu-22R 'Blinders' that were formerly in service.

Crew station

The Tu-22M has a crew of four: commander (left front), co-pilot (right front), communications officer (radio-*telegrafist*: left rear) and navigator (*shturman*: right rear). The crew is seated on KT-1 ejection seats which are effective at all altitudes at speeds of 130 km/h (80 mph) or greater for a single ejection, and a speed of 300 km/h (186 mph) for a simultaneous ejection of all four crewmen, because of the need for separation. They are fired upward, and so avoid the problems encountered with the downward-firing seats

After the break-up of the USSR, Russia was deprived of several of its most important weapons which had been based in the newly independent republics. For example, a large proportion of the Tu-22 fleet was based in Belarus. A well-known dispute arose over the Tu-160s left in the Ukraine – but Ukraine also inherited a force of Tu-22M3s. While the handful of Tu-160s soon became unserviceable, the 'Backfires' and their well-trained crews were retained. Lt Gen Vladimir Antonets, the air force chief, stated that the Ukraine must have "forces of strategic deterrence" and the Tu-22M3 was "the most potent weapon of the air force."

This page: These Tu-22M3s are operated by the Russian navy's 240th Sep. Composite Aviation Regiment, based at Ostrov. This unit is one of naval aviation's primary training centres.

long-range missions, a problem that is not solely confined to Tupolev's 'Backfire'.

Combat use

The Tu-22M was used in combat in at least two conflicts. Two Tu-22M2 squadrons from the 185th Heavy Bomber Regiment were used to provide air support in breaking the siege of Khost in Afghanistan in December 1987, operating from Mary-2 air base in Turkestan. The attacks were conducted against Mujahideen bases and storage areas, often in massed formation. On occasion, the squadrons conducted simultaneous drops of 200 tonnes (196.8 tons) of ordnance against single objectives. In January 1988, they were replaced with Tu-22M3 squadrons from the 402nd Heavy Bomber Regiment. The final operations by the 'Backfire' over Afghanistan took place in October 1988 during the withdrawal of Soviet forces. A total of 16 Tu-22M3 bombers was committed to the operation, which was aimed at preventing Mujahideen attacks on withdrawing Soviet columns. The Tu-22Ms were initially armed with normal FAB-500 bombs, but later switched to FAB-1500 1.5-tonne and FAB-3000 3-tonne conventional bombs for these missions. Attacks were conducted against bases, or carried out as pre-emptive strikes against likely

of the 'Blinder', which were not safe below 250 m (820 ft). During Tu-22M3 production, consideration was given to substituting the new Severin K-36D zero-zero seats, but this did not pass beyond the test stage. Although a substantial improvement over the Tu-22 'Blinder', the Tu-22M cockpit is not a model of comfort. Toilet facilities are limited to a hospital-style bed pan. Russian crews have long complained of the lack of decent prepackaged food for

Tupolev Tu–22M3 'Backfire–C' Aviatsiya Voyenno-Morskoyo Flota

The Tu-22M 'Backfire' resembles few other aircraft of its size, combining a variable-geometry wing with engines buried deep in the fuselage. The former feature is common to other heavy strategic bombers, including the American B-1B and the Tupolev Tu-160. The latter feature is found more commonly on tactical strike aircraft, however, and most heavy bomber designs since the 1960s have had the engines mounted in pods below the wing. The M3 version, seen here, introduced several important changes over previous 'Backfire' versions, most noticeably its reprofiled nose, redesigned main intakes, lengthened fuselage and increased wing sweep back.

Avionics and systems

The Tu-22M3's flight control system includes the basic Bort-45 system and the ABSU-145M automatic flight control system, linked to the NK-45 navigation system. The NK-45 navigation complex includes two low-altitude RV-5 radio altimeters, a high-altitude RV-18G radio altimeter, an ARM-15M radio compass, a UHF ARK-U2 radio compass, a short-range RSBN-PKV radio navigation system, and the OSh-1 instrumented landing system. The aircraft communication system includes an onboard SPU-7 intercommunication system, two R-832M radios, one R-847 radio, one R-876 receiver, and a R-855-9M emergency transmitter in the LAS-5M dinghy. The basic aircraft sensor is the Leninets PN-A radar in the nose (PN-AD on the Tu-22M3). This radar, although permitting low-altitude target approaches, does not provide nap-of-the-earth capability. The Tu-22M retains optical bomb aiming capability, accomplished with a forward-pointing OPB-15T television sight.

Samolet 145

The aircraft design that became the 'Backfire' was designed to carry a substantially greater maximum bombload than either the earlier Tu-22 or Tu-16: 24 tonnes (23.6 tons) versus 9 tonnes (8.8 tons) for the earlier medium bombers. The configuration of the aircraft bore a slight resemblance to the Tu-22, having been based on studies of evolutionary versions such as the Samolet 106K. However, the new design developed under chief designer D. S. Markov mounted the engines inside the fuselage and employed vertical compression 'cheek' air intakes. The Samolet 145 was also the first Tupolev heavy bomber design to use variable-geometry wings, due to the demanding speed and range requirements of the new aircraft.

What's in a name?

In its early years, and particularly throughout the SALT controversy, the Soviet Union refused to confirm the exact designation of its new swing-wing bomber. For many years, the type was mistakenly referred to as the Tu-26, because Western 'experts' refused to accept the Tu-22M designation – which inferred that the 'Backfire' was simply a modified 'Blinder'. It was not until 1990, the last year of its publication, that Soviet Military Power (the US DoD's chronicle of the Soviet Union's armed forces) finally attached the designation Tu-22M to the 'Backfire'. Mischievously, the Soviets played the West at its own game. For example, the newspaper Izvestiya continually referred to the Tu-22M as "the aircraft referred to in the West as the 'Backfire'." Ironically, the NATO name was later adopted by the Russian crews themselves (and not for the last time), who preferred it to the awkward Russian 'Tu-dvadcat-dva-em-dva' (Tu-22M2).

Radar warning receiver

The fairings on the trailing edge of the Tu-22M3's fintip are the antenna for its Sirena-3 radar warning receiver.

Satellites v 'Backfires'

'Backfire' crews considered missions against US carrier battle groups to be their most demanding assignment. This was because the aircraft could not use terrain masking for the final approach phase of the mission, which made it more vulnerable to detection by US Navy Hawkeyes, or other surveillance systems. Although not widely known, the US examined the possible use of satellites, such as the DSP infra-red missile early warning satellite, under a programme codenamed Slow Walker, to detect 'Backfire' take-offs and terminal approaches when the use of its afterburner provided an IR signature detectable from space. The data from the satellite could then be passed to the carrier battle groups to provide an approximate early warning of the approach of hostile forces.

Above: The Tu-22M3s operated by the LII research institute at Zhukhovskii have been involved in a number of research projects. Recent trials include a joint LII and TsAGI study of supersonic laminar airflow, using an aircraft with a modified port wing section. The laminar wing tests were flown on this aircraft, the LII's Tu-22M3LL testbed, which may be the Tu-22M3 prototype reincarnated (note the vestigial refuelling probe). A Tu-22M3 has also been used as a mothership for space vehicle re-entry designs – releasing a telemetered satellite mock-up, with parachute, at speeds of up to Mach 2.

Top: The 240th Sep. Composite Aviation Regiment (operator of this Tu-22M3) is based at Ostrov, south of Pskov. As a composite training unit, it operates a variety of types. The regiment is attached to the Baltic Fleet, but can also support missions for the Northern Fleet.

ambush positions. Some missions were conducted at night, and, in one mission the city of Herat was severely damaged. A witness to one of the raids remarked, "the mountains turned into valleys." The final missions in January 1989 were conducted near the vital Salang tunnels.

The Tu-22M3 was later used in operations in the 1995 Chechen conflict, mainly in bombing attacks near Groznii. Although the Russian press referred to mass carpet bombing attacks by 'Backfires' against the city, General P. S. Deneikin – the commander of the Russian air force and himself a former 'Backfire' pilot – stated that there had been in fact only a few Tu-22M missions. Ironically, the Chechen leader, Dzhokar Dudayev, was also a former Tu-22M3 pilot.

'Backfire' replacement?

In 1983, preliminary design work began on a possible successor to the Tu-22M 'Backfire' bomber. It took two parallel paths: a new version of the Tu-22M armed with a new weapon system, and an entirely new Sukhoi design. The Sukhoi OKB had been working on a follow-on to the Su-24 'Fencer' frontal strike aircraft called Su-24BM, grew too large and was cancelled in 1983. However, the concept was revived shortly afterward as a possible successor to the Tu-16, Tu-22 and Tu-22M. The new aircraft was called T-60S. The preliminary design studies were for a large 80-tonne (78.7-ton) aircraft with twin engines, using air intakes mounted over the wing. The design was intended to incorporate stealth characteristics. Work began on a prototype aircraft at the Komsomolsk-na-Amur plant in the mid-1990s, with an aim to begin flight trials around 2000. However, by 1997 it had become apparent that the Russian air force would not have the funding for such an aircraft. Although the T-60S has not been cancelled, its budget has been slashed so severely that it may become simply a technology demonstrator until the budget improves.

In its place, the Long Range Aviation is considering an upgrade programme for the Tu-22M3 'Backfire'. A prototype of an improved version was completed in 1990 as the

Tu-22M4, but, by the time it entered trials, production of the Tu-22M at Kazan had almost ended due to a lack of funding. The 1997 plan called for an upgrade rather than new construction. The development effort is designated project 245 or Tu-245, and full details of the effort had not been clarified at the time this article was written. The new aircraft is expected to be armed with the new Kh-101 stealth cruise missile being developed by MKB Raduga.

'Backfire' exports

Repeated reports of attempted sales of the Tu-22M have circulated since the early 1990s. The aircraft was displayed at the 1992 Farnborough air show, lending credence to the reports. At Farnborough, Tupolev representatives stated that government clearances to export the bomber were expected 'very soon'. At least two countries – China and Iran – showed serious interest in purchasing the Tu-22M. China's interest was reported as early as 1993, and there have been rumors that construction of bomber bases for Chinese Tu-22M 'Backfires' had been spotted in 1997. Iran first approached Russia about the Tu-22M in 1992. Its interest took a new twist in January 1994 when a Ukrainian delegation turned up in Teheran in an effort to sell used Tu-22M 'Backfire' bombers from existing Ukrainian inventory. Iran was unwilling to agree to such a sale in the absence of Russian assurances about obtaining spare parts, and the deal fell through.

Back to the future?

Ironically, the changing nature of the world situation may give the 'Backfire' a more central role in future Russian strategic planning than at the height of the Cold War. In the past, US intelligence agencies referred to the role of the 'Backfire' as the 'peripheral attack mission'. Although appropriate in the geographic sense of the word, its mission really was 'peripheral' to main confrontations along the Central Front in Europe, or in the event of the ultimate confrontation of strategic thermonuclear war. Scenarios of a NATO–Warsaw Pact clash, or an all-out Soviet-US thermonuclear exchange, no longer seem plausible. In their place, regional conflicts grow more likely. The 'Backfire', with its impressive conventional bomb capacity, has already been demonstrated in this role during the Afghanistan war. Russia is still embroiled in border conflicts along its southern periphery in the Caucasus and Central Asia, and future employment of the 'Backfire' in this troubled region remains likely.

The collapse of the Soviet Union has also seen the collapse of the Soviet army, and over the past five years the Russian army has atrophied due to a lack of funding. Its greatly diminished combat capabilities were all too evident from its embarrassing performance in the war in Chechnya. It seems unlikely that funding to rejuvenate the army will be available until well into the next century. At the

moment, the Russian General Staff is examining various options. One option that has emerged in 1996-97 as a realistic answer to the budget shortfalls is to place greater reliance on tactical nuclear theatre forces. This is in many ways reminiscent of the US Army's tactical nuclear doctrine under the Eisenhower administration's 'New Look' policy in the 1950s when the drain of funds into strategic nuclear forces threatened to render the army a hollow force. Russia's option is to declare its intention to use theater nuclear forces in response to any serious threat, even if only conventional, rather than relying on a large conventional army. At the moment, no such threat to Russia is plausible, be it from NATO, Ukraine or China. Nonetheless, military planning must consider a changing world situation, and prepare solutions. Under this doctrine, the 'Backfire' will play an important role. Its most likely technological competitor for deep-theatre nuclear strikes – theatre nuclear missiles such as the Pioner (SS-20) – were eliminated in the early 1990s as part of the Intermediate Nuclear

Forces (INF) treaty with the United States. The 'Backfire' remains the only major element of the former Soviet Union's theatre nuclear forces.

At the moment, it seems improbable that Russia will be able to afford a 'Backfire' replacement for this role. The Sukhoi T-60S is likely to remain in limbo given current budget realities. The Russian air force is barely able to afford enough funding for spare parts to keep the Tu-22M flying, and has had insufficient funding for adequate pilot flight time. Under the optimistic scenarios, the Russian air force will be able to fund a significant upgrade programme for the Tu-22M such as the Tu-245 proposal. This is not implausible, as the Russian air force and navy both have a significant number of the more recent Tu-22M3 aircraft in inventory. However, even this modest option may not be affordable, and from recent trends evident in the figures presented here, the Russian 'Backfire' force may continue to atrophy and shrink, starved of necessary funding.

Steven J. Zaloga

The 'Backfire' probably scoops the prize as the greatest of the West's Cold War bugbears. Few aircraft have been as feared or as mocked, as overestimated and as dismissed. A look back through the pages of Soviet Military Power, the great US chronicle of the USSR in the 1980s and early 1990s, shows that the Tu-22M was always considered to be a long-range strategic system. However, both it and the 'Blinder' have only ever been used in the medium-range theatre role, and no doubt will be so again.

Tupolev Tu-22 and Tu-22M Operators

Tu-22 'Blinder' Operators

Soviet Union

Upon the dissolution of the Soviet Union in December 1991, 'Blinder' strength had shrunk to less than half of its original production levels, through attrition, export and retirement. The Soviet navy began retiring its Baltic Fleet Tu-22R regiment in the mid-1980s and it was disbanded in 1989. Likewise, the reconnaissance regiment at Saki in the Crimea was in the process of disbanding in 1991, and had gone by 1994. Only six were still operational at Oktybrskoye in 1991, the remnants of the Black Sea Fleet regiment.

Most of the Soviet air force 'Blinder' regiments were outside of Russia in 1991. Prior to the USSR break-up, the Soviet air force was still operating 100 Tu-22Ks and Tu-22Ps with the 13th Heavy Bomber Division, and 55 Tu-22R reconnaissance aircraft with the two regiments of the 46th Air Army.

Above: In this line-up of Tu-22KDs, at Engels air base, the aircraft closest to the camera is wearing a Guards badge, while the second 'Blinder' is wearing a Tupolev emblem.

Tupolev Tu-22 'Blinder' Inventory, 1991		
Unit	Location	Inventory
46th Air Army, Long Range Aviation		
199 DRAP	Nezhin, Ukraine	26
290 DRAP	Zyabrovka, Belarus	29
15th Heavy Bomber Division, HQ Ozernoye, Ukraine		
121st Heavy Bomber Regiment	Machulishche, Belarus	34
341st Heavy Bomber Regiment	Ozernoye, Ukraine	32
203rd Heavy Bomber Regiment	Baranovichi, Belarus	32
Soviet Naval Aviation	Oktybrskoye, Ukraine	6

Russia

The heaviest concentration of the surviving 'Blinders' was actually in Belarus. However, the newly independent Belarussian government allowed Russian armed forces to maintain control over strategic forces on its soil, and this included the regiments of the 15th Heavy Bomber Division. Russia eventually withdrew the regiments back to Engels air base for disbandment, and, as of 1997, there were 92 Tu-22 aircraft at the 6213 BLAT (Base for the Liquidation of Aviation Technology) being 'demilitarised'.

Below: This eagle and shield badge was worn by the 'Blinders' of the 121st Heavy Bomber Regiment, formerly stationed at Machulishche air base, in the newly independent republic of Belarus.

Ukraine

The status of Tu-22 regiments on Ukrainian soil remained uncertain for several years, especially those under Black Sea Fleet control. Ukraine eventually took control of most of the 'Blinders' on its soil in 1993-94. In 1994, the total number of Tu-22s was 55, comprising 33 at the 18th Aviation Base, six at the 1339 ABR (Aviation Repair Base) in Belaya Tserkov, and 22 Tu-22Rs with the 199 DRAP at Nizhin. By 1995, the inventory had fallen to 50 Tu-22 aircraft in Ukraine subordinate to the 13th Heavy Bomber Division, including 17 Tu-22Rs attached to the 199 DRAP in Nezhin, and 27 aircraft being retired at the 18th Aviation Base in Ozernoye. These aircraft will remain in service until attrition and a lack of spare parts finally force their retirement.

Iraq

Iraq ordered the Tu-22 'Blinder' in 1973, with an initial order for 12 aircraft. The exact mixture is unknown, but is believed to have included at least 10 Tu-22B bombers. Iraqi pilots began training at Zyabrovka in 1973-74. Most of these crews were experienced pilots who had already trained in the Soviet Union. The Soviet instructors found their pupils very conscientious when it came to practical flight training, but very nonchalant in their academic studies. The 'Blinder' bomber squadron was based at Al-Walid. Iraqi Tu-22B bombers saw extensive combat use during the 1980-88 war with Iran, but there is no reliable figure for the number of losses. The Iraqi inventory after the war is variously reported as five to eight aircraft, which suggests four to seven losses, unless the Soviet Union provided additional aircraft. Some of the Iraqi aircraft were returned for overhaul to the Soviet plant at Ryazan.

Most sources suggest that at the beginning of Operation Desert Storm in January 1991, Iraq still had five to eight Tu-22s in service, although they saw no combat in that action. Reports conflict about the number of these aircraft lost during the war, but Iraqi reports claim that 'a handful' remained operational after the war.

Above: The dragon badge of the 341st TBAP was first worn in Afghanistan but was retained on its Tu-22Ps in later years.

Below: This 1977 photo is one of very few available that depict Libyan Tu-22s. It was taken during their delivery flight, by a VF-51 Phantom.

Libya

Considerable mystery surrounds the 'Blinder' in Libyan service. Many sources claim that as many as 12 to 18 'Blinders' were sold to Libya, but other sources put the number as low as seven to eight. Delivery of the aircraft took place from 1977 to 1983, and training of the Libyan pilots reportedly took place at Zyabrovka from 1976. However, repeated reports indicate that there were never sufficient numbers of qualified Libyan pilots for these aircraft, and that foreign mercenary pilots were employed. These aircrew have been described as coming from Pakistan, Syria, the Soviet Union and North Korea, though details remain sketchy. The Libyan 'Blinder' squadron was based at Obka Ben Nafi Air Base near Tripoli. At least four were lost in combat in Chad and elsewhere in the 1980s. Sources vary about the number still in inventory, with the consensus being six to eight. It is doubtful if many are actually serviceable, given the low level of pilot training, shortage of spares, and the Tu-22's notorious maintenance problems.

Tu-22M 'Backfire' Operators

Russia

The 'Backfire' has been deployed in both air force and navy heavy bomber regiments since it reached operational status in 1975. 'Backfire' regiments were generally organised into heavy bomber divisions. Three air force divisions comprised the 326th Heavy Bomber Division near the Baltic, the 22nd Heavy Bomber Division in the Pripyat region straddling Belarus and Ukraine, and the 13th Heavy Bomber Division in Ukraine. At least one Long Range Aviation 'Backfire' regiment was deployed near Irkutsk in Siberia and oriented towards The People's Republic of China.

An initial Northern Fleet 'Backfire' regiment was deployed near Olenya, and a second regiment began to be added in late 1991. The first Pacific Fleet 'Backfire' heavy bomber regiment became operational at Alekseyevka in 1979-80. The naval regiments were also organised into divisions: the 2nd Missile Carrier Division with the Black Sea Fleet, and the 5th Missile Carrier Division with the Northern Fleet. Overhaul of the 'Backfires' was undertaken at the 150th ARZ (Aviation Repair Plant) near Kaliningrad, and the 328th Aviation Repair Plant near Nikolayev, Ukraine for the Black Sea Fleet.

In order to minimise the wear and tear on the bombers, the Soviet air force deployed special training aircraft alongside the bombers, based on a modified version of the Tu-134 airliner fitted with the Tu-22M's radar and weapon control system. The air force version of these aircraft was designated Tu-134UBL and the navy's single Tu-134UBK. A total of about 90 Tu-134UBLs was completed between 1981 and 1983.

In 1988, 321 'Backfires' were in service, comprising 178 in air force regiments and 143 in navy regiments. As of time of the disintegration of the Soviet Union in 1991, about 370 'Backfires' were in service, with 210 in nine air force regiments and 160 in eight navy regiments. The 'Backfire' regiments were heavily concentrated in the European portions of the former USSR; about 315 of the 370 aircraft were west of the Urals in 1991. By 1991, the 'Backfire' fleet was beginning to suffer from serious maintenance problems due to shortages of spare parts. One estimate in 1991 put the operational rate at only 30-40 per cent of the force.

As of 1991, only 40 per cent of the 'Backfire' force was based on Russian soil, the other aircraft being based in Ukraine (26 per cent), Belarus (15 per cent) and Estonia (19 per cent). The CIS Ministry of Defence tried, with varying degrees of success, to place these types of aircraft under central control. The aircraft stationed in Estonia were returned to Russia, while those in Belarus remained in place but under Russian control. Ukraine attempted to retain control of all of its 'Backfires', although the naval regiments became embroiled in the controversy over the fate of the Black Sea Fleet. As of 1995, only 52 Tu-22Ms were in Russian air force service, and 79 in Russian navy service, for a total of 131 in European Russia. By 1996, these figures had fallen again to only 59 in air force service and 46 in navy service, for a total of 105 in European Russia, and perhaps 40 more in the Far East.

Tu-22M Deployment in the European former USSR*

Unit	Location	Strength		
Air Force (Long Range Aviation)		1991	1994	1995
43rd Training Centre	Ryazan, Russia	19	26	0
49th Heavy Bomber Regiment	Ryazan, Russia	0	0	1
52nd Heavy Bomber Training Regiment	Shaikovka, Russia	19	26	29
840th H. Bomber Regiment (326 HBD)	Soltsi, Russia	19	20	22
132nd H. Bomber Regiment (326 HBD)	Tartu, Estonia	18	0	0
402nd H. Bomber Regiment (326 HBD)	Balbasovo, Belarus	17	11	0
200th H. Bomber Regiment (22 HBD)	Bobruisk, Belarus	20	19	0
260th H. Bomber Regiment (22 HBD)	Striy, Ukraine	18	0	0
184th H. Bomber Regiment (13 HBD)	Priluki, Ukraine	0	14	12
185th H. Bomber Regiment (13 HBD)	Poltava, Ukraine	18	16	14
328th Aviation Repair Plant	Nikolayev, Ukraine	0	0	4
Sub-total		148	132	82
Navy		1991	1994	1995
240th Sep. Composite Av. Regiment	Ostrov, Russia	0	6	?
574th Missile Carrier Regiment (5 MCD)	Lakhta, Russia (Northern Fleet)	18	20	20
924th Missile Carrier Regiment (5 MCD)	Olenya, Russia (Northern Fleet)	32	20	20
5th Missile Carrier Regiment (2 MCD)	Veseloye, Ukraine (Black Sea Fleet)	22	19	7
943rd Missile Carrier Regiment (2 MCD)	Oktyabrskoe, Ukraine (Black Sea Fleet)	21	20	32
540th Missile Carrier Regiment (6 AB)	Kulbakino, Ukraine (Black Sea Fleet)	18	24	23
Sub-total		111	109	102
TOTAL		259	241	184

*west of the Urals and accountable under the CFE Treaty; there are at least two additional 'Backfire' regiments in the Far East

Soviet Tu-22M 'Backfire' Operational Strength

	1975	1976	1977	1978	1979	1980	1981	1982	1983	1984	1985	1986	1987	1988	1989	1990	1991
Air Force	10	20	30	50	65	75	90	100	115	130	145	160	165	175	195	195	210
Navy		30	35	50	65	75	85	90	100	120	115	115	120	130	125	130	160

Right: This Tu-22M3 was photographed at Shaikova air base and, like many current VVS aircraft, it wears the modern Russian flag along with its red stars.

Below right: This aerial view of Shaikova shows a typical Soviet/Russian airbase, hidden in a wooded area with the aircraft dispersed among large revetments.

Below: A Tu-22M3 of the Ostrov-based 240 Sep. Composite Aviation Regiment.

Lossiemouth Strike Wing

With its sophisticated weapons system and precise navigation capabilities, the Tornado is ideal for 'blue-water' anti-ship operations, armed with the hard-hitting Sea Eagle. The two-squadron GR.Mk 1B 'mini-fleet' is based in Scotland, tasked with both maritime and conventional overland attack operations.

Above: In recent years, the emphasis of maritime attack has begun to shift from 'blue-water' operations to those in coastal waters. In littoral operations, an overland approach and the use of laser-guided bombs has great application.

Left: The GR.Mk 1B is a conversion of the Batch 3 Tornado. Lossiemouth's aircraft are undergoing a series of modifications (STF 248 Nightbird NVG, STF 377 full maritime fit, etc) to enhance their effectiveness, while some have GP1 reconnaissance pod capability or the ability to carry the TIALD laser designation pod.

In the autumn of 1944, with the English Channel and southern North Sea effectively cleared of German shipping, RAF Coastal Command sent the main body of its strike force north to concentrate on the seas around Norway and Denmark. The move created two of the most powerful anti-shipping organisations available to the Allied forces: the Strike Wings at Dallachy and Banff. Both bases were located along the coastline on the southern side of the Moray Firth. Beaufighters from Dallachy and Mosquitoes from Banff launched daring raids into German-held waters, facing the ever-present risks of mid-air collision, barrage balloons, parachute bombs and walls of flak to press home complicated, well-drilled and devastating attacks against coastal shipping. Missions were further hampered by operating in the confines of Norwegian fjords. Although the end of the war was drawing close, the raids nevertheless proved to be among the most dangerous of the whole conflict, and losses were high.

Today, the inheritors of the RAF's proud maritime attack traditions are located in the same region of northern Scotland. A two-squadron wing of Tornados is based at Lossiemouth, just a few miles from the disused airfield at Dallachy. In the intervening 50-plus years, much about the anti-shipping mission has changed – electronics and missiles have radically altered the tactical situation and also dramatically increased the distances at which the battle is fought. Yet the basic principles have remained constant: the success of a strike rests heavily on the ability of the force to approach with as much surprise as possible, and to prosecute its attack with maximum compression. Now, as then, the warship is a vehicle with a high potential for a deadly concentration of defensive firepower, requiring a well-planned and precisely undertaken attack to defeat it.

From the end of World War II to the late 1960s, the RAF had no specialist anti-ship strike weapon, relying instead on regular fighter-bombers or long-range maritime patrol aircraft. Royal Navy experience with the Buccaneer demonstrated the type's outstanding capabilities in overwater and overland strike roles, and the RAF procured a land-based version, the S.Mk 2A. No. 12 Squadron, then at Honington, was the first recipient, acquiring its first Buccaneer in 1969. The unit was tasked with developing anti-ship tactics, many of which are still employed today. The first specialist weapon to be used was the TV-guided Martel, on which the squadron specialised. They were soon augmented by LGBs and anti-radiation Martels, and finally by the BAe Sea Eagle. No. 12's partner squadron was No. 208, which had formed on the Buccaneer at Honington in 1974, moving to Lossiemouth in July 1983 to specialise in Sea Eagle operations.

Following the Gulf War and the end of the Cold War, the RAF found itself with two squadrons of Buccaneers which, although still highly capable in the maritime strike role, were nevertheless becoming increasingly difficult to support as the airframes got older, while their avionics systems appeared ever more obsolete. By fortunate coincidence, the virtual disintegration of the Soviet Union and the removal of

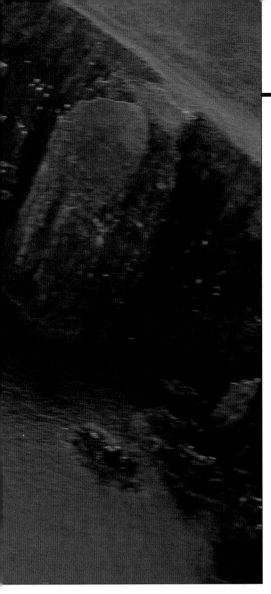

Above: A standard service load for Sea Eagle is two missiles, but the Tornado can carry four on shorter-range missions, as tested here by a BAe aircraft. Note that the Sky Shadow ECM pod has Saudi camouflage applied.

Right: The Sea Eagles are carried on dedicated launch rails which attach to the standard centreline pylons. Note the underslung faired-over intake for the missile's turbojet engine.

Below right: Control of the Sea Eagle is undertaken by this panel in the port console of the rear cockpit. The navigator can command a search bias before launch, as the tactical situation demands.

any major threat to Europe had created a surfeit of Tornados. Accordingly, the Buccaneers were retired, their place at Lossiemouth being taken by the two strike-assigned Tornado squadrons from Marham. In the attendant shuffling of numberplates, one Buccaneer unit (No. 12 Squadron) and one Tornado unit (No. 617 Squadron) retained their front-line status.

Each squadron has a nominal strength of 11/12 aircraft assigned, although with the overseas commitments of both Operation Warden in Turkey and Operation Jural at Al Kharj in Saudi Arabia, and the added burden of supplying aircraft to the summertime North American detachment, the squadrons have varying numbers of aircraft on strength. Although the two units are based in shelter complexes some way apart, on either side of Lossiemouth's runway, they operate closely. Crews and aircraft regularly plan missions and fly together, especially in the maritime role.

Within each squadron the individual aircraft differ according to fit, making life for the engineering staff all the more complicated. For instance, there are two standards of GR.Mk 1B (described below), and a handful of non-maritime twin-stick aircraft are assigned for training purposes. Many of the aircraft are equipped for night-vision goggles. Initially the STF 192 system was used, later replaced by the definitive STF 248 Nightbird system, which has a fully-compatible cockpit with special filters over the instruments rather than a less-than-ideal system of dimming. One of the twin-stickers is an STF 248 jet with maritime capability for full operational training.

Immediate plans will further complicate the life of the 'SEngO' (Senior Engineering Officer)

and his staff. A relatively new role, undertaken on UN monitoring operations over Iraq, is that of reconnaissance, using the Vinten Vicon GP1 camera pod. Lossiemouth plans to have three GP1-capable aircraft between the two squadrons, and will also acquire three aircraft with the SR(A)1242 upgrade which allows them to carry the TIALD system.

Tornado GR.Mk 1B

For operation in the maritime role, the aircraft were returned to British Aerospace for rework as GR.Mk 1Bs. The differences are relatively minor, and the 'B' suffix something of an anomaly (the GR.Mk 1B differs in far fewer respects from a standard early-batch aircraft than does, say, a TIALD-capable late-batch aircraft). Twenty-six aircraft were taken from Batch 3 production for GR.Mk 1B conversion, emerging with the architecture to allow them to carry and launch the Sea Eagle missile, including a different weapons programming unit and fire control panel in the cockpit. They were taken from the Buccaneers which the Tornados replaced.

However, further work is necessary before the aircraft is fully Sea Eagle-capable, as the missile requires dedicated pylons. Theoretically, the Tornado can carry four, but in practice the number is usually restricted to two, carried under the fuselage, although the capability to carry four missiles (with the second pair under the wing pylons) is retained. Completing the standard ordnance load-out are two 495-Imp gal (2250-litre) 'Hindenburger' fuel tanks on the main wing pylons, shoulder-mounted AIM-9Ls, and one BOZ pod and one Sky Shadow ECM pod on the outer wing pylons.

When the GR.Mk 1B first entered service the pylons were wired with only one 'Pan' (Panavia Standard) link for the Sea Eagle, restricting its operations to the reversionary mode only. These aircraft are currently known

as 'Maritime' standard. The fleet is slowly receiving the full STF (Special Trials Fit) 377 treatment which allows the aircraft to fire the Sea Eagle in the fully-computed mode, raising the configuration to 'Maritime Plus'. STF 377 was developed by TEDIT (Tornado Engineering Development Investigation Team) at Marham, with the work carried out at St Athan. The upgrade installs four 'Pan' links per pylon, enabling the missile to receive all the necessary data from the aircraft.

STFs are a useful means of quickly introducing modifications to satisfy purely the RAF's conversion needs. Originally, the STF was a trials fit, installed on only a few aircraft. Now it is used for much larger conversion programmes, negating the need to have the installation cleared by the multinational Panavia consortium and its customers' equivalent, NAMMA.

At present, the RAF Tornado fleet is undergoing the GR.Mk 4 Mid-Life Update, although the GR.Mk 1Bs are scheduled to be the last to enter the programme. While the reconnaissance-dedicated GR.Mk 1As are re-emerging as GR.Mk 4As, it is unlikely that the 'B' suffix will survive the modification process. A key element of the upgrade is the Mil Std 1760 databus architecture, which provides physical and electrical compatibility with all weapons designed to that standard, with only software changes required to switch between weapons.

No. 12 Squadron

Formed at Netheravon in February 1915, No. 12 Squadron spent most of World War I on corps reconnaissance duties in France, and remained in Europe until 1922 as part of the occupation force. It was reformed in 1923 as a day bomber squadron, at first with DH.9As and then with Fairey Fawns. Between 1926 and 1931 it had the distinction of being the only RAF squadron equipped with the Fairey Fox. This bomber was faster than the RAF's fighters of the day, and made No. 12 something of an elite unit. The name 'Shiny Twelve' was adopted on account of the highly-polished Foxes. The type also provided the squadron with a ready-made badge (a fox's mask). Today the squadron is the proud owner of a piece of fabric from the tail of one of its Fairey bombers, still bearing the squadron badge. Harts and Hinds followed, before the squadron adopted the monoplane Fairey Battle.

On the second day of World War II the unit took its Battles to France as part of the AASF. When Germany invaded in May 1940, the Battles were found to be hopelessly vulnerable in the face of the Messerschmitt Bf 109 and the squadron was cut to pieces, despite the bravery of its crews. Two days into the invasion No. 12 dispatched five Battles to bomb a bridge on the Albert Canal – none returned but the bridge was dropped and two squadron members, Flying Officer Garland and Sergeant Gray, were posthumously awarded the Victoria Cross. On the next raid only one of six aircraft returned. What was left of the squadron was evacuated to the UK, where a new lease of life as a night-bomber squadron awaited. Wellingtons were used at first, including participation in the first 'Thousand Bomber' raid, but from November 1942 the Lancaster was the primary equipment.

No. 12 survived the post-war demobilisation, acquiring Lincolns in 1946 and Canberra B.Mk 2s in 1952. With the Canberra B.Mk 6 it saw action in Malaya and at Suez. After a brief dormancy it was reborn in the V-force as a Vulcan B.Mk 2 operator at Coningsby (later Cottesmore), the principal role being the delivery of WE177 free-fall weapons. When the Cottesmore Wing was broken up, Nos IX and 35 Squadrons went to Cyprus, while No. 12 was disbanded, on 31 December 1967.

On 1 October 1969 'Shiny Twelve' bounced back with a new aircraft and a new role, becoming the first RAF user of the Buccaneer S.Mk 2. Based at Honington, No. 12 pioneered the use of the Martel missile for anti-ship missions, and later introduced the Sea Eagle after a move to Lossiemouth in 1980. No. 208 Sqn joined No. 12 in the maritime attack role, both squadrons retaining an overland capability and providing crews and aircraft for participation in the Gulf War. In 1993 No. 12 took over the Tornado aircraft from Marham's disbanding No. 27 Sqn to continue its dual maritime/overland tasking.

'Shiny Twelve' employs a fox's mask as its squadron badge, proudly repeated on the fin of its aircraft. The unit was the most recent RAF squadron to convert to the Tornado, having operated the much-loved Buccaneer for many years.

In theory any GR.Mk 4 will be able to fire Sea Eagle, but in practice it will require the reinstatement of the original Pan Standard links (removed in the update process) before it can do so in order to be compatible with the non-Mil Std 1760 weapon. Similarly, the dedicated Sea Eagle pylon will also be required.

Maritime attack role

Both squadrons at Lossiemouth share the maritime mission, although it only accounts for 40 per cent of their tasking. The remaining 60 per cent is concerned with the standard overland role for which the Tornado GR.Mk 1 was originally designed. The GR.Mk 1B conversion programme removed none of the overland capability, and both squadrons regularly practise low-level overland flying, plus both free-fall and guided (LGB) weapon deliveries, while taking their turns at manning the UN peacekeeping detachments. However, just as the other Tornado squadrons have speciality roles (Nos II and 13 on reconnaissance, Nos 14 and 17 on TIALD/LGBs, and Nos IX and 31 on ALARM), so Nos 12 and 617 specialise in the maritime attack role, or ASUW (Anti-Surface Unit Warfare) to give it its correct title. New squadron members arrive at Lossiemouth trained in the overland role, but dedicated maritime training is undertaken on the unit.

For both Lossiemouth squadrons the maritime attack role is a secondary one. The majority of peacetime training sorties are conducted as overland attack missions, with the accent on low-level flying and radar offset deliveries.

Work-up time is four to six months. As well as the basics of how to perform the ASUW role, the syllabus also emphasises the ability to recognise a wide range of ships. Indeed, 'visident' techniques are practised throughout the tour on the squadron, with regular intelligence updates and recce briefings/quizzes included in most mission briefings.

In the ASUW role the Tornado is an admirable tool, although inevitably comparisons are drawn with the Buccaneer it replaced. The Buccaneer routinely flew with four Sea Eagles, as opposed to the Tornado's normal two, and the fully-computed mode was always available. Furthermore, the Blue Parrot radar of the Buccaneer had a greater range than that of the

Tornado, which enabled the Buccaneer to use its radar outside the distance at which the force would commit to an attack (tactic initiation). What makes the Tornado an advance on the older aircraft is its complex nav/attack system, which allows it to undertake very sophisticated attack profiles which were beyond the capabilities of the Buccaneer, no matter how proficient the crew may have been. Such profiles have become increasingly important as ships' defences have become smarter, further-reaching and more lethal. Furthermore, the Tornado's GPS allows simpler co-ordination between it and Nimrod MPAs, in turn providing exact co-ordination of missile launches from multiple directions. The Tornado is still able to launch from well outside the coverage of all known ship's area anti-aircraft defences.

Weapons

Tornado GR.Mk 1Bs have two weapons theoretically available for ship attack, the Sea Eagle missile and the 1,000-lb laser-guided bomb. The latter requires the launch platform to approach close to the target, putting the aircraft well inside a lethal hemisphere of

defences. They would rarely be used in blue-water operations, but do have an application for littoral (coastal) work.

Sea Eagle is a sea-skimming missile which flies at Mach 0.85. It is a fire-and-forget missile, allowing the launch vehicle to take evasive action as soon as it is launched. It employs mid-course inertial guidance and terminal radar guidance, and has an off-boresight launch capability. The Marconi radar seeker incorporates EPM (electronic protection measures) and decoy rejection capability. The maximum range is quoted by *Jane's Air-Launched Weapons* as 110 km (68 miles) – the minimum is 8 km (5 miles).

From nose to tail the Sea Eagle missile consists of five main body sections. In the nose is the radar seeker, fuse and gyro pack. Behind this is the electronics section with missile control systems, electrical power and radar altimeter. In mid-body is the high-explosive semi-armour-piercing warhead, quoted by the aforementioned *Jane's* volume as 230 kg (507 lb), behind which is the fuel tank. Finally comes the propulsion section. This features a Microturbo TRI-60 three-stage axial-flow turbojet with low IR signature and smoke-free burning, aspirated by a duct which leads from an under-slung intake. External conduits provide electrical connections between the body sections, and large fixed cruciform wings are attached to the fuel section for lift and stability. Around the engine are four smaller fins, with actuators, for flight control.

Missiles are suspended from dedicated Sea Eagle launch rails which are attached to the underfuselage pylons with two harness points. The rails each have two MACE (minimum area crutchless ejector) saddle lugs. A recent innovation (another product of TEDIT) is the SEAL (Sea Eagle Loader), which consists of a missile

trolley with four independently adjustable wheels. The trolley, complete with missile, can be pushed under the aircraft and the weapon offered up to the pylons with great accuracy by adjusting the heights of the four corners – much quicker than using the old 'Wendy' loader.

Planning and tasking

Maritime Tornados can operate in four- or six-ship formations. In April 1997 the maritime tactics (MARTACs) were rewritten to include a basic formation of four aircraft, so that up to 16 aircraft could attack a single ship or Surface Action Role (SAG). The addition of four-ship tactics to the traditional six-ship formation was a response to a number of factors. Weapon-to-target matching was an important consideration: the original MARTACs were designed for use against a 'Kirov'-class sized target, which is now a highly unlikely one in the post-Cold War

world. The four-ship is certainly more flexible in terms of multiplying the attack force to meet the tasking requirements. A maximum Lossiemouth push would be two four-ships from each of the squadrons – 16 aircraft in all.

Unless one strikes a key spot, several hits are required to stop a modern warship of respectable size. So formidable are current warship defences that to stand any chance of achieving enough hits to cripple the vessel, the missiles must all arrive at the target within the space of a few seconds. If a ship's captain is presented with a missile every 30 seconds or so "he'll just laugh at you," according to one Tornado pilot. Maximum time compression is a prerequisite against any modern warship, but methods of attack vary depending on the sensor and defence fit of individual vessels. The aim is to overwhelm the ship's defensive systems: against some it may be better to concentrate all

the missiles into attacking from one direction; against others, sending in missiles from different directions may achieve better results.

To fully explain the full-standard 'Maritime Plus' GR.Mk 1B, colloquially known as the 'Grib', its mission and its capabilities, one must follow the example of an attack on a large SAG. As with most combat missions, the sortie is begun with the receipt of a tasking from higher command. The tasking specifies the nature of the target, and whether the attack is to be an HVU (high-value unit) or attrition type. In the latter the force can hit anything it can within the SAG, whereas the HVU attack specifies an individual target. This category can obviously include the aircraft-carrier or cruiser at the heart of the SAG, but also vital logistics vessels.

If at all possible, maritime attack Tornados would always work with a Nimrod (or MPA of similar capabilities) providing precise targetting information. This Nimrod is in full operational fit with underwing FLIR turret and BOZ pods.

Other important information usually in the tasking consists of the latest known position of the SAG, which allows the crews to draw basic threat radii on their maps, and the nature of the defences to be expected and attack support available. The latter two pieces of information define the tactics to be used and drive the line of attack to be followed. Extrapolating the line of attack back from the expected position of the target to a position outside the maximum threat radius defines a 'gate' through which the Tornados may fly as they commit to the attack. The nature of the defences will also decide whether a single-axis or a split-axis attack is undertaken, and whether the firing should be made from short or long range. Missile-firing range does not influence the accuracy of the attack to any great degree; MPA (maritime patrol aircraft) information, radar picture interpretation (if used) and SAG density are of more importance. However, the tactical situation and rules of engagement may dictate a short-range

launch, which may in turn place the aircraft in a more vulnerable position if the SAG possesses far-reaching defences. Also in the tasking will be various time brackets, specified altitudes and routing information to ensure deconfliction among friendly forces.

Routing

With route planning and briefing behind them, the crews strap in. One of the first tactical jobs of the navigator is to get the Surpic (surface picture), which can often be acquired while the aircraft is still on the ground via HF radio. During major maritime manoeuvres this is broadcast every 15 minutes, usually being provided by an MPA such as the Nimrod MR.Mk 2P. Throughout the transit to the 'gate' the Tornado crew continues to update the SAG layout. A lot can happen in 15 minutes, and a wily battle group commander can employ many tactics to render the Surpic less useful. Rapid direction changes are commonplace, while one sneaky trick is to draw the group in very close together so that their individual identities become lost, before spreading the group out again. The friendly MPA then has to redraw the Surpic, and reidentify the HVUs.

No. 617 Squadron

Although any other squadron worth its salt would vehemently debate the issue, few people could deny that No. 617 Sqn – the 'Dambusters' – ranks among the world's most famous military units. Formed from a nucleus of No. 106 Sqn crews at Scampton on 21 March 1943 specifically for one mission, No. 617 achieved everlasting glory for its actions on the night of 16/17 May 1943 during Operation Chastise, the raid against the Ruhr dams. Furthering its special bombing tasks, No. 617 went on to specialise in Tallboy and Grand Slam bombing attacks. During the course of these the squadron made its first acquaintance with Lossiemouth and the anti-shipping mission when, in partnership with No. IX Sqn, its specially-modified Lancasters flew from Lossiemouth (and its satellite, Milltown) on three Tallboy raids against the German battleship *Tirpitz*. The last of these proved successful, leading to considerable argument between the two squadrons for many years as to which dealt the telling blow. Recent evidence proves that it was No. 617.

A 'Six-foot' 'Grib' taxis out for a dusk mission. The lightning flash fin markings have been adopted from the official squadron badge.

With Germany defeated, No. 617 was earmarked as a Tiger Force squadron for service in the Pacific theatre. Despite the war's end, No. 617 did spend some time in India in 1946 before it returned to the UK and conversion to the Lincoln at Binbrook. Canberra B.Mk 2s and B.Mk 6s followed, the latter being used in anger over Malaya, before the squadron became the first Vulcan unit to be formed at Scampton. It first operated the Vulcan B.Mk 1 (with Blue Danube and Violet Club free-fall nuclear bombs) and then the B.Mk 2 (with Blue Steel as the primary armament until 1970 and WE177 thereafter).

On 31 December 1981 the Vulcans stood down, 'Six-foot' receiving its first Tornado GR.Mk 1s in April 1982. They were flown in the overland role from Marham, with squadron personnel taking a prominent role in the Tornado operations in the Gulf War. Indeed, the detachment at Tabuk was initially established as No. 617 (Composite) Sqn, while the squadron's CO later led the TIALD laser designation detachment. With the reshuffle of strike forces in 1993/94, the two Marham Tornado squadrons moved north to replace the retiring Buccaneers in the maritime/overland role at Lossiemouth. While No. 27 Sqn lost its front-line identity to become the Chinook OCU, No. 617 stayed intact, effectively replacing No. 208 Sqn (which also became the numberplate of a training unit).

Lossiemouth Strike Wing

Long-distance overwater navigation is traditionally an imprecise art, but the introduction of plug-in Garmin GPS kits to the GR.Mk 1B has greatly improved accuracy. Occasionally navigators have the luxury of an oil rig or island from which to get a radar update for the INS but, when fitted, the GPS is the main navigation aid. In time of war or tension, all of the 'Gribs' would have at least one GPS, and in most cases two (Garmin and Racal units). During peacetime exercises, the use of non-GPS aircraft requires measures to deconflict the formation on the ingress, using time separation for a trail formation or distance separation in a parallel spread formation.

Finding the target

Locating a group of warships may sound an easy task but, given the ranges involved and the lack of coastal reference points, is a far more sophisticated affair than one might at first imagine. The relentless fluidity of the situation is the main problem, as all three participants in the equation – patrol aircraft, attackers and ships – are all on the move. Attack support from an MPA greatly enhances the Tornado's chance of success. Nimrod uses its Searchwater radar and sensitive ESM equipment to plot the positions and identify the hostile vessels. The fitment of GPS to all of the Nimrods enables them to keep a precise plot on their own position, but not all of NATO MPAs have this equipment. In such cases the MPA's own precise position can be less easy to ascertain if GPS equipment is not fitted, especially if it has been on station for some hours and the INS has had time to drift. For the attackers in the Tornados a key concern is the timeliness of the information, measured by the T-fix. The T-fix is the elapsed time since the last target location upgrade, and is set to zero every time an amended position is received. The ramifications of a high or low T-fix will be explained later.

In the ideal scenario, GPS-equipped Tornados will be working with a GPS-equipped Nimrod, using what is known as Tac Note 28 for target positional (Tarpos) data. This provides a low T-fix, maximum compression, maximum accuracy and radar-silent firing of missiles, the perfect combination for a successful attack. Tac Note 28 has largely replaced the VASTAC (Vector Assisted Attack) used by the

Buccaneer and Tornado until recently, and consists of the Nimrod passing Tarpos data directly to the Tornados crews.

VASTAC Tarpos data was similar, except that it was only passed to the leader of the Tornado formation, and was presented as a range/bearing from his position. The lead crew had to convert this position into lat/long co-ordinates and then broadcast them to the rest of the formation. The result was not as accurate and often led to poor missile compression. In some cases aircraft would attack different targets. VASTAC is still practised with non-GPS MPAs. Tac Note 28 is a great improvement, as it can be used by each individual aircraft in the formation. In its basic form, the transmission is a coded voice message.

If a Nimrod is not able to provide dedicated support in the form of Tac Note 28, then the Surpic is the main means of locating the target. The Surpic provides positional information on all ships in the area, stating the lat/long position of the HVU at the centre of the SAG, and the remaining vessels in the group as range/bearings from the HVU. This allows the crew to draw a north-orientated picture of how the battle group looks, which can be rotated to align with the direction of attack. As mentioned earlier, the Surpic is refreshed every 15 minutes, so is

not as accurate as the near-real time Tac Note 28 steer.

Radar probe

As a last resort, when no Nimrod or targeting MPA is available at all, then the formation has the option of going active by sending in a probe. One aircraft leaves the formation and presses in towards the area where the expected target position is, using its own radar to locate the ships. This would probably only be used against unsophisticated vessels, as it is extremely risky for a number of reasons. Firstly, the target may be a lot closer than imagined, and when the Tornado pops up to begin the radar search, it may find itself within long-range missile range of the ship. Furthermore, the overt use of the radar will be picked up very quickly by the ship's highly sensitive ESM equipment, ruining the element of surprise. Unfortunately, the Tornado's RHWR is not as sensitive as the ship's ESM equipment.

Radar searches are generally conducted at about 4,000 ft (1220 m), from where the radar has line-of-sight out to about 80 nm (148 km; 92 miles). A phenomenon occasionally encountered is anomalous propagation (more commonly known as a radar 'trap', or 'anoprop'), where meteorological conditions such as temperature inversions or sharp humidity gradients form a layer which bounces the radar energy off rather than letting it through. In such cases the radar may not be able to see through from the 4,000-ft search height, and the probe crew have to drop down in altitude by steps until they are below the 'trap' and the radar can function again. The 'anoprop' can also have a beneficial effect insofar as it may be possible to achieve the full radar range from low level, the energy bouncing off the underside of the 'trap'. Once the target has been located, the navigator slews the crosshairs on to the blip and marks it, which sets the T-fix to zero. The probe then passes the Tarpos to the remainder of the formation, and rejoins for the attack run.

This No. 12 Sqn jet is in the standard maritime fit, with large tanks, BOZ pod and Sky Shadow ECM. In wartime, a pair of AIM-9Ls would be carried on the inboard pylon rails for self defence. The fin tip mounts the fore- and aft-looking antennas for the GEC-Marconi ARI18241/2 RWR.

British Aerospace Sea Eagle

Development of the Sea Eagle began in the early 1970s as a successor to the AJ 168 Martel missile, and was loosely based on the body of the Anglo-French weapon. Originally designated P3T, the Sea Eagle was developed to meet Air Staff Target 1226, issued in 1973. In 1976 design studies were funded, with a project definition contract issued in 1977. Full-scale development began in 1979, and construction of the first production weapons was initiated in 1982, the same year that the capabilities of the sea-skimming anti-ship missile had been graphically and painfully demonstrated to the UK MoD by Argentine Exocets in the Falklands War. Production ended in 1992.

The results of a test firing are indicative of the kind of damage possible with the Sea Eagle. A large vessel would require several hits to stop it.

Following evaluation trials in 1984, Sea Eagle entered service in 1985, initially for carriage by the Buccaneer (four) and Sea Harrier (two). Subsequent fixed-wing types to carry the missile were the Tornado GR.Mk 1B (from 1994), and the Agave radar-equipped maritime attack Jaguars of the Indian Air Force. ENAER of Chile test-flew the missile on its aborted A-36M Halcón. Unconfirmed reports suggest that the missile has also been supplied to Saudi Arabia for use from its Tornados. A helicopter-launched version, used by Indian Navy Sea King Mk 42Cs, has two strap-on solid-propellant booster rockets to provide initial acceleration. Other developments not proceeded with included a ship-launched version and the Golden Eagle, a long-range version with an imaging IR terminal seeker and datalink.

The missile's vital statistics include a launch weight of 1,323 lb (600 kg) for the standard version, of which 507 lb (230 kg) is the warhead. It is 13 ft 7 in (4.14 m) long, with a body diameter of 16 in (0.4 m), while the span of the main wings is 3 ft 11 in (1.20 m). The Microturbo TRI-60 engine weighs about 110 lb (50 kg), and burns kerosene. The main radar seeker, built by GEC-Marconi, operates in J-band, while the radar altimeter is a C-band unit.

Skirting the Skye coast, a 'Shiny Twelve' Tornado displays the medium sea grey scheme being introduced fleet-wide. This is particularly effective over water in most light conditions.

Using a probe does not give the accuracy provided by a Nimrod, and there is no real means of differentiating between vessels in a group. Experienced navigators can identify small ships from large ones by the nature of the radar return, but identification of individual vessels is largely accomplished by comparing previous intelligence information with the layout of the SAG as presented on the radar screen. While this is not important in an attrition attack, it does lessen the chances of an HVU attack achieving its primary goal.

With the theoretical Tarpos fixed, the formation initiates the 'tactic', passing through the 'gate' and flying towards the Tarpos. Ingress is generally undertaken at low level, flying hands-on in good visibility or using a radar height-hold autopilot function, with cues from the radar altimeter, in bad weather or at night. The terrain-following radar is not used as its emissions could be easily detected by the ship's

Once into the 'tactical' phase of a mission the Tornado GR.Mk 1B would rarely fly this high unless acting as a 'probe'. The fitment of the 495-Imp gal 'big jugs' restricts maximum wing sweep from 67° to 63.5°.

ESM equipment. Night-vision equipment will be used for anti-ship work following full conversion of the Lossiemouth fleet.

Ingresses are usually made in single track formations. The 'donkey trail' is easy to manoeuvre and offers good deconfliction in poor visibility. Until the tactical change in 1997, parallel tracks were also employed, offering far better visual cross-cover for spotting enemy fighters, but proving more difficult to manoeuvre. The attack run is generally flown at 480 kt (551 mph; 887 km/h), this proving to be slow enough to be fuel-efficient yet still providing sufficient 'fighting' speed in case the formation gets bounced.

Attack tactics vary according to the type of target being engaged, missile profile to be employed and the flying conditions, but all are designed for maximum missile compression. There is a universal matrix for MARTACS, allowing different attacks depending on the tactical situation. The simplest is the direct single-axis attack with visual spacings, which can be flown in good visibility. The formation flies through the 'gate' (in some ways corresponding to an overland IP), runs into the launch point and fires simultaneously. This maximises compression as all are essentially firing from the same point at the same time. The single-axis attack has the effect of saturating a sector of the ship's defences. An alternative is a visual split-axis attack. In this the formation can attack 'single-side' or 'double-side' before firing. Although individual sector saturation of the ship's defences is reduced, there are now two sectors under attack simultaneously.

At night or in poor weather the MARTACs incorporate 'mechanisms for a graceful degradation to full co-ordinated IMC work'. The full IMC attack is the most difficult to master, as it relies on accurate navigation and timing across the formation as a whole. It is for this kind of tactic where the sophisticated nav/attack system of the Tornado really comes into its own. Such attacks differ from the visual methods principally by having wider separation between the aircraft (because of the inability to safely fly close in poor visibility), and consist mainly of multi-axis attacks.

Split-axis attacks are more difficult to accomplish as wind becomes a factor. Introducing a second LOA (line of attack) means there will be a discrepancy in missile flight time to the target from one formation to the other. Attacks are planned backwards from the time the missile theoretically arrives at the target, each formation having to adjust its launch times to cater for differing wind directions relative to the LOA. The question of whether to attack with a single- or split-axis tactic, and indeed the parameters of the amount of 'split' for the latter, depends largely on the expected nature of the ship's defences according to prior intelligence reports.

Deceptive variation

An interesting variation is the single-side attack. In this the formation approaches in single-trail, and at the split point all turn obliquely away from the Tarpos, and all to one side. To a ship that may be tracking the formation, this looks like a change in direction away from the Tarpos, perhaps caused by the formation detecting a threat from the ship's defences.

Low-level overwater flying is generally not a problem in good weather, but haze and a 'mill-pond' surface can combine to create 'fishbowl' conditions. This is where sea and sky merge and the horizon disappears, making the calculation of height more difficult.

In fact, the deception is intended – with all of the aircraft nicely spaced along the new oblique track, they can all turn simultaneously back towards the Tarpos and fire their missiles to cover a wide sector of the defences.

A key feature of the Tornado's nav/attack system is its tied waypoint function. When an attack is planned, a theoretical Tarpos is entered ('X'). As described above, all timings are worked back from the time the missile theoretically hits the target, and so with the waypoints from the theoretical Tarpos. Working back, these consist of missile launch point, turnpoint on to LOA, formation split point and the 'gate'. All of these four waypoints can be tied to 'X', so that each always has the same range/bearing relation to 'X' wherever 'X' happens to be. As the formation nears the target area, it would hope to receive updated Tarpos information, which can be fed into the system to provide an updated 'X'. The tied waypoint function automatically shifts the other waypoints so that the final attack waypoints remain exactly as planned, only terminating at the new Tarpos.

LOA change

A tied-waypoint function also exists for a change in line-of-attack. This presents considerable additional challenges, and is usually only employed in the circumstances of a hitherto unseen defence system popping up to threaten the Tornados on their original LOA. The operation of the LOA change is as simple as pushing a few buttons, but the ramifications are far greater than those for a simple Tarpos alteration. In this case the shape of the attack profile remains the same, but is rotated to align with the new LOA. With a Tarpos move the attack shape is merely shifted, with all orientations remaining unchanged. Not so for an LOA change.

The four pre-attack waypoints are all swivelled to their new positions, but for each aircraft to fly this new route precisely would severely disrupt the timings of the attack across the formation. In reality, it is only the final one of these points (missile launch point) that is time-critical, so in an LOA-change scenario each crew goes it alone to ensure that they make their missile launch at the correct time and place, and on the new LOA. The navigators need to make rapid calculations to achieve a

precise launch, further complicated by the need to introduce altitude deconfliction to avoid any of the self-navigating Tornados hitting each other. This breaks down some of the tactical advantages of a standard attack, but does ensure the attack is pressed home.

Firing the missiles

Launching the Sea Eagles is not a complex task, as the missile itself takes the range/bearing data it needs directly from the aircraft's nav/attack system, and there is only a single-target capability for each launch. The navigator selects the missiles, the launch mode and search bias. With this information downloaded automatically, and the theoretical Tarpos fixed in their computers, the weapons are ready to go. Firing is then undertaken manually, the crew calling 'Magnum' over the comms to signify missiles away. The missiles have a pre-set handed station bias, so that on firing their paths immediately diverge so that they deconflict from each other as they leave the aircraft.

Sea Eagles can be fired from low (below 1,000 ft), medium (between 1,000 and 10,000 ft) or high level (above 10,000 ft), and from ranges usually between the maximum range of over 50 nm (57 miles; 92 km) to a normal short-range launch at about 20 nm (23 miles; 37 km). The type of launch being used will obviously dictate the exact nature of the missile profile, but in most cases the general pattern is similar.

As the weapon drops away from the Tornado, the caps which have protected the intake and exhaust (and incidentally reduced drag) are blown out and the engine fires up. The Sea Eagle descends towards the sea's surface using a radar altimeter. During the descent, readings from the rad-alt are fed to the

missile's computer to determine the sea state, which in turn will determine the initial low-level cruise height. Throughout this phase the inertial platform and computer keep the missile heading towards the Tarpos, as downloaded from the aircraft's system.

Search pattern

Inside 20 nm out from the Tarpos, the Sea Eagle climbs to begin its 'Ambit' – a radar search for the target. The seeker always looks first at the theoretical position of the Tarpos. If the conditions and circumstances of the attack are perfect, that is where the target should be. However, there are many variables which may degrade the precision of the Tarpos plot, and the missile automatically adjusts its radar scan pattern to cater for these, varying the scan volume according to computations governed by pre-set algorithms.

Launch range naturally affects the scan pattern, because the longer the missile flies in its 'blind' inertial phase, the further the target ship is likely to have moved, which in turn requires a larger scan volume to acquire it. An even more important factor is the value of the T-fix. If it has been a long time since the aircraft received an accurate Tarpos update, with a correspondingly high T-fix, the missile again needs to scan a large volume around the theoretical predicted position. However, if, say, the Tornado is operating with Tac Note 28 steers, the T-fix will be virtually zero at launch, and only a small scan volume is required.

Adjusting the scan volume is accomplished

A pair of No. 12 Sqn Tornados launch from Lossiemouth. Anti-ship missions are flown as four- or six-ships, or multiples thereof, depending on the nature of the target. Most overland missions are flown as a four.

Lossiemouth's other units

Since its establishment in 1939, Lossiemouth has been an important base in both training and operational roles. Acting as a major bomber training centre and maintenance unit for much of World War II, the airfield became a naval air station (HMS *Fulmar*) in 1946, home to advanced and weapons training squadrons, and best-known as the headquarters and training base of the Royal Navy's Buccaneer force. Handed back to the RAF in 1972, 'Lossie' continued its association with the Buccaneer, and latterly has become the RAF's principal operational fast-jet training location while maintaining its maritime traditions with the two front-line units.

Blessed with excellent flying weather thanks to being in something of a rain-shadow cast by the mountains to the south (the 'Lossie Bowl'), located close to range facilities at Tain and Garvie Island, and with the large tracts of low-level training areas in northern Scotland only minutes away, the base is ideally suited for operational training. In 1974 Jaguar type training began, formalised as 226 OCU on 1 October. Today this role continues, the OCU now being designated No. 16 (Reserve) Squadron. No. 15 (Reserve) Squadron, the Tornado weapons conversion unit (previously No. 45 Sqn/TWCU), moved in from Honington in 1994 to be closer to the training areas. Both units operate from the extensive apron area. The resurgence in fast-jet training activity is set to be increased from 1998 by the arrival of further Tornados with No. 15(R) Sqn, as the unit will assume the type conversion role from the disbanding Trinational Tornado Training Establishment at Cottesmore. The busy fast-jet schedule is further swelled by numerous visitors, notably during NATO maritime exercises.

A detachment of SAR Sea King HAR.Mk 3s is also maintained at Lossiemouth, provided by No. 202 Sqn 'D' Flight. The coastal location and proximity to the Scottish mountains make the Lossiemouth flight one of the busiest in the UK. Two helicopters equip the detachment, held on 24-hour alert.

No. 15 (Reserve) Sqn is the RAF's Tornado type conversion and tactical training unit.

Above: Jaguar training has been undertaken at Lossiemouth since 1974. 226 OCU is now known as No. 16 (Reserve) Sqn.

Below: This immaculate Sea King HAR.Mk 3 is from No. 202 Sqn 'D' Flight, the Lossiemouth SAR detachment.

by partitioning the radar's available scan volume into cells, and then using smaller or larger numbers of cells to create different sizes of scan volume.

With a low T-fix and a short range launch, where the ship has had little time to move from the Tarpos, the missile's computer will begin with a two-cell 'Ambit', with the scan pattern centred on the Tarpos. The radar operates a 'pinball' search, looking from corner to corner of each cell before moving to the adjacent cell, in a series of straight lines. If nothing is found, the radar automatically adds more cells to its search pattern, so widening the area being covered. Even though the missile is flying swiftly throughout its 'Ambit', the scan pattern remains centred on the Tarpos.

Before launch the navigator can enter a search bias into the weapon's computer. The

Sea Eagle will always start its 'Ambit' looking at the Tarpos, but if no target is found the bias function will then tell it to look in the desired direction rather than gradually increase its scan volume in all directions from the Tarpos. The bias function handles left, right, long and short searches, and is entered based upon the navigator's own interpretation of events. If the Tornado is attacking a ship from astern, the navigator will enter a 'long' bias, as the ship is most likely to have moved beyond the Tarpos relative to the LOA. If the missile does not see a target in its initial 'Ambit', it will then automatically look beyond rather than increase the scan area all round.

In all HVU attacks the aim is to keep the scan pattern as small as possible given the tactical circumstances. The missile has no ability to discriminate targets, and once it has found one it will go for it. The only means of target

discrimination is to isolate the HVU by position, and keeping the radar's scan pattern as small as possible reduces the chance of another vessel being acquired by default. Similarly, the search bias function can also be used to increase the likelihood of targeting the right vessel by biasing the search away from other vessels in the group.

All of the missile sequence described above applies to a launch in the fully-computed mode, that is from an aircraft with the four 'Pan' links in the pylon. For other aircraft, the Sea Eagle can only be employed in the reversionary, or line-of-sight, mode. Without the necessary links, the non-STF 377 Tornado cannot supply the Tarpos data into the missile's computer, and has to rely instead on using pre-set missile profiles to launch the weapon accurately.

In the reversionary mode the Sea Eagle has no off-boresight capability, and requires the aircraft to be flying on the precise LOA towards the Tarpos. It flies out in a straight line, using inertial guidance, and pops up for its 'Ambit' after a pre-set distance. Unlike the fully-computed launch described above, the centre of the search pattern is constant with relation to the missile, rather than the Tarpos. Consequently, the scan area moves forward as the missile flies along. It locks-on to the first target it sees ("Like a Pit-bull in a butchers," as one pilot described it) rather than looking for the desired target at the pre-loaded Tarpos. The radar search pattern itself is also pre-set, and armed with these parameters the crew can work out the optimum launch point to hit the desired target by working back from the Tarpos.

Terminal phase

Once the Sea Eagle has acquired its target, the missile immediately drops back down to low level. It continues its run towards the target, using the active radar to constantly refine its position as it streaks towards the ship. At 1 nm from the target the weapon enters a shallow terminal dive, aiming to hit the vessel at a height of ⅔ of the initial (inertial phase) cruising height. This is calculated to produce its explosive effect as close to the waterline as possible without running the risk of hitting the sea before striking the ship.

Design of the warhead includes an armour-piercing function and a time-delayed fuse, so that the missile will penetrate inside the ship before exploding. The piercing qualities of the missile also allow it to penetrate hulls even when striking a glancing blow. The explosion of the warhead is augmented by the ignition of any residual fuel, while the body itself causes considerable damage through kinetic energy alone. However, as mentioned earlier, it is calculated that it would require several hits to cripple or sink a large modern warship.

Thankfully, Sea Eagle has not yet been called upon to be used in anger, although a handful have been fired for training purposes. When the GR.Mk 1Bs do fly Sea Eagle training missions, usually during NATO maritime exercises, the characteristics of the missile are simulated by the aircraft themselves. Run-in and 'tactic' are performed as normal, but instead of turning away right after 'Magnum', as would be the case in a live launch, the Tornados then descend and accelerate to mimic the Sea Eagle as closely as possible. At the appropriate range

they pop-up for the simulated 'Ambit', and by using a boresighted radar pattern can simulate what the Sea Eagle's radar would have seen and acquired (that is, the target nearest to the centre of the radar display). They then drop down again and fly towards the acquired target, making a visual identification as they pass over it to assess the success, or otherwise, of the attack. These missile 'impersonations' also give the ship's crew very valuable training in handling attacks from sea-skimming missiles or very low-flying aircraft.

A role under review

Until 1997 the ASUW role was primarily geared towards blue-water (i.e., open sea) operations against large warships, chiefly those of a the Soviet navy surface action group, and for which the Sea Eagle was optimised. With the removal of this threat in recent years, thought has been expended on other areas more applicable to today's political environment. Other developments, such as the appearance of ever more 'stealthy' ships and the proliferation of Western-equipped vessels within the fleets of potential adversaries, have further provoked discussion about the role of the maritime strike aircraft.

NATO Northern Flank types of operations are no longer likely, with the emphasis having

Skimming the sea at low level, the Tornado makes for a difficult target for ship's defences. During simulated Sea Eagle attacks, the Tornado itself flies on towards the target to imitate the missile, presenting shipborne defenders with a superb opportunity to test their skills.

shifted to littoral operations. For this the Sea Eagle is less than ideal, for it has no capability to discriminate vessels from small islands, although when employed in short-range mode can be as effective as any weapon system. In the littoral role a missile such as the Norwegian Penguin (as carried by F-16s) is generally a better weapon, although the Tornados can make more effective use of laser-guided bombs than for blue-water ops. Coastal targets provide the bonus of being able to be approached overland, thereby using the superb terrain-following abilities of the Tornado to the full in order to mask the run-in up to bomb or missile release. As coastal vessels are much smaller, the weapon-to-target matching can be reduced, resulting in the introduction of the four-ship formation.

If blue-water operations were to ever make a resurgence, which is unlikely in the current climate, several upgrades would be desirable, including JTIDS and further-ranging radar for the Tornado, and a Sea Eagle that flew faster

A 'Shiny Twelve' pilot pulls hard after a toss-bombing attack on Tain range. Sea Eagle missiles are rarely seen on the Lossiemouth Tornados, which are usually fitted with practice bomb carriers and a variety of 'blue bombs' which simulate the ballistics of full-size weapons.

and lower, featured better EPM and had a waypoint facility, so that it could fly the deceptive moves rather than the aircraft. One item on the 'shopping list' catered for in the GR.Mk 4 update is the provision of FLIR.

For now, it must be remembered that ASUW is a secondary role for the Lossiemouth Tornado squadrons, and in addition to keeping current in this important capability, both units train hard for the overland role for which the Tornado was originally designed. It is in this role that the crews and aircraft would most likely be called to action, but if ever the need arises for potent ship-killers, the Lossiemouth Strike Wing is ready to assume the mantle from its illustrious predecessors. **David Donald**

Boeing/McDonnell Douglas
F-15 Eagle
Variant Briefing

A few years from now, in 2003, aviation historians will face the centennial of manned flight. They will begin to tally the achievements of various aviators and aircraft, and consider their relative places in the history of flight. When they do, it will be hard not to notice the record of one particular aircraft, an air superiority fighter from the late 20th cen-tury. This particular aircraft will have served for over three decades, and will still be in service at the time of the assessment. It will

have served in at least four different air forces, participating and fighting in numerous military engagements as well as several wars. Finally, this impressive aircraft will likely have achieved something that no other warplane fulfilling this kind of mission could match: a perfect record in its original designed role (air-to-air). The aircraft is the Boeing/McDonnell Douglas F-15.

Developed in the closing days of the Vietnam War, the F-15 is one of the most successful aircraft programmes the Air Force has ever run.

Conceived at a time when the US Air Force (USAF) was spending the bulk of its tactical aircraft production dollars on designs that origi-nated with the US Navy (USN), the F-15 was as much a expression of service ego as it was a combat fighter. Even today, the USAF's 'top guns' are usually found flying versions of the F-15 over many of the most tense regions of the world. This is not likely to change any time soon, since the Eagle's planned replacement – the Lockheed Martin F-22A Raptor – is proving

Developed as a fighter with a wide margin of performance and technological superiority over its rivals, the F-15 Eagle has held the position of the world's best fighter for 20 years. To prove the versatility of the basic design, the Eagle has also become a highly successful precision attack platform while losing none of its fighting prowess.

Above: F-15s based in Alaska, Iceland and on the US East Coast regularly intercepted Soviet patrol aircraft. The busiest 'Bear'-hunting unit was the 57th FIS, an interceptor squadron based at Keflavik in Iceland. Here two of its F-15Cs shadow a Tu-142M 'Bear-F Mod 3' as it transits through the GIUK Gap. F-15s routinely fly with only light armament on such sorties to extend the useful life of the live missiles.

Below: One of the types which the F-15 replaced was its immediate predecessor in the St Louis factory: the F-4E. Examples of both are seen here cavorting during the change-over period of the 110th TFS/Missouri ANG. The 110th is the flying unit of the 131st Fighter Wing, and appropriately operates from a ramp across the runway from the McDonnell (now Boeing) factory at St Louis-Lambert Field (also a major civilian airport).

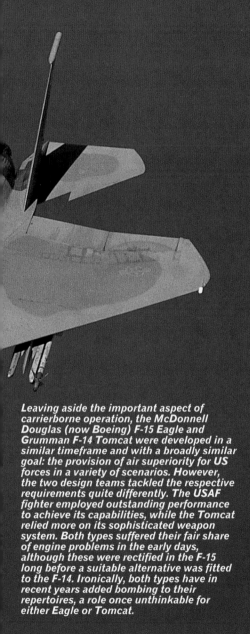

Leaving aside the important aspect of carrierborne operation, the McDonnell Douglas (now Boeing) F-15 Eagle and Grumman F-14 Tomcat were developed in a similar timeframe and with a broadly similar goal: the provision of air superiority for US forces in a variety of scenarios. However, the two design teams tackled the respective requirements quite differently. The USAF fighter employed outstanding performance to achieve its capabilities, while the Tomcat relied more on its sophisticated weapon system. Both types suffered their fair share of engine problems in the early days, although these were rectified in the F-15 long before a suitable alternative was fitted to the F-14. Ironically, both types have in recent years added bombing to their repertoires, a role once unthinkable for either Eagle or Tomcat.

flying it were even born. In fact, it is probably safe to say that the last F-15 aircrew has yet to be born, such are the expectations of planners and politicians in the countries that use this capable aircraft.

Development history

It goes without saying that governments and military services do some of their best work when they are under pressure from recent failures or shortcomings. Never was this more true than when the USAF began to rethink its plans for tactical aircraft in the late 1960s. Just five years earlier, USAF planners would have said that their vision of future Tactical Air Command (TAC) and tactical air forces structure was going to be a mix of McDonnell F-4 Phantom II and General Dynamics F-111 fighter-bombers. These two jets were considered to be a means of decreasing the number of airframe types in the various services (there was a planned F-111B variant for USN fleet air defence), and saving money in the long run.

However, a funny thing happened on the way to then-Secretary of Defense Robert S. MacNamara's (the 'S' actually stood for 'Strange') vision of the future: the Vietnam War. Vietnam highlighted the need for more than supersonic speed, beyond-visual-range (BVR) air-to-air missiles, and tactical nuclear weapons over a battlefield in order to impress local pilots on their home ground. On the contrary, the same minds that conceived the somewhat premature 'commonality' concept of the F-111 'Aardvark' fighter-bomber were also those that placed many of the restrictive rules of engagement (ROE) on US aviators. As much as anything, confining ROE and a lack of training in the art of air-to-air combat (i.e., 'dogfighting') made those fliers and their supersonic aircraft look and perform so poorly in Southeast Asia. On top of this, the F-111 began to suffer developmental and cost difficulties (the USN

to be prohibitively expensive to produce (something between $110 and $158 million per aircraft, depending on whose figures you use), and will not be in squadron service for at least five to 10 years. This means that F-15s will probably continue to be on active USAF duty for a minimum of another two decades. It also means that the air superiority and strike potential of the USAF, Japan, Israel and Saudi Arabia will continue to be based upon a design that was conceived long before the pilots who are now

Above: Two views of FSD aircraft highlight the major aerodynamic changes applied to the aircraft during the course of the flight test programme. The early configuration (left, possibly the first aircraft) has the original straight tailplane edges and straight wingtips. The later photograph (right) displays the tailplane dogtooth adopted at an early stage, and the angled wingtips which were first flown in March 1974. All of the FSD aircraft retained the original small airbrake and two large fin-top fairings throughout their careers. Note how the Dayglo high-conspicuity panels faded quickly in the desert sun.

Above: One of the hardest-working Eagles was the second TF-15A. Here it is seen testing the conformal fuel tanks which greatly increased range/endurance with little penalty.

This is how the F-X design looked in 1969/70, with a more pointed, slightly upturned radome, small vertical fins and ventral fins. The fin arrangement was modified following 1970 NASA research. In addition to AIM-7 Sparrows, this impression shows the F-X carrying the cancelled AIM-82 short-range AAMs.

F-111B version was cancelled), and it began to look like the USAF could not even buy its own aircraft any more. The result was a series of defeats in the skies over Vietnam that only began to be solved with the end of MacNamara's tenure as Secretary of Defense. Things were about to change for the better, though.

Even before the departure of Secretary MacNamara, the USAF leadership had begun to look into the shortcomings of their efforts in the skies over Southeast Asia. Perhaps most shocking was the ineffectiveness of USAF fight-ers against the tiny North Vietnamese Air Force (NVAF). Built around Soviet-made MiG-17s and -21s, and guided by a sophisticated ground-controlled radar system, they achieved impressive results. When integrated with Soviet-supplied V75SM/SA-2 'Guideline' surface-to-air missiles (SAMs), radar directed anti-aircraft artillery (AAA), and an integrated command, control and communications (C^3) system, North Vietnamese airspace was decidedly lethal.

Most upsetting for USAF leaders was an arcane number known as the 'kill/loss ratio', which compares the number of enemy aircraft killed with the number of friendly aircraft lost to enemy fighters. During World War II, American air forces had a kill/loss ratio of around 8:1. Korea was even better, with the Americans dominating the Communist air forces by a ratio of 13:1. However, Vietnam changed all that. USAF air units only averaged a kill ratio of around 2:1 and, at several points, less than 1:1. Worse yet, this loss of air superi-ority by the USAF over North Vietnam meant that many strike aircraft were lost, and even more air strikes were forced to drop their weapons or miss their targets.

Air superiority

Under USAF doctrine, first established at what is now the Air University at Maxwell AFB, Alabama, air superiority is something that American air forces are expected to take and hold any time that friendly aircraft transit a volume of conflicted airspace. Furthermore, that doctrine holds that having and holding air superiority over an opponent is just a step on the way to air supremacy, which means that an enemy cannot even make use of its own airspace during a conflict. During the Flaming Dart/Rolling Thunder phase (1964 to 1968) of

Above: In ADTAC service the Eagle replaced the F-106 Delta Dart. Here Tactical Air Command F-15As from the 49th TFW formate with F-106As of the 5th FIS, which was itself an Eagle operator between 1985 and 1988. Note the rarely-seen AIM-7 carriage on the wing pylon.

Left: Between 1983 and 1989 the 318th Fighter Interceptor Squadron at McChord operated the F-15A/B as the premier West Coast interceptor unit, the 48th FIS at Langley providing a similar function in the east. Both units received a few aircraft equipped to launch the ASM-135A ASAT.

Navy's 'Topgun' school at NAS Miramar, California (now integrated into the Naval Strike and Air Warfare Center at NAS Fallon), and a vast improvement in the Navy kill/loss ratio (roughly 13:1) during the Linebacker campaigns in 1972. The USAF, though, chose to take a different path to the future.

The Air Force has always been a service that has chosen to leverage new technology to gain an edge in combat. In each case, rather than find better ways of using existing equipment, the USAF chose to make a technological leap to achieve a capability 'overmatch' against an opponent. Therefore, in the matter of creating a new air superiority fighter, it was only logical

the air war against North Vietnam, at no time did the American forces have more than short periods of local air superiority. Air supremacy, the true goal of any air campaign, was only achieved late in the war, during the two Linebacker campaigns in 1972, and then at a high cost to the USAF. All too often in Vietnam, bad ROE, poor doctrine and leadership, as well as equipment developed for use in a thermonuclear war with the Soviet Union, forced the Air Force to win its victories through the payment of lost lives and aircraft.

These were just some of the lessons that were taken into account when the Air Force leadership initiated a pair of fighter aircraft studies on just what kind of new aircraft they really wanted in the 1970s. It should be said that the Navy was running its own set of air warfare studies at the same time, with the intention of creating a new generation of fighter/fleet air defence aircraft to replace the classic F-4 Phantom II. The result of these studies would be the F-14 Tomcat, with its mighty AIM-54 Phoenix long-range missile system. The Navy also did a highly critical in-house study of existing air-to-air weapons and tactics, know as the Ault Report (after Captain Frank Ault, the chairman

of the study panel). The Ault Report proclaimed that the performance of existing aircraft and missiles could be greatly improved though better quality control and assurance by contractors, and better tactical/weapons training of aircrews. The result was the creation of the

The F-15 is a big fighter by any standards, but this size is emphasised when compared to the RAF's diminutive Hawk. The 'tennis court' wing is lightly loaded, combining with the high thrust-to-weight ratio to provide superb manoeuvrability.

Landing at Tel Nof, an Israeli F-15A displays the 'barn door' airbrake. In IDF/AF service the Eagle opened its account as early as 1977, and in a series of skirmishes with Syrian aircraft has achieved a kill tally of at least 40 for no loss. Two Syrian MiG-25s were downed in 1981 and another in 1983.

that the USAF leadership would choose to design and build an aircraft that would be technologically superior to any other in the world for a generation. To this end, they formulated what would become the F-15 Eagle in a paper requirement known as F-X.

F-X requirement

The USAF F-X specification laid out for the American aircraft industry what the service expected from the new fighter. It was an ambitious requirement, which would give the new fighter capabilities that were unheard of in the 1960s. While the F-X fighter would be no faster (approximately Mach 2.2) than the Phantom, and would carry the same armament as the F-4E, it would improve on virtually every other feature of the classic McDonnell design. Range, manoeuvrability and sensors

Deliveries of Eagles to Saudi Arabia will total 170 when the current contract is completed. This figure comprises 75 Cs, 23 Ds and 72 Ss.

would all be vastly improved, with significant room for future systems growth in the design. The plan was that the F-X fighter would be able to beat any other fighter that it would face in the foreseeable future, with the growth capability to hold the 'overmatch' for a generation beyond that.

However, that future looked decidedly dangerous in the Cold War years of the late 1960s. On the other side of the world, the Soviet Union had just unveiled a new family of fighter designs at its 1967 Domodedovo air show near Moscow. Along with a host of new bomber and attack aircraft designs, the prototypes of what would become the MiG-23/27 'Flogger' and MiG-25 'Foxbat' fighters were openly shown to the world for the first time (American Corona-series photo-reconnaissance satellites had probably detected them earlier at their various flight test centres). Along with improved versions of older designs like the MiG-21 'Fishbed' and Su-7/17/20 'Fitter', this show of Soviet air power was a shock to the military leaders of the West. In particular, the variable-geometry 'swing wing' of the 'Flogger', and the fantastic speed of the 'Foxbat' (one reconnaissance version was clocked at Mach 3.2 on a run over Israel), were seen as

signs that the Soviet Union was about to field a generation of aircraft that would leave the existing fighter designs of the West in the proverbial dust.

Soviet surprise

Today, in light of the disintegration of the Soviet Union and the Warsaw Pact, it is hard to remember that there was near-panic in the defence departments and ministries of Free World nations around the globe when these designs were shown to the world. Taken, as they were, with other new weapons such as the new deep-diving, high-speed nuclear attack submarines like the 40+-kt (46+-mph; 74+ -km/h) ALFA/Project 705-class, they prompted real fear that Soviet technology was as good – or even better – as that of the West. It is in this context that the F-X requirement must be viewed, if one is to understand its ambition and vision.

The fundamental concept for the F-X fighter was to take the basic weapons package of the F-4E Phantom II (four AIM-7 Sparrow AAMs, four AIM-9 Sidewinder AAMs, and a 20-mm rotary cannon for close-in fighting), and place it onto an airframe that would maximise its combat potential. To do this, the following design parameters were emphasised to the contractors competing for the F-X contract:

Range: The unrefuelled range of the F-X would be several times that of the F-4, and the aircraft would have the ability to fly missions in and out of so-called 'large' theatres of operations. The standard for this was the operating area of Southeast Asia, where tactical aircraft flying out of Thailand would have to refuel at least twice to conduct missions over North Vietnam. The F-X would be able to fly such missions, with a comfortable reserve of 'combat' fuel without aerial refuelling.

Sensors: During the Vietnam War, US aircrews frequently faced the problem of Vietnamese MiG interceptors popping up from masking terrain to make surprise attacks on American formations. The radars of early EC-121 and E-1/E-2 Airborne Warning and Control System (AWACS) aircraft could not 'see' through the heavy clutter of mountainous terrain that is an integral part of the North Vietnamese landscape. Therefore, the F-X radar system would be one of the first designed for look-down/shoot-down operations against small aircraft flying at low altitude in such terrain. In addition, the F-X radar would be capable of scanning a volume of airspace vastly greater than that of the various radars on different models of the F-4. Greater dependence would be placed on off-board sensors like the planned E-3 Sentry AWACS, and a new generation of Identification Friend or Foe (IFF) gear.

Avionics: The F-X fighter would be designed to take advantage of the new generation of solid-state electronics that was being developed as a result of the US space programme in the late 1960s. The idea was to produce an aircraft that, while being the most complex tactical fighter ever built, would have reliability and mission generation capabilities better than those it would replace.

Cockpit layout: One of the biggest development areas in the F-X concept would be to make the cockpit a better place from which to 'fight' the new aircraft. The two-man cockpit

Above: An aircraft of the AETC's 325th Fighter Wing (F-15 training unit) performs a typically spirited run and break. Its noise, agility and power/weight ratio have made the F-15 a firm air show favourite since it first appeared.

Right: The only Eagles to be manufactured overseas are those of Japan, built under licence by Mitsubishi. Low-rate production continues towards a planned JASDF requirement of 224, to equip seven squadrons and an aggressor unit. This pair is from 202 Hikotai, the first operational recipient and F-15 OCU.

of the F-4 had been so cluttered and complex that aircrews over Vietnam had actually 'turned off' low-priority systems so that they could focus on the ones that literally meant 'life and death' in combat. The poor visibility from the Phantom's cockpit would somehow have to be improved. In addition, while a two-man crew was not completely ruled out, the F-X requirement made it clear that a one-man crew was the most desirable alternative. Given what would be expected of the new fighter, clearly a complete rethinking of cockpit design would be required, utilising new concepts like Hands-on-Throttle and Stick (HOTAS) and the Head-Up Display (HUD) to make possible the improvements in workload efficiency.

Airframe: For the first time, a combat fighter would be stressed to take combat loads in excess of 7*g*, with a potential for growth to a 9*g* capability. Extensive use of titanium would be encouraged, as well as new and exotic composite materials. The airframe would be designed for combat survivability and air-to-air performance, so that the F-X fighter would be tougher and more capable than any other in the world.

Engines: From the start, the USAF saw the advantages of a twin-engined design on reliability and survivability, and emphasised this in the F-X requirements document. The engines of the F-X would be high-technology fighting turbofans, which would deliver much more thrust and fuel efficiency than the turbojets of the previous generation of fighters. This would allow the most efficient use of the F-X's large planned fuel load. It also would allow the F-X to be able to meet the requirements for top speed and sustained turn/climb performance, without the continuous use of afterburner.

Many other requirements were covered in the F-X specification, but these were the ones that translated into the basic design that would eventually become the F-15 Eagle. While analysts with more limited perspectives might have questioned some points of the F-X requirement (straight-line speed, armament, etc.), nobody would ever deny the ambition of what had been conceived.

Competition and development

It is one thing to write a visionary aircraft specification, but quite another to turn that mass of paper, numbers and ideas into a predictable fighter aircraft ready for squadron service. This was the challenge that faced American industry when it received the F-X Request for Proposals (RFP) in 1968. Three companies – McDonnell Aircraft, North American Aviation and Fairchild-Republic Aircraft – submitted bids and proposals to build the new jet. It was an entirely 'paper' competition, meaning that the winner had to be decided on the basis of its proposal. There was to be no competitive fly-off between prototypes, or even a second 'best-and-final' chance to put a new design forward in the event of a losing bid. Remarkably, all three designs had generally similar layouts, with twin engines, single-man crews, and large high-mounted wings. The Air Force Systems Command decided in late 1969 to award the F-X contract (now designated F-15) to McDonnell, whose twin-tailed design showed the powerful lines that are so familiar to aviation enthusiasts today.

With the contract won, it was now up to the McDonnell Aircraft engineers and technicians to turn their proposal into a producable aircraft. Relatively few developmental and financial problems arose with the aircraft, in part because McDonnell Douglas Corporation (MDC) had so many other aircraft programmes going at the time. The Vietnam War was demanding huge numbers of airframes to replace lost aircraft, and McDonnell Douglas had more and larger contracts to make them than any other American manufacturer. With just two of its many programmes, the F-4 Phantom II and A-4 Skyhawk, MDC produced over 8,000 aircraft over a period of two decades, meaning that the company had vast financial and industrial resources to deal with any problems that cropped up. By comparison, many of its

Above: Long after its air-to-air capability had been proven beyond doubt, the F-15 acquired a strike/attack role in the form of the F-15E. A combination of advanced sensors, weapons versatility and sophisticated onboard processing and displays makes the 'E' arguably the most capable warplane in the world today.

Below: The most radically modified Eagle to date is the S/MTD aircraft, fitted with large foreplanes and thrust-vectoring to investigate automatic and short take-off/landing performance. The aircraft is currently flying in the ACTIVE programme (bottom), with axisymmetric thrust-vectoring, which may lead to a tailless Eagle.

competitors, such as Grumman and General Dynamics, had only one or two major projects to support them, and nearly went bankrupt completing them in the double-digit inflation of the early 1970s. In addition, the extensive engineering experience of the MDC team meant that it was frequently getting new ideas for improvements and features directly from fresh combat experience in Vietnam and the Middle East.

Eagle rollout

It is no wonder that when the first prototype Eagle rolled out of McDonnell's hangar in St Louis in 1972, it had a deadly look to it. Interestingly, the basic layout of the F-15 was almost identical to many of its competitors (such as the F-14 Tomcat and MDC's own F/A-18 Hornet), and enemies (like the MiG-25 'Foxbat', MiG-29 'Fulcrum', MiG-31 'Foxhound', and Su-27/30/35 'Flanker'). These twin-tailed, dual-engined designs were prevalent among the third-generation fighters of the day, and remain a model for today's fourth-generation low-observable/stealth tactical aircraft. However, under the skin of the new fighter were systems and ideas light-years ahead of any other pure air-to-air fighter in the world. For example, the cockpit of the Eagle was arguably the finest ever designed to that time, incorporating the new HOTAS/HUD technology with a 'bubble' canopy that gave the pilot an unsurpassed view from the cockpit. When pilots began to fly the new aircraft, they felt that they were not so much sitting in the F-15 as riding on top of it. The various cockpit elements had been carefully considered and balanced by a design team led by a talented young engineer named Eugene Adams. The result was an aircraft that let the pilot keep his head 'out' of the cockpit, and 'into' the fight. By the standards of the mid-1970s, it was a revolution. These days, 'Gene' Adams is a living

legend in the aerospace business, with engineers from all over the world making the pilgrimage to visit him at air shows and conferences whenever possible.

Combat: the Eagle's record

It was in the crucible of combat that the F-15's true record was forged. One early computer model of the F-15 equipped with the all-aspect AIM-9L Sidewinder AAM against a force of improved MiG-21 'Fishbed' fighters showed a kill ratio of 500:1 in favour of the Eagle. So absurd were these studies that there was a joke about how the USAF really only needed to build three production F-15s. Two fighters, one each for the Pacific and European theatres, and a single two-seat trainer for use in the continental US. While patently obvious that more F-15s would have to be built, it was still an indicator of the Eagle's future combat performance.

The first F-15s to see combat were those supplied in the late 1970s to the Israeli Air Force (Heyl Ha'Avir). Just months after their delivery in December 1976, they were committed to battle against Syrian MiGs in Lebanon. On 27 June 1977, IDF/AF Eagles shot down four Syrian late-model MiG-21 'Fishbed' fighters, with another going to an Israeli-built Kfir C2. Two years later, in September 1979, a second air battle took place, this time resulting in the downing of another five MiGs. This began an unbroken string of Israeli Eagle victories over Syria, currently reported as an astounding 57:0 (the actual number has never been officially confirmed and is likely to be somewhat less than this, but the fact remains that IDF/AF Eagles have enjoyed total supremacy over other fighters in the region). Perhaps as many as 40 kills were achieved during a two-day period on 9/10 June 1982, known as the 'Beka'a Valley Turkey Shoot'. During this time, IDF/AF fighters shot down approximately 90 Syrian aircraft of all types (Su-20s, MiG-21s, -23s, and -25s), as well as destroying almost 20 SAM batteries, for the loss of just one IDF/AF F-4 Phantom. Since that time, the Syrians have rarely seen fit to tangle with the IDF/AF.

The second Eagle user to take the aircraft into combat was the Royal Saudi Air Force (RSAF), which took delivery of its first F-15C/Ds in 1981. During the height of the Iran/Iraq War, Iranian aircraft began to attack neutral shipping in the Persian Gulf, including tankers operating in Saudi territorial waters. On 5 June 1984, two Saudi F-15s engaged a pair of Iranian F-4s, claiming the destruction of both (the Iranians admitted only to the loss of a sole Phantom). In this single action, sovereign control of Saudi airspace was assured until the outbreak of the 1990 Gulf Crisis. With the coming of the war in 1991, the RSAF got two more combat kills, both by Captain Ayehid Salah al-Shamrani. The Japanese have (reportedly) never been forced to use their Eagles in anger. The Eagle was designed to deter aggression by the forces of the former Soviet Union, Russia, China and North Korea, and the pilots of the Japanese Air Self-Defence Force have carried out their mission with professionalism and pride. Interestingly, the USAF was the last user of the Eagle to take it into action, on the first night of Operation Desert Storm on 16

January 1991. A total of five USAF squadrons flew against Iraq, amassing no fewer than 35 air-to-air kills during the war and shortly after. Most were gained by F-15Cs with the Multi-Stage Improvement Programme (MSIP) modification, but one was achieved by a two-seat F-15E with a Paveway II laser-guided bomb.

Future Eagle developments

As the Eagle starts its third decade of active service, it is reasonable to wonder what comes next. Some USAF and industry analysts would say that the end of the Eagle era is in sight – but do not believe it yet. The F-22A Raptor is impending, but there is no guarantee of when it will arrive in any useful numbers. With estimated F-22A production costs running in the range of $110 million each, more than a few members of Congress are placing a great value on the 1,000 or so Eagles and Strike Eagles in service today. Therefore, new systems modifications and upgrades for the Eagles are going to be common for the next 10 years or so, until the Raptor fleet comes into service. Some of them will include:

Joint Tactical Information Data System (JTIDS): Provision for installation of the JTIDS was part of the MSIP upgrade, but the high cost of the early fighter terminals meant that very few were bought. Only the 390th FS of the 366th Wing at Mountain Home AFB, Idaho is completely equipped with this marvellous system, which provides two-way exchanges of data relating to everything from radar and threat data to weapons and fuel status. New low-cost JTIDS terminals (known as MIDS) are on the way, and will probably be installed within the next few years. Global Positioning System (GPS) receivers and two-way satellite communications terminals are also likely to be installed in all of these aircraft.

Weapons: The Eagle force is fully equipped with the AIM-120 AMRAAM missile, but not all the weapons systems of the F-15 are as capable. In particular, the third-generation AIM-9 Sidewinder has been totally outclassed by foreign competitors like the Israeli Python-4

Above: On 14 October 1997 this F-15D was flown at Mach 1-plus over Edwards AFB by Brigadier General 'Chuck' Yeager to commemorate the 50th anniversary of the first recognised flight through the sound barrier.

Right: Former enemies unite: a pair of F-15Es of the 48th FW's 492nd FS formate with two MiG-29s from the Luftwaffe's JG 73. In theory the MiG-29 possesses some notable advantages in air combat over the Eagle, but in the few instances of actual fighting between the two the F-15 has emerged victorious, thanks in the main to its formidable BVR capabilities.

In addition to the two CONUS-based ANG units (Massachusetts and Oregon), one other Eagle squadron has a dedicated air defence tasking (as opposed to general battlefield air superiority duties). The 199th Fighter Squadron's primary function is to protect the island group of Hawaii.

and the Russian R-73 (AA-11 'Archer'). From early in the next century, the F-15 force will be the first USAF aircraft to be equipped with the new AIM-9X Evolved Sidewinder AAM. AIM-9X, along with a new helmet-mounted sight and cueing system, will be able to fire at high off-boresight targets at near BVR ranges, without even turning into the target. In addition, the Strike Eagle community will be receiving its share of the new generation of GPS-guided air-to-ground munitions such as the GBU-31 Joint Direct Attack Munition (JDAM), the AGM-154 Joint Stand-Off Weapon (JSOW), and the future Joint Stand-off Surface Attack Missile (JSSAM).

All of these modifications are designed to keep the Eagle and Strike Eagle population credible until they are completely replaced, sometime in the second decade of the 21st century. Studies also continue into advanced aircraft based on the F-15 airframe, incorporating thrust-vectoring, stealth, bigger wings and even a lack of vertical tails. Right now, the F-15C and F-15E remain the finest aircraft in the world for their chosen roles. Until the F-22A Raptor enters service, it is likely to stay that way. **John D. Gresham**

Additional variants material by David Donald
Production data by Craig E. Kaston

F-15 Eagle Variants

RPRV

Although the Eagle is considered somewhat 'normal' today, in the early 1970s its twin tail and fixed-geometry wing configuration involved a number of unknown factors. The Soviets, for example, had significant problems with their early production MiG-25 'Foxbats', partially due to unpredicted 'holes' in the flight envelope of the new aircraft. It is important to remember that most of the second-generation fighters of the day had been designed for straight-line dash speed, not for the kinds of low-speed/high angle-of-attack (AoA) manoeuvres that were a staple of aerial combat over Vietnam, the Middle East, and the Indian sub-continent. While visionaries like the famous Colonel John Boyd had codified the idea of 'energy manoeuvring' for heavily-loaded aircraft like the F-4 and F-105, the actual execution of such tactics was something that had to be mastered by veteran pilots. Ideally, pilots of even moderate skills should be able to explore the majority of a fighter's tactical traits and options, so a thorough understanding of the Eagle's aerodynamics was vital to bringing the new jet into service. Therefore, to increase the body of aerodynamic knowledge on twin-tail/twin-engine aircraft configurations, the USAF and the National Aeronautics and Space Administration (NASA) embarked upon a unique test programme.

It is easy to forget that computer access and time was a valuable commodity in the late 1960s. Incredibly, the average Western

NB-52B 52-0008 was the launch vehicle for the RPRVs, carrying them under a modified X-15 launch pylon. Drops were usually made from 45,000 ft (13715 m).

office worker today has more computing power in a desktop personal computer than was available to the entire USAF and NASA in 1969. Computer-aided engineering and modelling, which is a given for aircraft development today, was just being introduced to the aviation industry 30 years ago. This is why wind tunnel testing was so valuable in the 1950s and 1960s. However, wind tunnels can not easily replicate the low-speed/high-AoA characteristics of a particular aircraft design, so something else was required. That 'something' was a series of sub-scale models of the F-15, which would be dropped from an aircraft at altitude and then radio-controlled to execute the necessary test manoeuvres. Three such models were used in what was known as the Remotely Piloted Research Vehicle (RPRV) programme. The RPRVs were ⅜th scale models, made of fibreglass and aluminium, and cost around $250,000 each. They were 23 ft 10 in (9.94 m) long and weighed 2,425 lb (1100 kg). They were dropped from a NASA NB-52B Stratofortress (52-0008) at an altitude of 45,000 ft (13716 m), and were essentially high-performance radio-controlled gliders. Though unpowered, the RPRVs utilising Boyd's energy manoeuvring concepts could run several test manoeuvres before they came to a stop on the flat bed of Rogers

Dry Lake at Edwards AFB, California, on deployable skids. Alternatively, the RPRVs could be fitted with a parachute, this being snagged by a helicopter for recovery. In addition, aerodynamic changes suggested from wind tunnel testing or earlier RPRV flights could be incorporated into the models and flown again at a fraction of the cost and risk of trying it on a manned aircraft. So successful were the RPRV

flights that NASA later ran a similar programme called HIMAT (HIghly Manoeuvrability Aircraft Technology), and is doing so again in support of the Joint Strike Fighter (JSF) programme today. One of the F-15 RPRVs, known as the SRV (Spin Research Vehicle) remained in use with NASA on spin tests long after the F-15 test programme had ended. It could be fitted with an optional long nose section.

At the end of their test glides, the RPRVs were recovered in one of two ways. Shown at top is one of the vehicles turning in for its landing, having deployed skids which protected it when it was brought in to land on the dry lakebed (above). Alternatively, the RPRV deployed a parachute in mid-air, which was in turn snagged by a waiting helicopter using similar equipment to that used for mid-air recovery of reconnaissance drones (left).

F/TF-15A FSD Category I

There was no Eagle prototype as such, the initial F-15 contract providing for the construction of 12 Developmental Test aircraft (called Category I), comprising 10 F-15As and a pair of two-seat TF-15As. The designation YF-15A is often seen (erroneously) in connection with these aircraft. Category I testing was undertaken by McDonnell Douglas pilots, although most of the work was undertaken at Edwards AFB, where the aircraft provided the AFSC with the data and experience necessary to 'fine tune' the new fighter, which by now had been christened the 'Eagle' by the USAF.

Rolled out at St Louis on 26 June 1972, the first F-15A (F-1) was then ferried inside a C-5A to Edwards, from where it made its first flight on 27 July 1972, flown by Irving Burrows. The first flight lasted 50 minutes and reached 320 mph (515 km/h) and 12,000 ft (3658 m). Subsequent envelope expansion took the Eagle to above 60,000 ft (18290 m) and Mach 2.3, the limiting speed factor being the temperature at which the acrylic canopy glazing began to melt.

The remainder of the Category I fleet flew soon after, F-2 flying on 26 September. The final Category I aircraft, F-10, flew on 16 January 1974.

On 7 July 1973 the first TF-15A two-seater (TF-1) flew, followed by TF-2 on 18 October 1973. The two-seater was nearly identical to the F-15A apart from having a second seat added under a lengthened canopy. There was no space for the

71-0280 was the first F-15 to be completed, and is seen here on the occasion of its rollout ceremony at St Louis on 26 June 1972. The AIM-7 Sparrows were dummies.

provision of the ALQ-135 ECM system, but otherwise the TF-15A carried the same equipment.

The developmental/test programme progressed well, although some modifications were needed to various systems and structures. The biggest of these included removing a 4-sq ft (0.37-m²)

Below: 71-0280 turns for landing over the dry lakebed runway at Edwards during an early test flight. The Category I aircraft initially all wore this blue scheme with high-visibility Dayglo panels.

Left: The first three Category I aircraft prepare for test flying at Edwards. 71-0281 (centre) was principally an engine testbed, while 71-0282 (right) was the first aircraft with radar, hence the lack of nose boom.

Aircraft	Serial	Ship	Comments
F-15A-1-MC	71-0280	F-1	Category I Test. Envelope expansion, handling qualities, stores carriage. Preserved, Lackland AFB
F-15A-1-MC	71-0281	F-2	Category I Test. Engine test. Later to NASA; now retired. Preserved at Langley AFB
F-15A-2-MC	71-0282	F-3	Category I Test. Avionics development; APG-63; airspeed tests. AECS Eagle. To Robins ALC
F-15A-2-MC	71-0283	F-4	Category I Test. Structural test A/C; later to MDC as test and production chase aircraft
F-15A-2-MC	71-0284	F-5	Category I Test. Cannon/stores tests. To Ground Instruction Trainer, Goodfellow AFB
F-15A-3-MC	71-0285	F-6	Category I Test. Avionics test; missile firing. Later to MDC as production chase aircraft
F-15A-3-MC	71-0286	F-7	Category I Test. Armament, fuel, stores test. Preserved at former Chanute AFB
F-15A-4-MC	71-0287	F-8	Category I Test. High AoA; Spin tests. To NASA; now retired. Stored Edwards AFB
F-15A-4-MC	71-0288	F-9	Category I Test. Integrated engine/airframe investigations
F-15A-4-MC	71-0289	F-10	Category I Test. Radar and avionics test. To MDC as production chase aircraft
TF-15A-3-MC	71-0290	T-1	Category I Test. Two-seat test. To MDC as production chase aircraft. Converted to S/MTD demonstrator (canards, 2-D engine nozzles). To NASA
TF-15A-4-MC	71-0291	T-2	Category I Test. Bailed to MDC. Sales demo aircraft. DRF/Strike Eagle Demonstrator; Reconnaissance Technology Demonstrator (Peek Eagle)

A pair of two-seat TF-15As was included in the initial Category I test, this being the second aircraft (TF-2). The addition of the second seat required some internal rearrangement and the loss of ALQ-135 ECM provision.

section of each wingtip, giving the previously squared-off tips a raked planform. Along with this came modifications to the leading edges of each wing which, combined, eliminated a serious buffet problem occurring during near-sonic manoeuvring. Early attempts to cure the problem included mid-span wing fences, but in March 1974 the cropped-tip solution was devised by Edwards engineers. This was vitally important, because the MDC designers had decided, unlike the Navy and

71-0286 was used for armament tests. Here it is seen with the dogtooth tailplanes but retains the uncropped wingtips.

Grumman with the F-14, to build the Eagle with a fixed-sweep wing. While the F-14 with its variable-geometry wing had the ability to 'redesign' itself in flight, it did so with a significant weight and performance penalty compared to what was planned for the F-15. During the design process, the MDC engineers had a saying – 'Not a pound for air-to-ground' – which indicates what they really had planned for the Eagle. In their minds, the F-15 was going to be a pure air-to-air fighter, with every design and engineering decision being made in that direction. That explained a fixed wing with a shape and structure optimised for ACM.

In addition, there was a need to modify the flight control system for high-*g*

manoeuvres, and to improve crosswind taxiing performance. Another change involved the fuselage-mounted airbrake. Designed to provide a rapid and repeatable source of drag (thus eliminating the need for a drag/spin chute), it proved to be too small in the early flight tests. Eventually, the size of the airbrake was doubled, and a spine added to provide structural stiffness (the spine was deleted in production models). Another early mod was the addition of a dogtooth in the leading edge of the tailplane, required to overcome a flutter problem.

Finally, there was the matter of the Eagle's planned in-close weapons system, the new Philco-Ford 25-mm GAU-7 Gatling gun, designed to take advantage of a new system of 'caseless' ammunition. With this type of 'bullet', the shell's cartridge case is consumed during firing, so that the problems of case ejection at high speed (possible impact damage from the cases hitting the aircraft) are eliminated. In fact, most US tank main gun rounds use caseless rounds. However, in the early 1970s, the technology was brand-new and had significant problems, especially in the

feed system. After something over $100 million had been spent on the effort, the USAF decided to cancel the programme, and ordered the installation of the classic General Electric six-barrelled 20-mm M61A1 Gatling gun. There also had been plans to equip the F-15 with a new short-range air-to-air missile (AAM), the AIM-82. With a planned ability to 'look' up to 50° off-boresight, and a wide field-of-view seeker head, the new missile would have been a powerful weapon. However, the AIM-82 programme was cancelled in the early planning stages, and AIM-9 Sidewinder AAMs were fitted instead.

Overall, the new aircraft's problems were relatively minor, and the biggest threats to its becoming a production fighter were mostly political. The continued desire of politicians and the pubic for the Department of Defense to standardise on just one kind of fighter to reduce costs is hardly new. However, despite their outward similarities, the F-14 Tomcat and the F-15 Eagle are very different aircraft, with mission capabilities that require the unique traits each brings to its given roles.

The F-15 has been produced in blocks, which have primarily been used to help keep track of the various customer/model breakdowns. Unlike the F-16 Fighting Falcon and F/A-18, Eagle production blocks are not necessarily indicative of any particular model, equipment, or mission.

Above: 71-0287 was the spin test aircraft and carried a recovery chute above the rear fuselage.

Right: 71-0285 (nicknamed 'Killer') was decorated with various 'kill' markings denoting successful missile shoots against drones.

F-15A FSD Category II

In addition to the 12 Category I aircraft, eight other single-seat Operational Test/Full-Scale Development (FSD – Category II) airframes were constructed in FY72. These

were closer in standard to the production F-15As. Category II testing was undertaken by the USAF Joint F-15 Test Force, later rechristened F-15 Combined Test Force and

still in business at Edwards as the 415th Flight Test Squadron of the 412th Test Wing.

Initial plans for the F-15 test fleet had envisaged some attrition, but as this did not occur some of the Category II aircraft were considered redundant. Indeed, two of the batch took no part at all in the test

Carrying the badges of Air Force Systems Command and Tactical Air Command on the intake, 72-0114 prepares for a Category II flight test. This was the first aircraft to be fitted with an electronic countermeasures system.

Aircraft	Serial	Ship	Comments
F-15A-5-MC	72-0113	F-11	Category II Test. Operational test. Stored at MASDC. To Rome Air Development Center for antenna test
F-15A-5-MC	72-0114	F-12	Category II Test. Operational test with ALQ-135
F-15A-5-MC	72-0115	F-13	Category II Test. To Ground Instructional Trainer, Sheppard AFB
F-15A-5-MC	72-0116	F-14	Category II Test. Operational/Climactic test. (Later to Israel)
F-15A-6-MC	72-0117	F-15	Category II. Not used in testing, later to Israel
F-15A-6-MC	72-0118	F-16	Category II Test. Operational test. (Later to Israel)
F-15A-6-MC	72-0119	F-17	Category II. Modified on production line for project Streak Eagle. Displayed at Air Force Museum
F-15A-6-MC	72-0120	F-18	Category II. Not used in testing, later to Israel

programme. Both of these, together with a further pair, were supplied to Israel under Peace Fox I. These were refurbished for operational use, although they retained the small speedbrake which characterised the test aircraft. They were delivered on 10 December 1976, Israeli pilots having first flown the Eagle in September 1974. One further Category II aircraft was used for the Streak Eagle programme.

72-0118 was used briefly on operational tests, but was subsequently transferred to Israel, along with three other Category II test aircraft.

Streak Eagle

However impressive the early Eagles may have been, air show manoeuvres in the hands of a skilled test/show pilot hardly build a reputation, and so another means was found to highlight the F-15's combat potential. One of the most important characteristics valued in a fighter is the ability to rapidly climb to altitude to intercept incoming enemy aircraft, so it was decided to prepare an Eagle for the attempt to break a number of time-to-altitude records. Most were held by modified versions of the F-4 Phantom and the MiG-25 'Foxbat'. In April 1974 the USAF issued MDC a $2.1 million contract to modify a Category II F-15A (72-0119) under Project Streak Eagle. Started in 1974, under the programme the basic aircraft was modified though the removal of much of the combat equipment, including the gun, weapons control units, the radar, a number of actuators, and even the paint, which weighs 50 lb (23 kg). The fin-top pods were replaced by small mass balances. In all, the MDC Streak Eagle team managed to shave off some 1,800 lb (817 kg) which, along with special cable 'hold-back' release system and a minimum fuel load, helped the Streak Eagle take back some eight time-to-flight records in 1975.

Run in the winter cold of January and February 1975 (to improve the efficiency of the engines), from Grand Forks AFB, North

The Streak Eagle blasts off from the Grand Forks runway on one of its successful time-to-climb record attempts. Before the record attempts the aircraft had worn a tail badge proclaiming it as the 'Aquila Maxima' (ultimate eagle).

Dakota, the Streak Eagle did all that was asked of it. The records, which ran up to 30000 m (98,425 ft), represented a measure of the fighter's ability to get into the air and bring weapons to bear. Even though a specially modified Su-27 'Flanker' would later grab many of the Streak Eagle's records, the 'bare aircraft' had done its job. Around the world in squadron ready rooms, the word went out that you could not outclimb an F-15 Eagle. For that alone, the $2.1 million the USAF spent on Project Streak Eagle was well spent.

Altitude (m/ft)	Time (sec)	Date	Pilot	Previous record
3000/9,843	27.57	16/1/75	Major Roger Smith	34.52 (F-4A Phantom II)
6000/19,685	39.33	16/1/75	Major W. R. MacFarland	48.79 (F-4A Phantom II)
9000/29,528	48.86	16/1/75	Major W. R. MacFarland	61.68 (F-4A Phantom II)
12000/39,370	59.38	16/1/75	Major David W. Peterson	77.14 (F-4A Phantom II)
15000/49,212	77.02	16/1/75	Major David W. Peterson	114.5 (F-4A Phantom II)
20000/65,617	122.94	19/1/75	Major Roger Smith	69.8 (MiG-25 'Foxbat')
25000/82,021	161.02	26/1/75	Major David W. Peterson	192.8 (MiG-25 'Foxbat')
30000/98,425	207.8	1/2/75	Major Roger Smith	243.86 (MiG-25 'Foxbat')

F-15 FSD demonstration/test

Even before the Eagle entered service, MDC was 'recycling' the old pre-production aircraft to test some new ideas, such as the use of special aluminium-lithium alloys in wing panels and employing the Eagle as a specialised 'intruder' aircraft for air-to-ground missions. Much of this work was taken on by a veteran of the test wars, 71-0291 (TF-2), which had already done so much for the F-15 programme. 71-0291 started its post-test career as an air show demonstration aircraft, showing the world just what the Eagle could do. Decked out in a 'Thunderbirds'-style red, white and blue

Bicentennial paint scheme, it travelled over 34,000 miles (54716 km) around the world, demonstrating the F-15's impressive performance to allies, enemies and potential customers. Showing off the Eagle's superb handling qualities, TF-2 did an excellent job of introducing the new fighter to the world. It subsequently became McAir's principal test platform for a variety of programmes and is still in use as such today.

Other FSD aircraft were also used for continuing tests, some receiving a white paint scheme with blue, Dayglo or red trim.

In the mid-1980s TF-1 (71-0290) was used to test upper wing skins made of aluminium-lithium (Al-Li) alloy. The aircraft shows the scheme used by several FSD aircraft for subsequent tests.

In 1977 71-0282 was used to test the Advanced Environmental Control System (AECS), receiving a sharkmouth in addition to the AECS badge on the intake. The aircraft also had unusual formation lights on the port side of both fins.

71-0291 embarked on a major sales drive after its initial testing duties were complete. It sported French markings (below) for just four days in April 1976, together with flags from the nations that it had visited, while later in the year it adopted Bicentennial markings (above).

F-15A/B

In March 1973 the USAF officially ordered its initial batch of 30 Eagles, with the first unit delivered to an actual USAF unit on 4 November 1974. This first operational Eagle was a two-seat TF-15A trainer (73-0108) which was christened 'TAC-1'. In October 1978 the TF-15A was redesignated as the F-15B in recognition of its fully combat-capable status. 'TAC-1' went to the F-15 Replacement Training Unit (RTU), the 555th Tactical Flying Training Squadron (TFTS) at Luke AFB outside Phoenix, Arizona. As the RTU began to turn out qualified F-15 pilots, the first combat unit to field the new aircraft began to get its new mounts: the 1st Tactical Fighter Wing (TFW) with its distinctive 'FF' ('First Fighter') tailcode, based at Langley AFB in the Virginia Tidewater. On 9 January 1976 the 1st TFW was declared operational, having turned in its F-4E Phantoms for the new Eagles. The first 42 F-15s were painted in a unique 'Air Superiority Blue' paint scheme, but practical experience showed that it attracted enemy eyes more than conventional camouflage. Beginning with F-15A 73-0100 and F-15B 74-0137, a new two-tone 'Compass Ghost' scheme was introduced, consisting of Light and Dark Ghost Gray.

The following year saw the first overseas USAF unit – the 36th TFW at Bitburg, West Germany ('BT' tailcode) – receive its Eagles. The same year, the 57th Fighter Weapons Wing ('FW') at Nellis AFB near Las Vegas, Nevada activated the 433rd Fighter Weapons Squadron (FWS) to develop tactics for the Eagle, as well as conducting testing of new weapons and systems. Eventually, the 18th TFW ('ZZ') at Kadena AFB, Okinawa, the 21st Composite Wing ('AK') at Elmendorf AFB, Alaska, the 32nd Tactical Fighter Squadron ('CR') at Soesterberg, Netherlands, the 33rd TFW

Above: **One of the last active-duty units to receive the F-15A was the Minot-based 5th FIS 'Spittin' Kittens', part of ADTAC's US air defence organisation. Three US-based ADTAC units acquired the Eagle, although its career was brief as the CONUS defence mission was handed over to the ANG.**

'Nomads' ('ZZ') at Eglin AFB, FL, and the 49th TFW ('HO') at Holloman AFB, New Mexico joined the 1st as front-line combat Eagle units. In addition, numerous other USAF reserve and Air National Guard (ANG) units would eventually operate the F-15, primarily supporting continental air defence operations of North America. Most of these units were equipped with the 360 single-seat F-15As and 58 two-seat F-15B fighter/trainers that were eventually produced for the USAF.

A major area of improvement was the powerplant. In the 1970s the practice of

designing advanced turbofan engines that could function in the rough-and-tumble environment of air-to-air combat was still more art than science. Such engines, while vastly more powerful and fuel efficient than the turbojets that had powered the previous generation of fighters (like the F-4 Phantom), were very sensitive, and tricky to operate. They tended to experience compressor stall during high-AoA manoeuvres and rapid power shifts of the throttle. In addition, the designers of the F100-series engines at Pratt & Whitney had never anticipated the kinds of loads and manoeuvres that the Eagle pilots would put their engines through. In the beginning, pilots at early F-15 bases like Luke and Langley literally flew the fan blades off their engines.

In response, the USAF and Pratt & Whitney began an effort that continues

73-0100 was the first F-15A to introduce the 'Compass Ghost' colour scheme, introduced for lower conspicuity in European skies.

today: to make their 'fighting' turbofans safe and responsive to everything that modern fighter pilots can do to them. Initially, this meant strengthening the engine blades, and teaching the pilots to 'fly' the throttle safely through potential stall conditions. Frequent groundings and delays with engine production fixes caused something of a crisis in the late 1970s, when F-15 airframes were being accepted and placed in storage pending delivery of their engines.

'TAC-1' was the first Eagle delivered to the USAF, delivered to the 58th TFTW at Luke AFB, Arizona.

Aircraft model	Block number	Starting serial	Ending serial	Number in block	Comments
F-15A	7	73-0085	73-0089	5	
F-15A	8	73-0090	73-0097	8	
F-15A	9	73-0098	73-0107	10	
F-15B	7	73-0108	73-0110	3	(ex TF-15A-7-MC)
F-15B	8	73-0111	73-0112	2	(ex TF-15A-8-MC)
F-15B	9	73-0113	73-0114	2	(ex TF-15A-9-MC)
F-15A	10	74-0081	74-0093	13	
F-15A	11	74-0094	74-0111	18	
F-15A	12	74-0112	74-0136	25	
F-15B	10	74-0137	74-0138	2	(ex TF-15A-10-MC)
F-15B	11	74-0139	74-0140	2	(ex TF-15A-11-MC)
F-15B	12	74-0141	74-0142	2	(ex TF-15A-12-MC)
F-15A	13	75-0018	75-0048	31	
F-15A	14	75-0049	75-0079	31	
F-15B	13	75-0080	75-0084	5	(ex TF-15A-13-MC)
F-15B	14	75-0085	75-0089	5	(ex TF-15A-14-MC)
F-15A	15	76-0008	76-0046	39	
F-15A	16	76-0047	76-0083	30	
F-15A	17	76-0084	76-0113	30	
F-15A	18	76-0114	76-0120	7	
F-15A		76-0121	76-0123	3	Cancelled
F-15B	15	76-0124	76-0129	6	(ex TF-15A-15-MC)
F-15B	16	76-0130	76-0135	6	(ex TF-15A-16-MC)
F-15B	17	76-0136	76-0140	5	(ex TF-15A-17-MC)
F-15B	18	76-0141	76-0142	2	(ex TF-15A-18-MC)
F-15A	18	77-0061	77-0084	24	
F-15A	19	77-0085	77-0119	35	
F-15A	20	77-0120	77-0153	34	
F-15B	18	77-0154	77-0156	3	(ex TF-15A-18-MC)
F-15B	19	77-0157	77-0162	6	(ex TF-15A-19-MC)
F-15B	20	77-0163	77-0168	6	(ex TF-15A-20-MC)

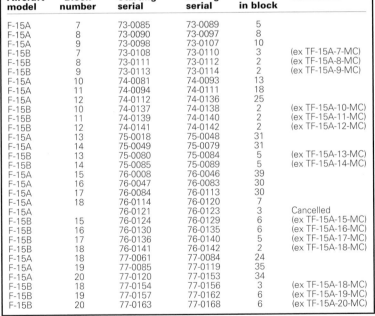

The training wing at Luke (58th TFTW) received most of the initial batch of F/TF-15As. These red/white stripes were tested (as were black and white) for high conspicuity in the training role, but not adopted.

Four splinter schemes (designed by Keith Ferris) were tested by the 58th TFTW in early 1977. The small multi-coloured band on the rudder denotes that this is the wing commander's aircraft. Note the false cockpit.

As F-15C/Ds were delivered, the older Eagles were cascaded to ANG units, including one on each coast dedicated to US air defence missions. The West Coast unit is the 123rd FIS/142nd FIG, Oregon ANG, flying from Portland.

F-15B companion never carried the FAST/CFT tanks, although these flew on some test aircraft. Aircraft were initially fitted with the IC-7 ejection seat, although this gradually gave way to the ACES II through retrofit. Avionics development lagged behind that of airframe with the result that many aircraft were delivered without ECM equipment, which was slowly enhanced throughout the F-15A/B's career.

Eventually, digital fuel control systems were added for the throttles, which automatically monitored the air and fuel flow, avoiding the need for the pilots to worry about engine flameouts at a critical moment in a dogfight.

In service, the F-15A and its two-seat

F-15A/B Baz

In 1973, the Shah of Iran evaluated the Eagle as a possible air superiority fighter for use by the Imperial Iranian Air Force (IIAF). However, the IIAF eventually bought the competing Grumman F-14A Tomcat with its mighty AIM-54A Phoenix AAM, for use against the perceived Russian threat to the north. That was the only foreign sale Grumman ever achieved of the Tomcat. The Eagle had more success in export sales. Great Britain, Canada, Australia and France all evaluated the F-15 in the mid-1970s, although none ever became a customer.

It fell to the Israeli Air Force (IAF/Heyl Ha'Avir) to become the first overseas customer for the F-15. Still smarting from the heavy losses that it had suffered during the Yom Kippur War in October 1973, the IAF faced enemies equipped with the same

MiG-23 'Flogger' and -25 'Foxbat' fighters that had inspired the Eagle's original development. Committed as always to providing its pilots with the best aircraft that Israeli and American taxpayer money can buy, the IAF was anxious to purchase the new fighters to protect its tiny country.

The first batch of F-15As, delivered as Peace Fox I, were Category II/FSD aircraft (72-0116, 72-0117, 72-0118 and 72-0120) updated to the full F-15A standard, albeit retaining the small speedbrake. Ironically, when the four aircraft were delivered on Friday 10 December 1976, the ensuing celebration of their arrival (which ran into the Jewish Sabbath) caused a public furore that eventually toppled the Labour Party government the following year. Eventually, the IAF received 26 F-15As and F-15Bs, including a single attrition replacement example in 1982.

With the Heyl Ha'Avir, the Peace Fox II

Aircraft model	Block number	Starting serial	Ending serial	Number in block	Comments
F-15A	5	72-0116	–	1	Category II Test Aircraft
F-15A	6	72-0117/-0118/-0120	–	3	Category II Test Aircraft
F-15A	17	76-1505	76-1514	10	Peace Fox II
F-15A	18	76-1515	76-1523	9	Peace Fox II
F-15B	16	76-1524	76-1525	2	Peace Fox II (ex TF-15A-16-MC)
F-15A	18	76-0120	–	1	ex-USAF attrition replacement

F-15A/B entered service with 133 Squadron at Tel Nof in late 1978, and was soon in action against the air forces of its Arab neighbours. Subsequent actions, including the famous 1982 Beka'a Valley air war, have seen the IDF/AF's Eagle vistory tally rise to between 40 and 50. Named Baz (eagle) in service, the F-15A/Bs have been progressively updated with local equipment

and weapons (bringing them to roughly F-15A MSIP standards), and have been the only operational A/Bs to be equipped to carry the Type 1 CFT (including the refurbished FSD machines).

Following Desert Storm a batch of ex-USAF F-15A/Bs was earmarked for delivery to the IDF/AF, to be mainly used for training purposes. This was believed to be part of the deal by which Israel stayed out of the Gulf War, despite having suffered Iraqi 'Scud' attacks.

Block	Serial	Former user
F-15A-7-MC	73-0087	110 FS MO ANG
F-15A-8-MC	73-0093	122 FS LA ANG
F-15A-8-MC	73-0094	122 FS LA ANG
F-15A-9-MC	73-0101	122 FS LA ANG
F-15A-9-MC	73-0102	122 FS LA ANG
F-15A-9-MC	73-0104	122 FS LA ANG
F-15A-9-MC	73-0105	122 FS LA ANG
F-15A-9-MC	73-0107	122 FS LA ANG
F-15A-10-MC	74-0085	199 FS HI ANG
F-15A-10-MC	74-0098	199 FS HI ANG
F-15A-12-MC	74-0122	122 FS LA ANG
F-15A-12-MC	74-0125	122 FS LA ANG
F-15B-7-MC	73-0110	110 FS MO ANG

To date, it is doubtful if any of these aircraft have undergone the MSIP upgrade. They will probably be used for spare parts before they are scrapped, sometime in the next few years.

Israeli F-15As were swiftly in action after arriving in-country. All of the earlier models have been operated by 133 Squadron.

F-15A ASAT

While few doubted the air-to-air potential of the original F-X design, it is unlikely that anyone considered that it might become the first space fighter. However, by the late 1970s, this was seriously being considered

as a result of the rapid growth of the Soviet Union's military space assets, which were in direct support of its armed forces. Military space satellites tend to travel in one of a few designated types of orbits. Communications and navigational satellites are generally placed into high orbits, including the favoured geosynchronous

band 22,300 miles (35887 km) above the equator. Little can be done to harm space vehicles in such high orbits. However, many of the most valuable military support satellites work in much lower orbits, only a few hundred miles above the surface of the Earth. They include photo-reconnaissance and naval radar reconnaissance vehicles, as

well as some electronic listening or 'ferret' satellites. Much of the Soviet Union's ability to target and strike military units of the Western and NATO forces hung on data from these low-orbit satellites. In particular, its navy was absolutely dependent upon a series of low-altitude, nuclear-powered radar ocean reconnaissance satellites

F-15A 76-0086 was the first aircraft modified to carry the ASAT missile. It performed the first launch (against a point in space) in January 1984. Three more were fired against celestial infra-red sources.

The ASM-135A was carried on the centreline. It consisted of two stages, the first (aft portion) utilising an AGM-69 SRAM motor. The forward part was based on the Altair III. Note the cameras for recording weapon separation.

(RORSATs) to target enemy naval forces and convoys. The need to destroy or 'negate' the orbital 'aircraft' of an enemy was clear to anyone who cared to study the problem.

The answer came in the form of the F-15, which had demonstrated the ability to fly to altitudes of more than 100,000 ft (30480 m) during Project Streak Eagle. By using an F-15 as essentially the first stage of the ASAT system, the rest of the weapon could be made both relatively small and highly accurate. So small, in fact, that the proposed weapon could be carried on the belly of a standard F-15A with only minimal modifications. With this idea, a contract was issued to Vought (now part of Lockheed Martin Loral) in 1979 to build a batch of ASAT vehicles for test purposes. Based on the AGM-69A Short-Range Attack Missile (SRAM-A) first stage with an Altair III second-stage, the ASM-135A weapon was the biggest AAM ever built in the United States. It weighed 2,700 lb (1225 kg) and measured 17 ft 10 in (5.43 m) in length.

The idea was that – using tracking data and cueing from the North American Defense Command (NORAD) command centre at Cheyenne Mountain near Colorado Springs, Colorado – an ASAT-equipped F-15 would be launched and placed in a parking orbit until the proper launch 'window' arrived. Then, with NORAD controlling the intercept, the F-15 would initiate a 'zoom' climb, much like the profile flown during Project Streak Eagle. At 80,000 feet (24384 m), near the top of the parabolic climb profile, the pilot would launch the weapon on a pre-programmed course, and then return to base. The ASAT missile would then fly to the intercept point, guided by an onboard infra-red seeker. There, the missile would fly directly into the target satellite,

76-0084 releases an ASM-135A during one of the five ASAT launches, of which only one was against a live target. The weapon was released at about 80,000 ft (24385 m), the F-15 in effect providing the first of three stages. The small kill vehicle was infra-red guided and relied on kinetic energy to destroy the target.

with the energy of the two vehicles' closing speed (something over 11,000 mph/17700 km/h) providing the final 'kill' mechanism. In addition to fulfilling all the requirements previously mentioned, the Vought ASAT had the advantage of being able to engage satellites out to altitudes in excess of 600 miles (965 km). This would provide an engagement envelope that included virtually all of the known Soviet low-orbit systems, including the nuclear-powered RORSATs. Even better, it would do so at a fraction of the cost of a co-orbital or nuclear-armed ASAT mechanism.

By the early 1980s the device was being carried in captive-carry tests on F-15s, and plans existed to deploy a pair of USAF Reserve F-15 squadrons at Langley AFB in Virginia (48th FIS) and McChord AFB in Washington (318th FIS). Indeed, a few suitably-modified F-15s had already been delivered to these units.

However, just as firing tests got underway, the Democratically-led US Congress decided that the F-15-based ASAT system violated the very space-based weapons treaty that it had been intended to circumvent. Most of the early ASAT work was done by two F-15As (77-0084 and -0086) based at Edwards AFB. After just five firing tests, the first of which took place in

January 1984, the Congress voted to ban further testing and deployment, and the programme was officially cancelled. Only one launch took place against a target. In this 13 September 1985 test flown from Vandenberg AFB, a target satellite (Solwind

P78-1, a Gamma Ray Spectrometer observation satellite) was successfully destroyed. This type of ASAT system remains a tantalising idea, especially if tensions with foreign powers that heavily use space assets increase.

F-15A/B tests

A small number of production F-15A/Bs have been used for test programmes, including F-15A 77-0139 which was employed at Edwards as a test vehicle for the F100-PW-229 Improved Performance Engine. The most notable programme, however, was the IFFC/Firefly III study, which began with a February 1982 award to McDonnell Douglas to equip an F-15B (77-0166) with an Integrated Flight-Fire Control (IFFC) system, which allowed the onboard computer to tailor the flight control system to various weapon systems and delivery modes for air-to-air work. If a sensor was locked on to a target, the IFFC could automatically manoeuvre the aircraft to weapon release point. IFFC was demonstrated successfully against various air-to-air targets.

Meanwhile, General Electric was developing a parallel system known as Firefly III, which was to be used against air-to-ground targets. The sensor employed was the Martin Marietta ATLIS II acquisition/laser designation pod. This allowed the F-15 to achieve satisfactory bomb drops but incorporating complicated flight profiles. The system was not adopted, but the Firefly III work was of great benefit to the integration of the LANTIRN system with the F-15E.

Right: The F-15B has served the AFFTC well on both chase duties and with the Test Pilot School. Early aircraft have black nose tips, deriving from an initial decision to paint all F-15 radomes black. This was subsequently altered, but too late to change the colour of the tips.

The IFFC/Firefly III aircraft is seen armed with Mk 82s on MERs. The testbed investigated ways of accurately and automatically delivering both air-to-air and air-to-ground weapons.

The Firefly portion of the tests required laser designation/rangefinding, provided by an ATLIS II pod mounted on a revised hardpoint under the port intake.

F-15A 77-0139 was utilised as the testbed for the F100-PW-229 IPE engine, as used by late-production F-15Es, the F-15I and F-15S (as well as the F-16C/D Block 52).

F-15B S/MTD

In the 1980s, the USAF wanted to explore the value of tactical aircraft that did not require 2 miles (3 km) or more of concrete on which to take off and land. The US Navy and Marine Corps had been conducting operations of this sort for decades, and the fear that the Soviet Union and Warsaw Pact might fill NATO runways with holes was enough to prompt the Air Force to fund modifications to an F-15. The objective of the Short Take-Off and Landing/Maneuver Technology Demonstrator (S/MTD) programme, studies for which began in

1984, was to explore options to shorten the take-off and landing rolls of tactical aircraft, without resorting to the kinds of engineering compromises inherent in a Vertical/Short Take-Off and Landing (V/STOL) aircraft like the AV-8B Harrier II or V-22 Osprey. 71-0290 (TF-1, one of the Category I test aircraft) was equipped with a pair of forward canards (actually modified

In Phase I S/MTD testing 71-0290 retained standard F100s, but did have the revised cockpit, automatic landing system and canard foreplanes fitted.

F-15 Eagle Variants

F/A-18 tailplanes) and an automatic landing guidance (ALG) system to determine if it could take off and land on a strip of concrete only 1,500 ft (457 m) long and 50 ft (15 m) wide, on a wet surface and with a 30-kt (34-mph; 55-km/h) crosswind.

The canards were mounted at 20° dihedral, and could operate symmetrically or differentially, but were not in theory used for primary flight control. A glass cockpit and the heavier landing gear from the F-15E were installed. The aircraft first flew in this guise on 7 September 1988, with Larry Walker at the controls. After 43 flights, the aircraft was laid up for fitment of box-like two-dimensional thrust-vectoring nozzles

This view amply illustrates the two-dimensional thrust-vectoring nozzles added for Phase II S/MTD testing. The flaps at the rear closed for thrust-reversing, efflux being redirected forward through upper and lower louvres.

made by Pratt & Whitney. In addition to thrust-vectoring up to 20° off-axis, the nozzles incorporated full reverse-thrust capability via a system of upper and lower louvres.

With its new nozzles, the S/MTD first flew at St Louis on 16 May 1989 before

transferring to Edwards for the second phase of testing, which lasted until 15 August 1991. The first in-flight vectoring was accomplished on 23 March 1990. The modifications reduced landing run to as little as 1,366 ft (416 m), while take-off rotation was demonstrated at 42 mph (68 km/h). Much of the STOL/MTD work has led to features designed into the F-22A Raptor, as well as the new Joint Strike Fighter design.

NF-15B ACTIVE

The ACTIVE (Advanced Control Technology for Integrated VEhicles) programme is a joint project between NASA, USAF Wright Laboratory, Boeing/McDonnell Douglas and Pratt & Whitney. It utilises the S/MTD aircraft (71-0290/NASA 837) equipped with

new thrust-vectoring nozzles. Known as PYBBN (pitch/yaw balanced-beam nozzles), the new nozzles are axisymmetric and can deflect thrust up to 20° off-axis in any direction. F100-PW-229 IPE engines are fitted, although otherwise the ACTIVE (also

Left: ACTIVE is currently the main F-15 programme being undertaken at Dryden. The aircraft has now received a NASA number (837).

designated NF-15B) is similar to the Phase 2 S/MTD. The aim of ACTIVE is to study potential control effects for next-generation combat aircraft, notably the employment of supersonic thrust-vectoring.

Initial flight trials began in February 1996, followed shortly by the first thrust-vectoring flights. On 24 April the F-15 thrust-vectored supersonically for the first time, at Mach 1.2. On 31 October 1996 the NF-15B successfully demonstrated thrust-vectoring at Mach 1.95.

A third phase of the ACTIVE programme will be aimed at studies for the F-15 MANX tailless programme.

This close-up shows the vectoring nozzle of the F-15 ACTIVE, which can vector up to 20° in any direction. Unlike previous thrust-vectoring testbeds, ACTIVE is primarily concerned with supersonic thrust-vectoring, as well as investigating the use of thrust-vectoring to replace vertical tailfins (which greatly increase radar cross-section) of operational designs.

F-15A/B NASA

NASA has used three F-15s in the course of its experimental work, one of which is till in use (in addition to the joint-agency ACTIVE programme). These are as follows:

71-0281: This was the second F-15 built, and was used by NASA Dryden between December 1975 and October 1983. Initially it was used for testing the thermal insulation tiles for the Space Shuttle, a section of these being attached to the starboard wing and port wing glove. Other minor tests ensued before its return to the US Air Force.

71-0287/F-15 FRF/DEEC/EMD/HIDEC: The eighth FSD F-15A, '287 was originally the spin test aircraft, and was subsequently used as such (along with one of the ⅜th scale RPRVs) by NASA Dryden, which acquired it on 5 January 1976. Assigned the NASA number 835 and dubbed the F-15 Flight Research Facility, the aircraft then embarked on a number of programmes which tested a variety of integrated propulsion/flight control systems and other equipment.

In 1982/83 NASA 835 was fitted with a digital electronic engine control (DEEC) system to support the F100-PW-220 development effort, this engine being subsequently retrofitted to operational F-15s. In mid-1983 the aircraft was further used in the Engine Model Derivative (EMD)

programme, being fitted with improved engines that matured as the F100-PW-229 IPE as fitted to late-production F-15Es.

The aircraft was again used for advanced engine tests under the HIDEC (Highly Integrated Digital Electronic Control) programme, which combined an advanced digital engine control system (ADECS) with a self-repairing flight control system (SRFCS) and other advanced systems, including those which automatically controlled engine parameters to improve engine life and fuel efficiency. The result was an aircraft with a fully-integrated inlet-engine-flight control system, which demonstrated inflight self-repair of flight controls. In 1993 the HIDEC F-15 also demonstrated a touch-and-go at Edwards with the flight control surfaces in a simulated 'locked' position, control during the approach being made solely by symmetrical and differential throttle settings. NASA 835 is currently in storage at Dryden, used as a spares source.

74-0141/FTF-II: With NASA number 836 applied, NASA Dryden has operated an F-15B since 1994 as its Flight Test Fixture-II aircraft (having replaced the F-104 FTF-I). This aircraft carries a slab-shaped pylon (the actual FTF) under its centreline, which contains its own test instrumentation. The FTF-II provides a ready-made vehicle for a variety of small test articles and aerodynamic shapes. In 1996 tests of the X-33's thermal protection tiles were conducted using this aircraft.

71-0281 was acquired by NASA on 17 December 1975, and was initially used to test the thermal protection tiles for the Space Shuttle. They were attached to the starboard wing (above) and port intake (right). During the tests the tiles were subjected to 150 per cent of the dynamic pressure experienced during an actual Shuttle launch.

71-0287 began its NASA career continuing the spin tests it had performed while part of the F-15 test programme. Note the cropped fin-tip fairings and spin recovery chute.

'287 was subsequently modified as the HIDEC testbed, which digitally integrated control of the engines, inlets and flight controls. A self-repair system was incorporated.

This F-15B has taken over Dryden's FTF tasking from an F-104. The underfuselage instrumented Flight Test Facility is used to mount various small-scale experiments.

F-15C/D

In order to keep the F-15 as the world's premier fighter, MDC engineers began working on a second-generation Eagle design, known loosely as the PEP (Production Eagle Package)-2000, which would improve the performance of the fighter measurably. All areas of the design were looked at and subtly improved where necessary, although the resulting F-15C/D is externally very similar to the preceding F-15A/B. Internally space was found for an additional 2,000 lb (907 kg) of fuel, while the F-15C/D was the first operational model to be able to carry the conformal fuel tank (CFT).

CFT development had begun in 1974 as the Fuel And Sensor Tactical (FAST) pack. FAST packs are flush-mounted on the outer walls of the Eagle's engine bays and can easily be removed, although not jettisoned. Each provides the ability to carry up to 5,000 lb (2270 kg) of additional fuel or sensors, although the sensor option has never been exercised. Initial proposals covered various EW and reconnaissance fits, and even included one study to fit rockets in the rear of the pack for augmented heavyweight take-offs. The first airborne demonstration of a FAST pack-equipped aircraft occurred on 27 July 1974, using the second FSD TF-15A 71-0291, but it was the late 1970s before any significant order was issued to MDC for the new tanks. The advent of the twin crises in Iran and Afghanistan during 1979 changed the situation, and sufficient tanks were ordered to equip the entire 1st TFW. The 1st TFW had been assigned the air superiority mission for the newly formed Rapid Deployment Joint Task Force (RDJTF), which eventually evolved into the US Central Command – CENTCOM).

The ability to carry a load of over 43,000 lb (19505 kg) of fuel meant that the Eagle could self-deploy to an air base in the Persian Gulf, with either two stops or inflight refuellings. However, the enlargement of the SAC tanker force with the new KC-10A Extender and the drawdown of the bomber force meant that the new packs were rarely used.

F-15C/Ds use the Dash-1 CFT, which has simple small pylons for mounting the two Sparrow missiles. CFTs were not fitted, in service at least, to any F-15A/Bs apart from those operated by the IDF/AF. The Dash-3 CFT was tested for a while, notably on 71-0291 and the No. 1 F-15C, this featuring a series of small stubs for bomb carriage. The

Two views show the first F-15C, which was used for many armament tests. The curvature of the CFTs requires vestigial pylons to allow the carriage of AIM-7s, as opposed to the 'Eagle claws' used for AIM-7 carriage directly from the intake.

definitive bomb-carrying CFT was the Dash-4, as fitted to the F-15E.

The increase in fuel carriage has naturally raised the take-off weight, requiring airframe and undercarriage strengthening. A related change was made from the A/B's white-painted wheels to black. An important addition was an airframe overload warning system which allows the F-15C/D pilot to manoeuvre safely to 9 *g*, the F-15A/B being limited to 7.33 *g* in certain flight regimes. An additional UHF radio was added and the F-15C/D standardised on the new ACES II ejection seat. The first F-15C (78-0468) flew at St Louis on 26 February 1979, followed by the F-15D two-seater on 19 June.

Initial production C/Ds were powered by the same F100-PW-100 engines which had powered the A/B, but from November 1985 the F100-PW-220 was introduced. This new engine was slightly less powerful, but was considerably more reliable, thanks to the use of single-crystal blade technology and a digital engine control unit. The new engine had first flown in 71-0287 in 1982, and began to reach operational units in the spring of 1986. With digital control, the pilot was provided with carefree engine handling, being able to slam the throttles without fear of the stagnation problem which dogged the F100-PW-100. Combined with the new overload system, the DECU made the

F-15C/D the first fully carefree handling service aircraft. The F-15C/D officially dispensed with the 'turkey feathers' which covered the variable nozzles, although these had mostly been removed from F-15A/Bs for some time. This greatly eased maintenance.

Avionics systems were also improved,

Above: The 18th TFW at Kadena was the first recipient of the F-15C, this being the second production aircraft. Note that it retains the engine 'turkey feathers' which were subsequently removed from most production C/Ds.

Below: As the prime air defence unit in NATO's 4th ATAF region, the 36th TFW at Bitburg was quick to receive F-15C/Ds. A 5-minute 'Zulu' alert was maintained for many years. USAFE Eagles now serve with the 48th and 52nd Fighter Wings.

Aircraft model	Block number	Starting serial	Ending serial	Number in block	Comments
F-15C	21	78-0468	78-0495	28	
F-15C	22	78-0496	78-0522	27	
F-15C	23	78-0523	78-0550	28	
F-15C	N/A	78-0551	78-0560	10	Cancelled
F-15D	21	78-0561	78-0565	5	
F-15D	22	78-0566	78-0570	5	
F-15D	23	78-0571	78-0574	4	
F-15D	N/A	78-0575	N/A	1	Cancelled
F-15D	24	79-0004	79-0006	3	
F-15D	25	79-0007	79-0011	5	
F-15D	26	79-0012	79-0014	3	
F-15C	24	79-0015	79-0037	23	
F-15C	25	79-0038	79-0058	21	
F-15C	26	79-0059	79-0081	23	
F-15C	27	80-0002	80-0023	22	
F-15C	28	80-0024	80-0038	15	
F-15C	29	80-0039	80-0053	15	
F-15C	27	80-0054	80-0055	2	
F-15C	28	80-0056	80-0057	2	
F-15C	29	80-0058	80-0061	4	
F-15C	32	81-0002	N/A	1	RSAF (to USAF as 81-0056)
F-15D	32	81-0003	N/A	1	Eventually to RSAF
F-15C	30	81-0020	81-0031	12	
F-15C	31	81-0032	81-0040	9	
F-15C	32	81-0041	81-0056	16	(81-0056 is ex-RSAF 81-0002)
F-15C	N/A	81-0057	81-0060	4	Cancelled
F-15D	30	81-0061	81-0062	2	
F-15D	31	81-0063	81-0065	3	
F-15D	32	81-0066	N/A	1	RSAF (from 81-0003)
F-15D	N/A	81-0066	81-0067	2	Cancelled
F-15C	33	82-0008	82-0022	15	
F-15C	34	82-0023	82-0038	16	
F-15D	33	82-0044	82-0045	2	
F-15D	34	82-0046	82-0048	3	
F-15C	35	83-0010	83-0034	25	
F-15C	36	83-0035	83-0043	9	
F-15C	N/A	83-0044	83-0045	2	Cancelled
F-15D	35	83-0046	83-0048	3	
F-15D	36	83-0049	83-0050	2	
F-15D	N/A	83-0051	N/A	1	Cancelled
F-15C	37	84-0001	84-0015	15	
F-15C	38	84-0016	84-0031	16	
F-15C	N/A	84-0032	84-0041	10	Cancelled
F-15D	37	84-0042	84-0044	3	
F-15D	38	84-0045	84-0046	2	
F-15D	N/A	84-0047	84-0048	2	Cancelled
F-15C	39	85-0093	85-0108	15	
F-15C	40	85-0109	85-0128	21	
F-15D	39	85-0129	85-0131	3	
F-15D	40	85-0132	85-0134	3	
F-15C	41	86-0143	86-0162	20	
F-15C	42	86-0163	86-0180	18	
F-15D	42	86-0181	86-0182	2	

Left: F-15Ds incorporate all of the improvements of the C although, like the F-15B, they have no provision for the internal ALQ-135 ECM system. This was not fitted to a two-seat Eagle until the F-15E. These F-15Ds belonged to the 32nd FS.

the first F-15C/Ds emerging with the improved APG-63PSP (programmable signal processor) radar and better ECM equipment. From 1989 the APG-70 radar was incorporated, this being a much-modified APG-63. Using the same antenna,

the APG-70 had new signal processor systems which were nearly five times quicker than those of the APG-63, while able to handle much larger volumes. The result is a tactically superior radar allowing much more rapid changes between modes.

The ECM equipment was the ALQ-135B, with a characteristic rounded radome on the starboard tailboom (also seen on a few F-15A/Bs).

C and D model Eagles were rapidly delivered to front-line fighter units around

the world, and by the time the last of the second-generation F-15s had been delivered to the USAF, some 408 F-15Cs and 62 F-15Ds had been produced. F-15A/Bs displaced by the new model were largely distributed among ANG units.

Since the early 1990s the primary weapon of the F-15C has been the AIM-120 AMRAAM, seen here during an early test launch from a 3246th Test Wing aircraft flying from Eglin AFB.

In the immediate wake of the Iraqi invasion of Kuwait, the F-15Cs of the 1st TFW's 27th and 71st TFS were the first US warplanes to be deployed, arriving at Dhahran a week after the invasion, fully armed and ready to fight.

F-15C/D Akef

When the American C/D-model Eagles came on the scene, the IAF was already interested in a further procurement of the F-15. The result was Project Peace Fox III, which delivered 18 F-15Cs and eight F-15Ds from the FY 1980 and 1983 Eagle

production runs. In IDF/AF service the F-15C/D acquired the name Akef (buzzard). Later, five additional F-15Ds were delivered from FY90 production under Peace Fox IV, these probably being based on the modified F-15E airframe rather than the F-15D as the latter was no longer in production. Delivery of some of these aircraft was delayed as a punitive American response to the 1982

Israeli invasion of Lebanon (Operation Peace in Galilee). Nevertheless, the entire batch did eventually arrive, and continue to serve today in IAF service with 106 Squadron, which flies alongside the A/B-equipped 133 Squadron at Tel Nof. Like the earlier A/B models, they are equipped with locally-produced EW equipment, which replaces some of the equipment (such as

ALQ-128) removed from export Eagles. Weapons include the Python-3 and latest Python-4 AAMs, which have largely replaced the American AIM-9 Sidewinder. Armed with a much larger warhead than the Sidewinder, the Python-series missiles were designed to destroy the aircraft and the pilot, and take advantage of new targeting systems like helmet-mounted sights. Python-4 has a very good off-boresight capability which, combined with the helmet-targeting sight system makes it arguably the best short-range AAM in service today.

Israel's F-15C/Ds are operated by 106 Squadron at Tel Nof. This aircraft carries a Python-3 on the outer launch rail (AIM-9 on the inner).

Aircraft model	Block number	Starting serial	Ending serial	Number in block	Comments
F-15C	27	80-0122	80-0124	3	Peace Fox III
F-15C	28	80-0125	80-0127	3	Peace Fox III
F-15C	29	80-0128	80-0130	3	Peace Fox III
F-15D	27	80-0131	80-0132	2	Peace Fox III
F-15D	28	80-0133	80-0136	4	Peace Fox III
F-15D	35	83-0054	83-0055	2	Peace Fox III
F-15C	36	83-0056	83-0062	7	Peace Fox III
F-15C	35	83-0063	83-0064	2	Peace Fox III
F-15D	50/51	90-0275	90-0279	5	Peace Fox IV

F-15C/D (Saudi Arabia)

In the 1970s, as the relationship between Saudi Arabia and the US began to improve (partly as a result of the Iranian Islamic Revolution), the Royal Saudi Air Force (RSAF) began to consider procuring a force of high-end interceptors to replace the BAC Lightning. The belief was that they would be needed to provide protection of the

oilfields, Islamic holy sites and other facilities that were making the Kingdom one of the most important emerging nations in the world. However, the sale, which was tied to a force of Boeing E-3 Sentry Airborne Warning and Control System (AWACS) aircraft, became a lightning rod in the United States. Israel and its lobby in the

American Congress did everything possible to stop, and later to delay and limit, the sale of the aircraft to the RSAF. Eventually, the details of the sale became part of the contents of the Camp David Peace Accords between Israel, Egypt and the US.

Specifically, only 60 of the Eagle airframes would be allowed on Saudi territory at any time. Since the RSAF order was for 62 C/D-model F-15s, two would have to be held back as attrition aircraft. Later, an additional 12 aircraft were cleared for production and

This F-15C carries the striking eagle badge of No. 13 Sqn, RSAF, the unit responsible for the double-kill during Desert Storm. RSAF Eagles now carry dark grey markings in place of the traditional green.

Aircraft model	Block number	Starting serial	Ending serial	Number in block	Comments
F-15C	28	80-0062	80-0067	6	Peace Sun
F-15C	29	80-0068	80-0074	7	Peace Sun
F-15C	30	80-0075	80-0085	11	Peace Sun
F-15C	31	80-0086	80-0099	14	Peace Sun
F-15C	32	80-0100	80-0106	7	Peace Sun
F-15D	27	80-0107	80-0110	4	Peace Sun
F-15D	28	80-0111	80-0112	2	Peace Sun
F-15D	29	80-0113	80-0114	2	Peace Sun
F-15D	30	80-0115	80-0117	3	Peace Sun
F-15D	31	80-0118	80-0119	2	Peace Sun
F-15D	32	80-0120	80-0121	2	Peace Sun
F-15C	32	81-0002	–	1	Peace Sun (to USAF as 81-0056)
F-15D	32	81-0066	–	1	Peace Sun (from 81-0003)
F-15C	48 to 51	90-0263	90-0271	9	Peace Sun VI
F-15D	48 to 51	90-0272	90-0274	3	Peace Sun VI

delivery in FY90.

Procured under Project Peace Sun, the initial RSAF F-15s were ordered from the FY80 and 81 production runs, and began to arrive in the Kingdom on 11 August 1981, several having been retained in the US at Luke for training. Later in 1991, the further order of 12 attrition aircraft was contracted under Peace Sun VI, and were delivered at a rate of two per month starting in February 1992. They quickly showed their teeth when, on 5 June 1984, two RSAF F-15s shot down a pair of Iranian F-4 Phantoms over the Persian Gulf, making it clear to all that the new Eagles were not there just to let princes play in the sky. By 1990 a total of three RSAF Eagle squadrons were in service: No. 5 at Taif, No. 6 at Khamis Mushait, and No. 13 at the huge airfield at Dhahran. By this time, the political restriction of only allowing 60 RSAF F-15s had been dropped, and two dozen additional F-15Cs and F-15Ds were rushed from the USAF to flesh out the RSAF during the 1990/91 Persian Gulf crisis, these being used to form No. 42 Squadron at Dhahran. These latter aircraft were the only export Eagles fitted with the ALQ-128 fin-top bullet antenna, although the sensitive equipment was removed prior to delivery.

This pair of F-15Cs is from No. 13 Squadron, from the early delivery batches. The aircraft both carry the older AIM-9P Sidewinder, since superseded by the AIM-9L. The four squadrons of F-15C/Ds will be augmented in the Saudi air defence mission by 24 of the 72 F-15S aircraft delivered in the late 1990s.

Aircraft	USAF serial	RSAF serial
F-15D-24-MC	79-0004	4223
F-15D-24-MC	79-0005	4221
F-15D-24-MC	79-0006	4222
F-15D-25-MC	79-0010	4224
F-15C-24-MC	79-0015	4201
F-15C-24-MC	79-0017	4206
F-15C-24-MC	79-0018	4214
F-15C-24-MC	79-0019	4215
F-15C-24-MC	79-0023	4202
F-15C-24-MC	79-0024	4207
F-15C-24-MC	79-0028	4216
F-15C-24-MC	79-0031	4203
F-15C-24-MC	79-0032	4217
F-15C-24-MC	79-0033	4208
F-15C-25-MC	79-0038	4218
F-15C-25-MC	79-0039	4212
F-15C-25-MC	79-0043	4213
F-15C-25-MC	79-0051	4209
F-15C-25-MC	79-0052	4219
F-15C-25-MC	79-0055	4210
F-15C-26-MC	79-0060	4211
F-15C-26-MC	79-0062	4220
F-15C-26-MC	79-0063	4205

During the Gulf War, the RSAF's finest moment came when a pair of Eagles led by Captain Ayehid Salah al-Shamrani of No. 13 Squadron shot down a pair of Exocet-carrying Iraqi Mirage F1s.

F-15J/DJ

The second overseas customer for the Eagle was the Japanese Air Self-Defence Force (JASDF), which first evaluated the F-15 in 1975. The Japanese requirement for the Eagle was centred on the growing strength of the Soviet and Communist Chinese forces in the Far East, as well as the advancing age of their best existing fighters. These were the Japanese-built versions of the F-104 Starfighter and the F-4 Phantom, which had been procured in the 1960s. The JASDF versions of the Eagle (the F-15J is the single-seat version, and the F-15DJ a two-seat fighter trainer) differed

from their American brethren in being designed to be co-produced by Mitsubishi Heavy Industries (MHI) in Japan. Other than the deletion of a few sensitive items of equipment such as the ALQ-128 RWR, they were functionally identical to early-production C/D model Eagles in USAF service. Indigenous equipment to replace sensitive US items includes the J/ALQ-8 ECM system and XJ/APQ-1 radar warning receivers. Initially, the procurement, which was run under Project Peace Eagle, was to have been for 123 aircraft (18 aircraft in five squadrons), but by early 1998 totalled 213 (169 F-15Js and 44 F-15DJs) with further low-rate production likely to the currently planned total of 224.

02-8801 was the first F-15J, one of two built and assembled by McDonnell Douglas at St Louis. It wears the badge of the Koku Jikkendan (Air Proving Wing), the JASDF's Gifu-based trials unit.

Aircraft	Japanese Fiscal Year	Beginning serial	End serial	Number in block	Comments
F-15J	1980	02-8801	02-8802	2	Built by MDC (ex USAF 79-0280/81)
F-15J	1981	12-8803	12-8804	2	Built by MHI from knockdown kits
F-15DJ	1981	12-8051	12-8054	4	Built by MDC (ex USAF 79-0282/85)
F-15J	1982	22-8805	22-8815	11	First 6 are from knockdown kits by MDC
F-15DJ	1982	22-8055	22-8056	2	Built by MDC (ex USAF 79-0286/87)
F-15J	1983	32-8816	32-8827	13	
F-15DJ	1983	32-8057	32-8060	4	Built by MDC (ex USAF 81-0068/71)
F-15J	1984	42-8828	42-8844	17	
F-15J	1985	52-8845	52-8863	19	
F-15DJ	1985	52-8061	52-8062	2	Built by MDC (ex USAF 83-0052/53)
F-15J	1986	62-8864	62-8870	15	
F-15J	1987	72-8871	72-8895	17	
F-15J	1988	82-8896	82-8905	10	
F-15DJ	1988	82-8063	82-8066	4	
F-15J	1989	92-8906	92-8913	8	
F-15DJ	1989	92-8067	92-8070	4	
F-15J	1990	02-8914	02-8922	9	
F-15DJ	1990	02-8071	02-8073	3	
F-15J	1991	12-8923	12-8928	6	
F-15DJ	1991	12-8074	12-8079	6	
F-15J	1992	22-8929	22-8940	12	
F-15J	1993	32-8941	31-8943	3	
F-15DJ	1993	32-8080	32-8087	9	
F-15J	1994	42-8944	42-8950	7	
F-15J	1995	52-8951	52-8957	7	
F-15DJ	1995	52-8086	N/A	1	
F-15J	1996	62-8958	62-8959	2	
F-15DJ	1996	62-8089	N/A	1	
F-15J	1997	72-8960	N/A	1	
F-15DJ	1997	72-8090	N/A	1	

Initial F-15J production was undertaken at MDC in St Louis, where two aircraft were built, the first undertaking its maiden flight on 4 June 1980. The next eight F-15Js were supplied to Mitsubishi as knockdown kits (major sub-assemblies) for final assembly at MHI in Japan, the first of these flying at Komaki on 26 August 1981. All subsequent F-15J production was at MHI. Dual-control fighter/trainer aircraft (F-15DJs) were initially built at St Louis to supplement MHI F-15J production as it was ramping up. All F-15DJ production from FY 1988 on was by MHI (this coincides with MDC production conversion to F-15E). F-15Js began entering service (with 202 Hikotai) in 1981 after initial service testing had been performed by the Koku Jikkendan at Gifu.

Currently, the JASDF is conducting a major mid-life upgrade of the F-15J/DJ fleet, with will result in the aircraft being given a

F-15DJs are interspersed with the single-seaters throughout Mitsubishi production. This aircraft has an oversprayed brown scheme for service in the aggressor role.

'Plus' designation. This includes installation of an upgraded ejection seat, F100-IHI-220E engines (the licence-production version of the F110-PW-220), and an upgraded radar designated APG-63U, which is probably equivalent to the MSIP upgraded APG-70. Eventually, the indigenously-designed AAM-4 air-to-air missile (roughly equivalent to the US AIM-120 AMRAAM) will be fitted, when it comes into service.

One final note concerns the interpretation of JASDF F-15 tail numbers. Consider the example 72-8960. The numbers break down like this: 7 – last digit of fiscal year; 2 – type number (2 is assigned to F-15, F-86, T-1); 8 – basic aircraft configuration (8 = All Weather Jet Fighter); 960 – sequential serial number. The F-15DJ fleet has tail numbers that start at 050, while the F-15J force starts at 801.

F-15A MSIP

A Multi-Stage Improvement Program was developed in 1982 for the F-15A/B alongside that for the F-15C/D (described below). This was cancelled on cost grounds. Subsequently, however, those surviving F-15A/Bs considered to be in good enough condition for further useful service

After Desert Storm, the F-15C-equipped 32nd FS at Soesterberg transitioned to F-15A MSIPs.

life have undergone portions of the MSIP-II programme. The APG-70 radar and CFTs are not fitted, but the improved ECM system, cockpit changes and other facets of MSIP-II have been applied. Among other

to existing F-15A/Bs and retained by some early F-15C/Ds. The radar utilises some portions of the APG-70, and provides an improved tactical sensor with much greater speed and reliability. The radar is also a candidate for the upgrade of overseas aircraft fitted with APG-63.

MSIP A/Bs generally serve with ANG units, although the front-line 32nd FS at Soesterburg in the Netherlands was equipped with the variant after having rapidly transferred its C/D aircraft to the RSAF during the Gulf war. Early A/B aircraft not considered worthy of receiving MSIP improvements have either been placed in storage, dispatched to Israel or are due for near-term retirement.

changes the wheels have been changed to the black-painted stronger units of the C/D, and from the early 1990s the F100-PW-100 engines have been raised to Dash 220E standard, this being equivalent to the more reliable and digitally-controlled Dash 220s of the F-15C/D. The 9 *g* overload warning system is also fitted.

On 18 July 1997 an F-15 testbed flew with an upgraded radar for the first time, the APG-63(V)1 being intended as a replacement for the standard APG-63 fitted

F-15C MSIP-II

The Multi-Stage Improvement Program, handled jointly by McDonnell Douglas and the WR-ALC, was a means by which improvements could be incorporated on the production line and retrofitted to earlier aircraft. MSIP-II is the portion of the programme handling the F-15C/D. The main feature of MSIP-II was the adoption of the APG-70 radar and AIM-120 AMRAAM.

BVR AAMs have been in existence since the 1950s, but for much of that time they and their tactical advantages have been wasted by political and operational realities. The problem is simply described: you cannot reliably employ BVR missiles if you do not know exactly what the target aircraft is. Much of this stems from the need to avoid so-called 'friendly fire', or 'blue-on-blue', losses. In addition, given that neutral civil air traffic frequently still operates in the middle of combat zones (common in Southeast Asia and the Middle East), the last thing one wants to do is shoot down an airliner loaded with civilians, as a US Navy warship did to an Iranian Airbus in July 1988. Therefore, giving a pilot a positive identification has been a priority for almost four decades. The first successful effort was a system called Combat Tree, which was installed in F-4s of the 555th TFS in

84-0001 was the first aircraft built to MSIP-II standards, although it was some time before APG-70 and AIM-120 were integrated.

1972. Designed to cause an enemy IFF transponder to 'squawk' actively, it was used with some success during Linebacker I and Linebacker II over North Vietnam in 1972. While Combat Tree was an interesting start, the USAF was looking for something that would actively be able to tell the pilot exactly at what kind of aircraft he was shooting.

One intriguing possibility came in a programme called Musketeer in the 1970s, which looked at the possibility of counting the fan blades of an enemy aircraft while in flight. This is the same technique that submarines use to identify and track potential targets, obtaining a blade count from the emitted noise. The concept was immediately classified 'black' (meaning that it officially did not exist), and was renamed Non-Co-operative Target Recognition (NCTR). Quickly, several things became clear. While possible, the NCTR technology would require a huge amount of computing power onboard the aircraft, as well as a great deal of software development. A key part of this would be the cataloguing and creation of a threat library, which would be carried onboard the fighter to identify the

various target aircraft. Frankly, the technology that would make NCTR work – things like high-speed microprocessors and more rugged hard disk drives – simply did not exist when the concept was defined. However, by the mid-1980s the hardware necessary to bring NCTR into fruition was arriving, and was being integrated into an F-15 radar upgrade programme as part of MSIP.

MSIP was designed to give the Eagle's APG-63 radar the ability to utilise NCTR, as well as several other emerging technologies. They included being able to employ the new fire-and-forget AIM-120 AMRAAM, as well as several new radar modes such as track-while-scan features so that the F-15 could ripple-fire up to four AIM-120s at separate targets nearly simultaneously. In addition, there was something called 'Low Probability of Intercept', or LPI, which means that a radar is able to operate and detect aircraft without emitting enough power to be easily seen by an enemy utilising electronic support measure (ESM) 'ferret' gear, or tactical radar warning receivers (RWRs). This last operating mode required a great deal of work in an arcane part of computer science known as Digital Signal Processing (DSP), which allows LPI radars to become more sensitive in a combat environment. The result, though, changed the course of aerial warfare.

Left: The MSIP-II Eagles of the 390th FS, 366th Wing at Mountain Home AFB are JTIDS-equipped.

Hughes Ground Systems handled the MSIP-II upgrade for the APG-63, which involved the replacement of the radar's signal processor and computer systems, and the addition of several other 'black boxes'. When completed, the MSIP-equipped APG-63 was redesignated the APG-70. F-15C 84-0001 was the first MSIP-II aircraft, delivered on 20 June 1985. Begun in the late 1980s, MSIP-II was still incomplete when the 1990 Persian Gulf crisis arose. The capabilities of the MSIP aircraft were a closely guarded secret, although virtually every APG-70-equipped F-15 was dispatched to the Persian Gulf prior to the outbreak of war. When Desert Storm began on 16 January 1991, the MSIP-equipped F-15Cs began to cut a swathe through the few Iraqi aircraft brave (or foolish) enough to get airborne. Normally they would be detected by E-3 AWACS aircraft, which would then dispatch an MSIP-equipped F-15C to intercept the enemy aircraft utilising the LPI mode. Then, when an engagement was imminent, the Eagle would manoeuvre to 'see' the engine of the enemy aircraft ('down' the inlets or 'up' the tailpipe) with NCTR, and would usually down the target with an AIM-7 Sparrow AAM (the AIM-120 AMRAAM had yet to enter service).

The system was so good that it frequently identified aircraft by model and sub-variant, and the result was not one reported 'blue-on-blue' engagement during Desert Storm. This is not to say that MSIP is perfect, as the accidental shootdown of two United Nations UH-60s after the war proves. However, NCTR is better than any other technology yet identified in its ability to sort the good from the bad.

Quickly, regional/unified Commanders-in-Chiefs (CINCs) began to scream for more aircraft with the MSIP capabilities, and today one finds similar capabilities on all advanced versions of the F-14, F-16 and F/A-18. In addition, the foreign Eagle customers, all of whom have 'special' relationships with the US, have been receiving the upgrade for their F-15s.

MSIP-II also introduced other features, such as a new multi-function display armament control panel, new stick-top and throttle grip, and provisions for the JTIDS and MIDS tactical information distribution systems. ECM equipment is again improved, with ALR-56C RWR, ALQ-135B internal ECM system and enhanced ALQ-128. The UHF radio now incorporates advanced jam-resistant features.

The 33rd TFW at Eglin was the first recipient of full-standard MSIP-II F-15Cs with APG-70, and it was the wing's aircraft which scored the lion's share of kills during Desert Storm. These are from the 60th FS.

RF-15/F-15(R)

The performance of the Eagle made it a natural choice for a reconnaissance platform, and at an early juncture McDonnell Douglas proposed an RF-15 version. Although there were several schemes, the aircraft featured a redesigned nose housing a battery of cameras, and a redesigned lower fuselage incorporating IRLS and a side-looking radar. The idea was not proceeded with, the USAF relying instead on its existing RF-4Cs.

Much later, McDonnell Douglas privately developed the F-15(R) 'Peek Eagle', which employed the Reconnaissance Technology Demonstrator (RTD) pod carried on the centreline. This was a semi-conformal fairing which could be attached to standard Eagles for use in the tactical reconnaissance role, and which was internally

reconfigurable to cater for a variety of cameras, IR systems and other sensors. The pod was flight-tested in mid-1987 under the long-suffering TF-2 airframe (71-0291) but development proceeded no further.

A further reconnaissance aircraft was produced and flown in 1995, when an F-15D (82-0046) was modified to carry a Loral-Fairchild ATARS multi-sensor pod on the centreline as a potential alternative to a pod-carrying F-16. The first flight took place at St Louis on 26 April, and only one further flight was necessary to validate the concept. However, the future of the 'RF-15' is bleak due to the lower costs and greater availability of the F-16.

82-0046 takes off on the second of its two test flights carrying a multi-sensor reconnaissance pod on the centreline.

'F-15G' Wild Weasel

From an early date the two-seat Eagle was proposed as a potential successor to the F-4G Wild Weasel in the lethal SEAD role. Indeed, the long-term McDD test aircraft, 71-0291, was flown with a representative chin pod (similar to that carried by the F-4G).

In 1986 McDonnell Douglas received a study contract for a Wild Weasel VII based on the F-15D, but the programme progressed no further.

In 1994 another award was made, this time to study the use of the single-seat

F-15C in the lethal SEAD role, it being envisaged as a possible use of the F-15Cs made redundant by the service entry of the F-22. The F-15C would be fitted with a sophisticated 360° PDF (passive detection finder) including conformal cheek fairings, and be equipped to carry and fire the AGM-88 HARM. Flight tests of a PDF-equipped F-15C were undertaken in August 1996 to

prove the feasibility of fitting the equipment in an Eagle. Subsequently, the F-16CJ Block 50/52D has been adopted as the USAF's HARM-shooter, but the F-15C/PDF may possibly be resurrected at a later date.

In the absence of a dedicated Wild Weasel F-15, the F-15E has been cleared to carry the AGM-88.

As part of the ongoing lethal SEAD proposals for the Eagle, F-15C 78-0527 was fitted with an outer pylon capable of carrying the AGM-88 HARM missile. Another F-15C tested a direction-finding system in 1996.

F-15N 'Seagle'

McDonnell Douglas first presented a navalised F-15 in July 1971. The F-15N was initially proposed as a minimum-change model with strengthened landing gear, an

extended nosewheel strut to increase catapult launch angle of attack, arrester hook and folding wings. This met with little interest, so a more extensively redesigned

model was offered, including further strengthening, refuelling probe and additional high-lift devices, which included full-span slats and boundary-layer control. A Navy fighter study group then added AWG-9 radar and Phoenix missile capability, which eroded the F-15N's projected performance

to the point where it had no advantage over the F-14. McDonnell Douglas and radar manufacturer Hughes countrered with a reduced-weight Phoenix-capable aircraft with yet more high-lift modifications, but in the event the Navy remained faithful to its chosen design, the F-14 Tomcat.

Strike Eagle

While the cry of 'Not a pound for air-to-ground' was at the centre of the original F-15 design effort, it would be a lie to say that weapons delivery against ground targets was not considered. As early as 1980, the F-15As of the 1st TFW had a secondary air-to-ground support mission, and had procured the necessary bomb racks to conduct bombing operations. Trials during FSD had revealed the Eagle to be an excellent delivery platform for air-to-ground munitions, and only the need to get the air superiority fleet equipped kept a strike variant of the F-15 from coming to fruition. By the late 1970s, though, this was going to change. With the completion of the F-111 buy, TAC began to consider an all-weather, day-and-night interdiction aircraft. The machine that best met their requirements was the planned fleet of F-117A Nighthawk 'Stealth Fighters' that resulted from the successful Have Blue trials of the late 1970s.

However, General Wilber Creech, the legendary and long-lived commander of TAC at the time, was hardly ready to 'bet the farm' on a thread as thin as stealth aircraft

dropping precision munitions to win the next war. Like all good poker players (and 'Uncle Wilber', as he is known, is a pro), he decided to have an 'ace in the hole,' just in case the F-117 programme ran into problems, or failed to perform as planned. From this came the Enhanced Tactical Fighter (ETF, later named Dual-Role Fighter/DRF) programme, which would ostensibly be justified as a replacement/augmentation to the existing fleet of F-111 'Aardvarks'. TAC got away with the subterfuge thanks to the fact that the F-117 programme was almost

completely 'black,' and not something that most Congressional and Administration analysts were entitled to even know about. With the cover story in place, General Creech began the drive to develop the aircraft that eventually became the F-15E Strike Eagle.

Resplendent in a 'lizard' scheme, the Strike Eagle demonstrator lugs a heavy load of 'slick' Mk 82s. The aircraft belied its FSD origins by having two large fin-top fairings as opposed to the usual one.

F-15 Eagle Variants

The Strike Eagle initially wore a standard Compass Ghost scheme. Here it is seen carrying the Pave Tack acquisition/designation pod, similar to that used by the F-111F.

By this time, MDC and Hughes had decided to spend their own money to build a prototype ETF, and got to work using that hard-working airframe, TF-2 (71-0291, the second pre-production F-15B). MDC added a pair of FAST packs/CFTs, as well as equipping the ETF demonstrator with an

AAQ-26 Pave Tack laser ranging/designator pod on the belly. Hughes modified an existing APG-63PSP radar to explore some new ideas that had grown from the MSIP programme, one promising notion being to coax ground mapping and imaging from the basic Eagle radar system. With the addition of extra DSP hardware and software, Hughes was able to create synthetic aperture radar (SAR) modes, which allow for near-photographic views of ground targets to be 'taken' by the weapons system officer (WSO) in the rear seat of the two-seat F-15.

Also added to the ETF demonstrator was

a new 'glass' cockpit design with four MFDs and hand controllers, created by MDC's cockpit 'guru,' the legendary Eugene Adams. The Strike Eagle, as it was named, first flew in its new guise on 8 July 1980. The DRF competition between McDonnell Douglas and General Dynamics, which was offering the F-16XL, got under way in 1982. The Strike Eagle was aided in the DRF demonstration programme by an F-15B (77-0166), the No. 1 F-15C (78-0468) and two F-15Ds (80-0055 and 81-0063). The result was an impressive showing by McDonnell Douglas, fully justifying the

One of the weapons tested on the Strike Eagle was the General Electric GPU-5/A Pave Claw cannon pod, which contained a four-barrelled GAU-13/A 30-mm cannon (a derivative of the A-10's GAU-8/A Avenger) and 353 rounds of ammunition.

private venture capital put up for Strike Eagle. On 24 February 1984 the USAF announced its selection of the Eagle, which would be built as the F-15E.

F-15E

Having won the DRF competition, MDC engineers made a number of changes to this third-generation Eagle design, many of which set it apart from its air-to-air brethren. Much of the design is new, incorporating many elements that make it a better fighter than the normal Eagle.

Over 60 per cent of the F-15E's structural components were redesigned and strengthened. This meant that a fully loaded F-15E might weigh in at over 81,000 lb (36742 kg), so heavy that it would actually mould flat spots onto the tyres just sitting on the ramp. The forward fuselage was rearranged to incorporate the ALQ-135B internal ECM system, previously lacking from all two-seat Eagles. This system has two (as opposed to the F-15C's one) tailboom antennas. Fuel capacity was reduced slightly to 2,019 US gal (7643 litres) and the ammunition for the M61A1 cannon was reduced to 450 rounds.

Dash-4 CFTs were fitted as standard, these featuring a continuous lower pylon with various attachments for heavy weapons and Sparrow missiles, together with three upper stub pylons for lighter bombs. The versatile hardpoints, together

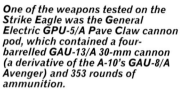

with the wing pylons, allow the F-15E to carry everything from cluster munitions to the 4,800-lb (2177-kg) GBU-28 'Deep Throat'. The Adams-designed 'glass' rear cockpit was retained, albeit with different sizes of MFDs and some refinements, while the front cockpit was configured with three MFDs and a Kaiser wide-angle HUD. The Strike Eagle's AAQ-26 Pave Tack pod was

replaced by the Low-Altitude Navigation and Targeting, Infra-Red, for Night (LANTIRN) pod system.

Developed by Martin Marietta (now part of Lockheed Martin), the LANTIRN system was designed to be able to be bolted onto a number of different aircraft types (A-10 Thunderbolt II/'Warthog', F-15 Eagle, F-16 Fighting Falcon, etc.). The AAQ-13

86-0183 was the first F-15E, although it did not have the redesigned aft fuselage and common engine bay, which were introduced on the second aircraft (86-0184).

navigation pod provides the aircraft with terrain-following radar (TFR) like that of the F-111, and night vision via a high-resolution Forward Looking Infra-Red (FLIR) sensor whose image can be projected onto a wide field-of-view HUD, while the AAQ-14 targeting pod incorporates a magnifying FLIR for acquisition and a laser rangefinder/designator for delivery of precision weapons like LGBs. While plans for installing LANTIRN on the A-10 fleet never proceeded because of cost, the system was integrated onto the F-15E and F-16C from the late 1980s. When properly integrated, as it is in the F-15E (the system is tied to the new SAR-capable APG-70 radar), LANTIRN is one of the most accurate weapons delivery systems in the world.

Arguably the most important part of the F-15E is the radar. based on the SAR version of the APG-63 flown in the Strike Eagle demonstrator, the F-15E's APG-70 differs from those fitted to its air-to-air cousins by having a SAR mode. This allows the crew to make accurate radar maps of the target area, allowing for precise designation of targets and cueing of other sensors such as the attack FLIR.

The biggest airframe change occurred in

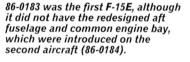

Compared to standard external stores carriage, the tangential arrangement of the F-15E allows large loads to be lifted with a reduced drag penalty. These weapons are CBU-89s.

Aircraft model	Block number	Starting serial	Ending serial	Number in block	Comments
F-15E	41	86-0183	86-0184	2	Production Lot I
F-15E	42	86-0186	86-0190	6	Production Lot I
F-15E	43/44	87-0169	87-0216	48	Production Lot II
F-15E	45	88-1667	88-1687	21	Production Lot III
F-15E	46	88-1688	88-1708	21	Production Lot III
F-15E	47/48	89-0471	89-0506	36	Production Lot IV
F-15E	49/50	90-0227	90-0262	36	Production Lot V
F-15E	51/52	91-0300	91-0335	36	Production Lot VI
F-15E	53	91-0600	91-0605	6	Production Lot VII
F-15E	53	92-0364	92-0366	3	Production Lot VIII

the rear fuselage, which was much modified to provide a common engine bay to permit the installation of either F100 or General Electric F110 engines. Despite this, only F100s have been used on the F-15E apart from one test aircraft (87-0180) which flew with the F110-GE-129 engine. The first 134 F-15Es were powered by the F-15C's F100-PW-220 engine, but subsequent machines have the F100-PW-229 Improved Performance Engine (IPE) installed, generating 29,100 lb (129.45 kN) thrust with afterburner. This engine first flew in an F-15E on 2 May 1990. The extra thrust is greatly appreciated due to the higher weights at which the F-15E operates. This extra weight also demanded a further beefing up of the undercarriage.

On 11 December 1986 the first F-15E (86-0183) undertook its maiden flight at St Louis, although it was devoid of any CFTs or pylons. Deliveries to the 405th TTW at Luke, the training unit, began on 12 April 1988. The first operational wing of Strike Eagles was the 4th TFW, assigned to Seymour Johnson AFB, North Carolina, which began to receive its aircraft on 29 December 1989. Unfortunately, it had only finished converting two of three F-15E squadrons from the F-4E when the wing was called to deploy to the Persian Gulf in August 1990. Assigned to the 4th TFW (Provisional) at Al Kharj Air Base, Saudi Arabia (along with a squadron of F-15Cs from the 36th TFW at Bitburg and two F-16 squadrons), they went to war with only half of the LANTIRN system installed. The targeting pods had been delayed by development problems, and only the navigation pods were available. However, every aircraft that could conduct night strikes was needed, and the F-15E's APG-70 SAR-capable radar (it also had all the MSIP capabilities) was ideal for hunting Iraqi 'Scud' missile launchers in the trackless

Much of the F-15E weapons clearance work is performed by the 46th Test Wing at Eglin AFB. This weapon is the 3,000-lb (1360-kg) AGM-130 rocket-powered glide-bomb with Mk 84 warhead.

deserts. Towards the end of the war, they even received about a dozen of the prized AAQ-14 targeting pods, allowing them to finally get into the precision weapons business with Paveway LGBs. Although two F-15Es were lost to ground fire, they did the job assigned, even managing to kill an Iraqi Hughes 500 helicopter with a Paveway II LGB.

After the war, the Strike Eagles finally received their full complement of LANTIRN pods, and got a chance to get fully operational, something they had been denied by the Gulf crisis. Despite the drawdown following the end of the Cold War, the F-15E continues to be procured, 12 attrition units being approved in FY97, and six more planned for FY98.

The original interceptor series of F-15s finished production in 1992, and all subsequent machines (apart from those being built in Japan) have been two-seaters utilising the basic F-15E airframe. This is believed to include the follow-on batch of 'F-15Ds' for Israel.

Left: The F-15E's systems make it a very accurate 'dumb' bomber. Here a 390th FS aircraft releases a pair of dummy Mk 84s.

Below: Seen at speed, this 46th TW F-15E carries a pair of GBU-31 JDAM weapons, in addition to AIM-120 AMRAAMs which are routinely carried on the wing pylon shoulder stations as a Sidewinder alternative.

F-15F/H/XP

With the USAF Strike Eagle programme coming to an end, the MDC marketing team was looking everywhere for ways to keep the F-15 production line 'warm' into the 21st century. Fortunately, the Strike Eagle's performance in Desert Storm made it an automatic choice for several nations that had been most involved in that conflict. In late 1991, the RSAF began to consider a buy of 24 modified F-15Es, which would have been equipped with only one seat. They would have had many of the F-15E features, including the common engine bay, F100-PW-229 engines, and the ability to carry LANTIRN pods if desired. However, the US Congress rejected any attempt to sell the aircraft. In its place came the F-15H, a downgraded two-seat F-15E. This, too, was vetoed, being replaced by a third proposal known initially as F-15XP (export). This was finally given the Congressional go-ahead on 10 May 1993, and emerged as hardware in the form of the F-15S.

F-15S

Following the F-15F sales effort, an industry rumour surfaced that the RSAF wanted 72 additional Eagles, although the type and purpose was unspecified. Eventually, the order crystallised for the F-15S. Originally, it was intended that the 72 aircraft of the RSAF buy would not have all the capabilities of the domestic F-15E. Once again, the power of the Israeli lobby in Congress came to bear, and the low-level TFR capabilities of the LANTIRN navigation pod were to be deleted so that the low-level penetration capabilities of the aircraft would be lessened. However, when word got out that the Israelis themselves were planning to procure a batch of Strike Eagles, the Departments of Defense and State decided to sell RSAF the new aircraft, designated F-15S, with only slightly downgraded equipment. Some modes of the APG-70 are down-tuned while, as with all export Eagles, nuclear weapon wiring is deleted and certain sensitive ECM systems are replaced with older equipment, or deleted altogether. Other systems which had originally been the subject of debate, such as CFTs and tangential stores carriage, were supplied. The aircraft are powered by the latest F100-PW-229 IPE engines.

The Saudi Eagles are essentially stock F-15E airframes, the first of which flew on 19 June 1995. The first was handed over in a ceremony at St Louis on 12 September. The programme is proceeding well, and the 27th, 28th, 29th and 30th aircraft were delivered in late 1997, with all 72 to be in service by the end of 1999. Twenty-four are to be optimised for the air-to-air role, with the remainder assigned a dual-role tasking like the F-15E. Combined with the purchase of precision weapons which include the AGM-65 Maverick and GBU-10/12 laser-guided bombs, the F-15Ss are expected to hold a set of targets at risk that includes everything from the traditional targets in Iraq to possible nuclear weapons and

terrorist facilities in Iran and Yemen.
F-15S serials observed so far run from 93-0852 to 93-0870.

Above: 93-0852 was the first F-15S to fly, albeit without any RSAF insignia. Dash-4 CFTs with Sparrow attachments are fitted.

Right: The 12 September 1995 handover ceremony of the first F-15S (5501) provided an excellent illustration of the Mod Eagle scheme in which the aircraft are delivered.

Below: The first RSAF aircraft sits outside the St Louis factory (now administered by Boeing). The initial RSAF squadron will be No. 55.

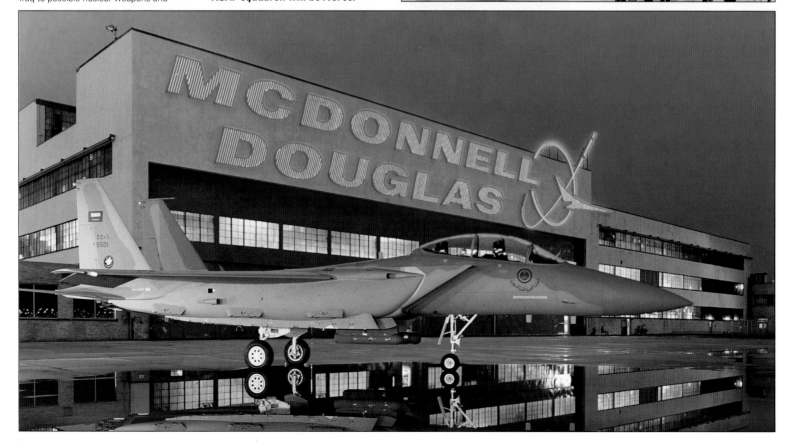

F-15I Ra'am

Facing stiff opposition from a developed version of the Lockheed Martin Fighting Falcon (the F-16ES), McDonnell Douglas was selected to provide the Israeli air force with a new long-range interdictor in November 1993, the order being officially received on 12 May 1994. This covered the provision of 21 aircraft, with four options (exercised in early 1996). Designated as the F-15I, and known in IDF/AF service as the Ra'am (thunder), the Israeli aircraft are essentially similar to the late-production F-15E, with F100-PW-229 engines, full-standard LANTIRN system and APG-70 radar. Some US ECM equipment is deleted, but is replaced by Israeli units. Likewise, Israeli weaponry, notably the Python-4 SRAAM, will be utilised.

The first F-15I made its first flight at St Louis on 12 September 1997, and deliveries began in January 1998. 69 Squadron at Hatzerim is expected to be the operator, and follow-on sales appear likely.

The initial batch of 21 F-15Is are covered by the Peace Sun V programme, with the follow-on four coming under Peace Sun VI. By the start of 1998 USAF serials reported were 94-0286 to 94-0289.

Right: The first F-15Is were delivered in January 1998, routing through RAF Lakenheath, where this example (the third F-15I) is seen. Although painted in full IDF/AF camouflage, the aircraft wore USAF serials and national insignia for their delivery flights.

Below: Lacking any paint apart from its USAF serial on the fin, the first F-15I completes its maiden flight from St Louis-Lambert Field on 12 September 1997.

Left: F-15Is wear the standard IDF/AF three-tone attack scheme as carried by F-4s and F-16s. The aircraft also carries the badge of 69 Squadron on the fin, and is armed with bombs, AIM-120s (outer shoulder) and Python-4 (inner shoulder). Outwardly similar to the F-15E, the F-15I incorporates certain Israeli-built components, notably in the EW suite where the standard US equipment is not available for export. Similarly, the weapons fit includes Israeli-designed ordnance, carried alongside US-built weapons. The IDF/AF has already stated a requirement for further fighter-bombers, and the likelihood of follow-on F-15I orders is high.

Export proposals

F-15H: As this article was written in late 1997, reports emerged that Greece may be in the market for a force of 40 Strike Eagles of its own. Now that it is facing an F-16C/LANTIRN/LGB/AMRAAM-equipped Turkish foe on one side, and a destabilised Balkans to the north, the Hellenic Air Force wants something to even the odds – that may well be another run of 40 Boeing F-15 Strike Eagles, which would be built to similar standards as the Saudi and Israeli models. Beyond that, details remain sketchy.

F-15U: Proposed to answer a requirement of the United Arab Emirates for between 20 and 80 long-range interdictors, the F-15U was essentially an F-15E tailored for the UAE. Final assembly was proposed to take place in the Gulf states.

F-15U (Plus): A further proposal was made to the UAE covering a significantly enhanced version with a larger clipped-delta wing, extra fuel, more weapon stations and internally mounted LANTIRN. Thrust-vectoring capability was offered as an option. Both U and U (Plus) were in competition with the F-16U, Eurofighter, Rafale and the Su-30MK. In late 1996 the UAE reduced the field to just the F-16U and Rafale, but subsequently reinstated the Eurofighter.

F-15K: Another important competition looming is that for a new fighter for South Korea, which is expected to order up to 120. An advanced version based on the F-15U (Plus) or F-15 MANX is expected to be offered by Boeing.

F-15XX

The F-15XX was an unsolicited proposal made to the USAF in the wake of the Advanced Tactical Fighter decision, which resulted in the Lockheed Martin F-22 being selected as the F-15's successor. The F-15XX was a stripped-down F-15 derivative offering better performance and reduced radar cross-section, and represented a low-cost approach to the ATF requirement. No work was authorised on the project, while the F-22/ATF programme has forged ahead largely unchallenged.

F-15 MANX

Using technology developed during the ACTIVE programme, and to incorporate further developments from Phase III ACTIVE testing, the MANX is an advanced F-15 derivative intended to feature advanced control systems. It will be stealthy and tailless (hence the acronym). A test specimen is expected to be built, and this may provide the basis for future versions being offered for export or for home consumption, including as a possible F-15E/F-117 replacement.

Poland's front-line 'Fulcrums'

A photo feature by Captain Andrzej Rogucki

While Poland and other Eastern European nations search for a 'NATO-compatible' fighter for the future, the sleek, and still impressive, MiG-29 'Fulcrum' remains the front-line combat aircraft of the Polish air force. This feature takes a look at the current operations of its recently-reinforced 'Fulcrum' force.

Above and left: Poland originally took delivery of 10 MiG-29 'Fulcrum-As' in 1989 along with three MiG-29UB 'Fulcrum-Bs'. Nine of the first batch of these single-seat aircraft survive in service (along with all of the trainers). They have now been joined by an additional nine 'Fulcrum-As' and one 'Fulcrum-B' acquired from the Czech air force in 1995/1996. The Czech aircraft arrived in their original three-tone camouflage, as seen here. On delivery to Poland, the MiGs were still in full Czech colours, with serials and squadron badges in place. These were quickly sprayed over and Polish markings and numbers applied over the repainted patches.

Right: Poland's MiG-29s are based at Minsk-Mazoweicki, near Warsaw, and make up the dedicated air defence element of 1.PLM (Pulk Lotnictwa Mysliwskiego/fighter aviation regiment) 'Warszawa'. 1.PLM also operates the MiG-21M and is one of the last remaining MiG-21 operators now in the Polish air force.

Below: The MiG-29 is powered by a pair of Klimov/Sarkisov RD-33 turbofans, seen here in full 'burner on departure from Minsk-Mazoweicki. At 'full chat', the RD-33 can develop 18,300 lb (81.4 kN) of thrust.

Above: The Mermaid badge of 1.PLM is the crest of the city of Warsaw. In June 1989, Poland became the fourth export customer for the aircraft after India, East Germany and Yugoslavia. Deliveries to Czechoslovakia began soon afterwards, in October.

Left: Two MiG-29s from 1.PLM attended the Royal International Air Tattoo at RAF Fairford in July 1997. The MiGs staged via RAF Bruggen in Germany, and were escorted by Tornados from No. 111 Squadron upon entering UK airspace (note the serial on the 'Fulcrum'!). This photo was taken from the accompanying MiG-29UB.

Below: In Polish service, the former Czech aircraft retained the tiger-striped fin band of 11 SLP. The MiG-29 was retired from the Czech air force in late 1993 and several attempts were made to dispose of them before they were finally sold to Poland.

Above: Clearly visible on this aircraft are the auxiliary inlet doors above the MiG-29's prominent LERXes. The MiG-29's engine intakes are covered by doors that deploy on take-off and landing to prevent FOD damge (if operating from a rough strip). The auxiliary inlet 'louvres' are an innovative way of ensuring maximum airflow into the engines.

Right: 1.PLM now has four two-seat MiG-29UBs to complement its 18 single-seaters. This is the last of the three 'Fulcrum-Bs' delivered by the Soviet Union.

Below: The MiG-29 has g limits of +7.5 g above Mach 0.85, and +9 g below.

Above: This 'Fulcrum' is one of three deployed to Israel during April/May 1997 for weapons and tactics evaluation with the IDF/AF (note where temporary Israeli markings have been painted out on the fin and the Polish squadron badge has been repainted on the nose). The evaluation was reportedly conducted over a two-week period and pitted the MiG-29, with helmet-mounted sight and IRST, against the F-16.

Inset, above right: The black and white striped missile body under the wing of this 'Fulcrum' is a Vympel R-27T AA-10 'Alamo' acquisition round. The R-27T is the medium-range IR-homing version of the missile, which comes with IR and SARH (R-27R) guidance. It is believed to have a range of 50 km (31 miles) and was designed for carriage by the MiG-29 and Su-27.

Right: The white-striped aircraft in this formation were part of the 'Republic of Pyrland' 'blue force' during the Operation Eagle's Talon '97 exercise. The MiG-23MF is a 28.PLM aircraft, while the MiG-21bis is from 9.PLM.

Left: This 1.PLM 'Fulcrum-A' (54) was previously 5414, of the Czech air force. The other aircraft transferred to Poland include 38 (previously 3810), 40 (4012), 56 (5616), 59 (5918), 77 (7702), 83 (8304), 86 (8606), 92 (9207) and 28 (4401) – the single MiG-29UB.

Right: This 1.PLM aircraft gained a special scheme based on the stork badges of EC 1/2 'Cigognes', 2ᵉ Escadre de Chasse (EC2), one of the most famous units of France's Armée de l'Air. There is a tradition of co-operation between the two units which dates back to 1993 when Polish pilots travelled to the Dijon home of EC 1/2, at the instigation of the French unit. In 1994, two Mirage 2000Bs visited Minsk-Mazowiecki and reciprocal visits (with aircraft) followed in 1995 and 1996. In June 1997, two MiG-29s and two MiG-29UBs flew to Dijon for a week-long visit. Since 1995 the French and Polish pilots have been conducting intensive air combat exercises during these exchanges. This 'Fulcrum' was painted up for the 1994 visit and a second aircraft (105) also wore a small EC 2 badge below the canopy.

Taiwan
(Republic of China)

In the short time that the Republic of China has been an 'independent nation' it has led a wholly troubled existence. Under permanent siege from mainland China, the Taiwanese have had to face this threat with unpredictable support from fickle allies. A worldwide trend towards *rapprochement* with the Communist People's Republic has increasingly sidelined the island republic, although – conversely – this has not prevented Taiwan's air power assets from growing; they are stronger today than ever before.

When the ancient regime was toppled in 1911, Sun Yat Sen, founder of the Nationalist Party (Kuomintang, or KMT) tried to unite all of China, but failed and resigned after only a few months. His successor, Yuan Shih Kai, tried to install himself as emperor, but died in 1916 as civil war broke out. China degenerated into a collection of feuding warlords, until the Nationalist army under Chiang Kai-shek imposed some degree of central control, re-establishing a government under Sun Yat Sen in 1923, – although warlords in the north remained active and outside the new government's control. Chiang Kai-shek took power in 1925, upon the death of Sun. The relative peace was destined to be short-lived. A nascent revolutionary movement formed behind the tiny Communist Party (former partners of the KMT) and its charismatic leader, Mao Tse Tung; an uprising on 1 August 1927 began a civil war which was to continue for 20 years, and arguably to this day. Japan invaded in 1937, occupying Manchuria and much of China's coastal regions. Internecine warfare was largely suspended during World War II, with both Communist and Nationalist forces fighting (and very occasionally co-operating) against the Japanese invaders. Although never a democrat, Chiang Kai-shek was a benevolent ruler, and was remarkably pro-Western. His struggle against the Japanese began well before the USA entered the war.

Birth of two Chinas

Once World War II was over, the Soviets liberated Manchuria and helped to form and equip the Communist Party's People's Liberation Army. The USA airlifted half a million KMT troops to key ports and cities to forestall a Communist take-over, and seven USMC regiments mounted an amphibious landing at Tientsin to allow the KMT to stabilise the area and disarm the Japanese. The US Marines departed in June 1946. Talks between the Communists and the KMT collapsed and full-scale civil war broke out again. After initial successes, the tide turned against the Nationalist forces, under Chiang Kai-shek, who were unable to use their superior air power. Peking and Tientsin fell in January 1949 and the Nationalists were eventually evicted from the mainland altogether (the latter formally became the Communist People's Republic of

China on 1 October 1949) and formed their own government and virtual nation state on the island of Formosa (or Taiwan) on 1 December 1949. Chiang Kai-shek organised a skillful evacuation, and encompassed in the 1.5 million who moved to Taiwan were 600,000 troops – a formidable army. The number also included China's leading scholars, industrialists and professionals, helping to shape the Taiwan we know today.

Isla Formosa ('Beautiful Island' in Portuguese) had been ceded to Japan in 1895, and had remained in Japanese hands until liberated in 1945. Under Japanese rule, the island was heavily industrialised and the best land was brought under cultivation. The island was restored to Chinese rule on 25 October 1945, still celebrated as Restoration Day. The KMT also retained the fortress islands of Quemoy and Matsu just off the coast of Fukien, near the ports of Amoy and Fuchow, the Pescadores, and also Tachen and Nanchi, evacuated in 1954.

Safe in their fortress, Chiang Kai-shek's forces formed the basis of a pro-Western and rabidly anti-Communist Republic of China, often known as Nationalist China, and sometimes as Taiwan. Chiang Kai-shek was determined not to repeat the failures which had led to the KMT's downfall on the mainland, and instituted a liberal programme of land reform, while dismissing corrupt and inefficient bureaucrats and officials. This 'nation' is small, with only 21 million people, and lies only 100 miles (160 km) off the coast of the mainland. The Communists in Peking claimed, with some justification, to rule the rest of China as a single nation, and made no secret of their wish to recover the missing territories of Taiwan and Hong Kong (one portion of which was a British Crown Colony in perpetuity, with the rest leased until 1997; all of the territory was returned on 1 July 1997). Chiang Kai-shek and his government were equally vehement in their claims to be the rightful rulers of all China, and were equally vocal in stating their intention to reunify the mainland and Formosa under their own leadership. The new state was initially theoretically committed to reunification through military action, though no timescale was specified.

During the Korean War, the possibility of an attempted invasion of mainland China by the Nationalists was sufficient to prompt the USA to send the carrier *Valley Forge* to the area to deter

any such move, which ran the risk of widening the complex conflict in Korea. The initial US attitude toward Taiwan seemed to be that its collapse was inevitable, and not worth trying to prevent. However, as it became increasingly clear that China was offering massive support to the North Koreans, relations between the USA and the Chinese Nationalists warmed. The USA started to consider Taiwan as a valuable bulwark against the spread of Communism in what it perceived as a vulnerable area. A Mutual Assistance Advisory Group was despatched in May 1951 which helped rebuild and re-equip the KMT's armed forces. Within three years, the RoCAF included two wings of F-84Gs, two more equipped with P-47s, one with P-51s, and one with B-25s and B-24s. Taiwan became a base for covert US operations over and around China, and many US spyplanes were shot down in the area.

The two nations competed fiercely for international recognition and legitimacy. The mainland state become the Communist world's favoured China, and Taiwan the recognised China of the West. Until 1971, Taiwan had China's sole seat in the UN, and was one of the five permanent members of the Security Council. Taiwan's leaders refused to seek recognition as an independent state, however, since this would have undermined their claim to the rest of China; this ensured that Sino-Taiwanese relations remained contentious. The refusal by either side to face the realities of history is perhaps best illustrated by the fact that even in 1997, a Taiwanese President was conducting a campaign to end his country's 'inexplicable and untenable' claim to Mongolia.

The Quemoy incident

Tension between the two Chinas intensified throughout the 1950s, finally exploding into a limited war in 1958, after a false start in 1954, when artillery duels between Quemoy and the mainland threatened to get out of control. In 1954, the USA sent warning signals to the Nationalists to 'cool it', dispatching two carriers and an F-86 wing to the area. In July 1958, trouble began when two Nationalist F-84Gs were attacked and downed by four MiG-17s, and this time the USA encouraged the Nationalists to respond. USAF fighters and USN carriers were sent to Taiwan, Japan and the immediate area to provide air defence for Taiwan, and to deter any invasion from the mainland. This freed the Nationalist fighters to go hunting for MiGs, which they did with alacrity, downing 31 MiGs for the loss of two F-86Fs until the fighting ceased in October. The war was fought almost entirely in the air, over the Taiwan Straits. Major air engagements saw the Chinese Nationalists winning a decisive victory over the Communist air force, and marked the first use of the AIM-9 in combat. In 1959 the victory was reinforced when the Nationalists downed five more MiGs, without loss to themselves.

In 1958 the seeds were sown for a complex and organic relationship between the USA and Taiwan. The air defence of Taiwan was shared with Task Force 13 of the USAF's Pacific Air Forces, while USAF and Central Intelligence Agency (CIA) reconnaissance and agent-dropping aircraft used Taiwanese airfields. From 1959, many missions were flown in Taiwanese markings, by Taiwanese pilots, although they were tasked by the CIA and the US military.

Above: The Beech T-34C has replaced the AIDC T-CH-1 at the Air Force Academy.

Below: The AT-3s of the Academy's Fighter Training Group wear this vivid scheme.

Above and below: No. 35 Squadron operates the AT-3(B) Tzu-Chung from Kangshan, alongside the AT-3 trainers of the Basic Training Group.

PEOPLE'S REPUBLIC OF CHINA

PEIKAN (Republic of China)

MATSU (Republic of China)

PAICHUAN LIEHTAO (Republic of China)

QUEMOY (Republic of China)

Straits of Taiwan

Sungshan
Chi Lung
Taipei
(Lungtan) Taoyuan
Hsinchu
Hsinchu

Chin Chuan Kang

Taichung
Changhua
Hsin Cheng
Hualien
Hualien

Chia Yi
Chia Yi

TAIWAN
(Republic of China)

PENGHU LIEHTAO/ Pescadores
(Republic of China)

Tainan
Tainan
Pingtung
Taitung
Kangshan
Kao-hsiung
Pingtung
Taitung
Kao-hsiung

Tung Chiang

South China Sea

Above: A single Boeing 727-109 remains in service with the Sungshan-based VIP unit.

Below: Three Fokker 50s were delivered in 1992, to replace VIP DC-3/C-47s.

Above and right: Twelve Beech 1900C-1s were acquired from 1988 onwards and most are used for transport and training tasks. Two B1900s (above) are used for navaid calibration.

Taiwan remained a pillar of the USA's Cold War strategy in the Far East throughout the 1950s and 1960s, though China's break with Moscow foreshadowed the end of the 'special relationship'. It became increasingly clear that Washington would build bridges with Beijing, and the first fruit of this came when Taiwan was ousted from the UN in October 1971, as mainland China was admitted. Readmission to the UN has remained a Taiwanese foreign policy goal ever since, though it has been unwilling to face the one solution which would have made this easy – recognition that reunification of the two Chinas would not happen. Without formal independence from China, it is difficult for Taiwan to refute the charge that it is merely a renegade Chinese province. Since 1971, therefore, a country of 21 million people, the 14th largest trading nation in the world, lacks a seat in the UN, and has formal diplomatic relations with only 30 countries. Parallel representation within the UN has been allowed before (with East and West Germany and North and South Korea, for instance), but seems unlikely in the case of China and Taiwan.

China's break with Moscow held out the potential promise of improved relations between the USA and the People's Republic, but China's support for North Vietnam prevented this from becoming a reality. Moreover, Taiwan's value as an anti-Communist bulwark was steadily declining as other Asian nations reached maturity as powerful, economically strong, free-market, pro-Western democracies.

US support withers

The end of US involvement in Vietnam removed the penultimate barrier to improved relations between the USA and China. The final barrier, of course, was the USA's close relationship with Taiwan. China's own break with the USSR in the early 1960s, and the replacement of Mao Tse Tung by men who were ostensibly more 'moderate', made China a potentially valuable US ally – well worth the sacrifice of Taiwan. Loyalty to a long-standing Cold War ally could come a poor second to expedience and self-interest. Taiwan's readiness to spend almost 50 per cent of its budget on defence, to strip its own defences to send F-5s to bolster Vietnam and to fly the most dangerous reconnaissance missions over Red China were put aside, and the country was virtually abandoned. CIA/Taiwanese U-2 overflights of the mainland ended in October 1974. Chiang Kai-shek died in 1975 and was succeeded by his son, Chiang Ching-Kuo.

The rise of the wily and chameleon-like Deng Xiao Ping in the PRC was of particular significance, since he was a man who could be seen as being a Communist leader with whom the West could 'do business'. Where the US led, other Western nations followed – some convinced that a reformed Chinese economy would be followed by a more general liberalisation. Others did not care if China became more liberal, and just wanted a share in the Chinese market and in the business opportunities presented by the People's Republic. The British government was by no means alone in barring defence exports to Taiwan, although its refusal to supply Rapier air defence SAMs was among the first such bans.

It soon became clear that a *rapprochement* between Washington and Beijing could, at a single stroke, cut off Taiwan from what had become

its sole source of arms. Taiwan immediately began to establish indigenous defence industries, and began looking elsewhere for military equipment. The Aero Industry Development Centre (AIDC) had originally been formed in 1969, from the Bureau of the Aircraft Industry formed in 1946, and was a subsidiary of the government's Chung Shan Institute of Science and Technology until July 1996 when it was reorganised under the supervision of the Ministry of Economic Affairs, as a first step towards privatisation.

First steps to self-sufficiency

Taiwan's indigenous aircraft industry had previously been limited to production of the Pazmany PL-1 Chiesou, a licence-built elementary/basic trainer based on an American homebuilt. The industry had been established as a means of encouraging economic and industrial development, but, once ties with the US began to loosen, there was a more urgent strategic imperative to produce indigenous combat aircraft. Between 1969 and 1976, AIDC produced 118 Bell UH-1Hs for use by the Chinese Nationalist Army (a handful served with the RoCAF on SAR duties). The next major product of the Taiwanese aircraft industry was the T-CH-1, a turboprop-powered derivative of the North American T-28, a type already in widespread RoCAF service. Some 50 T-CH-1s were built, based on the (armed) XT-CH-1B prototype, which won a competitive evaluation against the unarmed XT-CH-1A. The two prototypes flew on 27 November 1974 and 23 November 1973, respectively, and production aircraft were delivered between 1976 and 1981.

From 1973, AIDC licence-built some 242 F-5Es and 66 F-5Fs, giving the company invaluable experience in modern fast-jet manufacturing methods and techniques, and forging a useful link between AIDC, Northrop and a number of other US aerospace firms. The F-5E programme was accelerated following the US disengagement from Taiwan in 1974, while local content was dramatically stepped up in 1979, when the USA formally cancelled the 1954 mutual defence treaty and reduced official (financial) support for the project. A higher proportion of indigenously manufactured parts and sub-assemblies drove down costs, and gave AIDC more useful experience. By the end, 35 per cent of every AIDC-built F-5E coming off the line was of local origin. F-5E production was followed by development of the AT-3 indigenous jet trainer, 62 of which were delivered between 1982 and 1990.

Change of allegiance

In 1979, the USA disengaged from Taiwan. America switched diplomatic recognition from Taipei to Beijing on 1 January 1979, cancelling the mutual defence agreement with effect on 1 January 1980. As it disengaged, however, the USA did pass the Taiwan Relations Act. This promised that the USA would continue to help Taiwan to maintain a 'sufficient defence capability' and to resist anything that 'jeopardises the security or the social or economic system of the people of Taiwan'. It no longer committed the USA to actively defend Taiwan, however. The implicit promises contained within the act had a hollow ring. The reality of the new US position seemed to be illustrated by the 1982 agreement between the USA and mainland China to diminish arms sales to Taiwan over time, though no strict

timetable was given. The process appeared to be behind the White House's refusal to approve the export of J79 engines, which killed any prospect of Taiwan receiving 48 IAI Kfirs, and behind consistent US refusal to export the F-5G (later F-20) Tigershark or even second-hand F-4E Phantoms. More modern aircraft like the F-16 were specifically barred to Taiwan.

America did allow the export of 103 ex-Luftwaffe F-104Gs and 47 F-104Gs/F-104Js from Denmark and Japan. This allowed the RoCAF to finally retire its obsolete F-100 Super Sabres, bringing one F-104 unit up to full strength and allowing a second to form. It did not represent anything like the modernisation that was required, though, and prompted the development of the indigenous AIDC Ching-Kuo fighter (described in detail in Volume 26 of *World Air Power Journal*). Some US arms deliveries did take place, including the 1984 purchases of 12 C-130H Hercules (for delivery in 1986), and of 14 Sikorsky S-70C-1A helicopters.

Ruthless Chinese suppression of internal opposition and disregard of basic human rights did not cease as the PRC became more economically liberal, as was dramatically demonstrated when tanks crushed a student-led demonstration in Tiananmen Square in 1989. This led to a loosening of economic ties between the USA and China, and even to the imposition of a US arms embargo on 5 June 1989. Some other nations imposed similar embargoes and restrictions on military co-operation. In the light of Tiananmen, China's (unchanged) attitude to Taiwan was once more perceived as unacceptable, and the USA again strengthened its links and warmed its relations with Taipei. Many other nations signalled their disapproval of 'Red China', but were altogether less able to switch their allegiance, since they relied more heavily on the trade which they had built up with the People's Republic.

Increasing recent tensions

Taiwan made some attempts to defuse the tension building between the two Chinas during the 1990s, though such attempts were, in truth, doomed to failure, not least because Taiwan's very existence was a major affront to Chinese national pride, while the growing contrast between an affluent, advanced, liberal and democratic Taiwan and an impoverished, backward authoritarian China did little to reassure Beijing. Nonetheless, Taiwan took many steps to underline its informal, *de facto* recognition of the Communist regime and in May 1991 formally ended the so-called 'Period of National Mobilisation for the Suppression of Communist Rebellion'.

Taiwanese Presidential elections in March 1996 provided a flash point between the two Chinas, and eventually led to increased Western support for Taiwan. The first truly democratic election held in Taiwan, it was bitterly opposed by the mainland government. A democratic election was, perhaps, a threatening example for its own people, but, more significantly, Communist China feared that Taiwanese independence would assume an increasing visibility on the political agenda. It would send 'the wrong message' to some other Chinese possessions, principally Tibet, Xianjing and Mongolia. Independence for Taiwan had also always been bitterly opposed by the Taiwanese Nationalists themselves, most vocally by those who had fled

Detatchments of S-70C-1As 'Bluehawks' are positioned at several locations for SAR duties (above). The fleet is now being repainted (right) and some aircraft have gained prominent Red Cross markings (below right).

Left: The 1st Tactical Fighter Wing is the second wing to transition to the Ching-Kuo.

Above: The F-5s of the Tainan-based 1st TFW will be replaced by Ching-Kuos in 1998.

Left: Two squadrons of F-5s (the 3rd and 9th TFSs) still served with the 1st Fighter Group, 1st TFW in early 1998.

Above: Taiwan's aggressor unit, equipped with F-5E/Fs, uses red 'mainland-style' aircraft codes.

Taiwan's 48 Mirage 2000-5Eis (above and left) are tasked with high-altitude air defence. They are spread among three squadrons (Nos 41, 42 and 48) of the 2nd Tactical Fighter Wing, at Hsinchu AB. A total of 12 Mirage 2000-5Di trainers (above left) has also been ordered.

the mainland in 1949, since they insisted that the two Chinas must be reunified, under Nationalist rule. Some even feared that independence would inevitably mean a return to domination by Japan. By 1996, though, even the youngest army officers from 1949 were in their 60s, and their influence was waning. Among those actually born on Taiwan, there was less of an emotional attachment to the mainland, and a more clear-headed appreciation of the benefits of independence. Significantly, Taiwan's new President, Lee Teng Hui, was himself Taiwan-born. Lee had been appointed in 1988 upon the death of Chiang Ching-Kuo, and was democratically confirmed in office by the elections. While never openly espousing independence (still a dangerously alienating thing for a Taiwanese politician to support), Lee had long pressed for international recognition as a self-governing territory, and for Taiwan to become a member of the UN and other international bodies. Many people with similar political views to the President openly declared that reunification must wait until China had the same democratic, politically liberal, free-market system as Taiwan. Interestingly, Lee's National Party remained committed to eventual reunification in its constitution, and only the opposition Democratic Progressive Party formally supported independence.

Taiwanese independence was feared more on the mainland than was democracy on the island, since the ageing leadership of the PRC was still emotionally committed to reunification of China, and their appetites were already whetted by the preparations for the hand-over of Hong Kong. While Taiwan was a rebel province (albeit one ruled by people with a fanatical ideological hatred of the People's Republic), reunification was regarded as being possible and the existing situation was therefore tolerable. If Taiwan were independent, though, reunification might well become impossible. For many years, China had therefore maintained that it would invade Taiwan if the island declared independence.

With Lee's calls for international recognition (even though they stopped short of calls for independence), China became increasingly edgy. His private visit to the USA in 1995 further incensed the mainland leaders, who suspended dialogue with Taiwan. Threats of invasion became less veiled, while the possible justification for such an invasion changed from the threat of independence to 'chaos' on the island, or even to the 'fact' that Taiwanese politicians risked 'splitting the motherland'.

A real and growing threat

In the long run-up to the 1996 elections, China made every effort to intimidate the Taiwanese. Fujian province opposite Taiwan was declared a 'war zone' and massive exercises (including amphibious landings) were staged with great publicity. Missile firings were made into the Taiwan Straits, ominously close to the island. In March 1996 (the month of the election) firings were made against targets near Taiwan's main ports, Keelung and Kao-hsiung, within 20 miles (32 km) of the coast. The missiles fired were Dong Feng (East Wind) DF-15s, which carry a 500-kg (1,100-lb) warhead over a range of about 600 km (370 miles). Many experts believe the weapon cannot be reliably intercepted by missiles like Patriot.

This all had the effect of eroding the morale of the Taiwanese people and creating something of a climate of fear, in which some people were almost certainly dissuaded from voting for candidates whose line on independence was held to be 'too provocative'. Taiwan's stock market prices tumbled, as did the price of property and real estate on the island. Remarkably, the missile tests proved to be a step too far: stock prices rallied, while Keelung and Kao-hsiung became tourist destinations.

When it was most crucial, America failed to deter China strongly, adopting instead what was called a policy of 'strategic ambiguity', reminding Beijing that any attempt to reunify by force would be viewed with 'grave concern' but failing to state how that concern might be expressed. With President Clinton's perceived weakness and vacillation, this stance was hardly reassuring to the Taiwanese, nor was it necessarily a strong enough threat to the Chinese Communists. It was a serious error, since the danger of escalation was very real. While the US Navy amassed the largest fleet seen in the area since the Vietnam War (battlegroups based around the carriers *Independence* and *Nimitz*), junior Chinese officials told American counterparts that China would "attack Los Angeles with nuclear bombs" if the USA actively defended Taiwan. It was soon made clear that this was not official policy, fortunately.

In the end, however, China did not attempt an invasion. Some sources suggest that even without US help, such an invasion would have been prohibitively costly (if not actually doomed to failure). This is believed to have been the view of the Pentagon. A more real risk was that China would mount missile attacks against Taiwan's petrochemical industry, or that it would blockade the island, though fortunately these options were not exercised. Instead, the election of Lee (who gained 54 per cent of the vote, on a 72 per cent turnout) led only to a brief increase in the torrent of hostile rhetoric, and to a raised military posture on both sides of the Taiwan Straits.

The conclusion of the 1996 crisis marks only a breathing space for Taiwan, and the situation remains dangerous. China's long-held views have not been changed. Even as recently as 1995, China's President stated, "The peaceful reunification of the two sides of the Taiwan Straits is the unshakeable determination of the entire Chinese people. However, one cannot rule out the military option." An invasion of Taiwan by mainland forces would be inevitable if the People's Republic felt that it could do so without prohibitive cost, and without too severe an international reaction. For the time being, the USA is again a useful ally, but one which cannot be relied upon, and one which may again vanish when the memories of Tiananmen Square fade. This forces Taiwan to maintain strong and independent defences.

In the long term, invasion may become less of a threat. It is clear that China's naval superiority allows it to operate virtually unimpeded, and China could probably already impose a loose blockade of Taiwan. Future plans will increase Chinese capabilities in this area; simultaneously, China will become ever more capable of mounting strategic strikes against Taiwanese targets, by missile or by manned aircraft. The change of regime in South Africa has revealed that Taiwan did not receive nuclear weapons from the Apartheid regime, which makes 'nuclear blackmail' by the PRC more likely. Taiwan will be forced to continuously upgrade its defensive capabilities in the light of the emerging threats.

Jon Lake

Republic of China Air Force/Chung Kuo Kung Chuan

The Chinese Nationalist Air Force was generously equipped with a range of USAAF aircraft types during World War II, including P-51 Mustangs, P-40 Warhawks, P-47 Thunderbolts and even B-25 Mitchell and B-24 Liberator bombers. Many of them escaped to Taiwan when the Nationalists finally lost their toe-hold on the mainland.

Today the Taiwanese air force is almost entirely defensive in character, with only limited air-to-ground capabilities, sufficient to allow CAS/BAI operations in support of troops defending the country against invasion, and perhaps with the most limited ability to mount retaliatory or nuisance raids against coastal targets. To a certain extent this concentration on maintaining a defensive posture is merely realism. It would be quite impossible for a nation as small as Taiwan to mount any meaningful interdiction or strategic air campaign against mainland China, whereas it can realistically expect to be able to provide air defences sufficient to impose a heavy cost on any attacker.

Front-line ethos

Perhaps predictably enough, Taiwan's air force (the Republic of China Air Force/RoCAF) is commanded by a former fighter pilot, General Huang Hsien Yung, who has stated, "Our strategy is entirely defensive. Our mission is to intercept enemy aircraft." The vital importance of the fighter role is illustrated by the fact that the air force maintains a dedicated aggressor/adversary unit, regards one wing as a 'fighter weapons school' and has a Cubic ACMI (air combat manoeuvring instrumentation) range for high value air combat training. Heavy emphasis is placed on realistic training, and the RoCAF flies more live air-to-air gunnery sorties than many equivalent air arms.

The air force is organised along USAF lines, with a Combat Air Command looking after manned aircraft, an Air Defence Artillery Command and a Logistics Command. The air force has eight front-line wings based at eight major hardened air bases, with a training unit at a ninth similar airfield. Five of the wings are designated as Tactical Fighter Wings, one as a Composite Tactical Fighter Wing, one as a TFW/Tactical Training and Development Centre, and one as a Troop Carrier and Anti-Submarine Combined Wing. A Tactical Control Wing administers the Hughes Skynet air defence ground environment, into which the Hawkeyes are now integrated.

Above: No. 12 Sqn is the last operator of the AIDC R-CH-1 in RoCAF service. The R-CH-1s are based at Taoyuan.

Right: The Mirage 2000-5s of the 11th Fighter Group, 2nd TFW share their base with a detachment of No. 12 Sqn.

Above and right: No. 12 Sqn is Taiwan's last Starfighter unit. Its TF/F-104Gs are based at Hsinchu AB. At least two examples are capable of carrying the 'Stargazer' LOROP reconnaissance system in a (removable) extended nose.

Taiwan's first Ching-Kuo squadron was No. 7 'Wolf' TFS (above) of the 3rd FG, 3rd TFW, which transitioned from the F-104 in 1993. The second was No. 8 'Dragon' TFS (below).

Above: The 3rd TFW is based at Chin Chuan Kang AB. Unusually among RoCAF units, its Ching-Kuos all carry toned-down, but still clearly visible, squadron badges.

Below: This Ching-Kuo belongs to No. 28 Sqn, which converted to the type in 1995/96. Note the nose badge.

Above: The sudden approval of F-16 sales to Taiwan immediately cut short the AIDC Ching-Kuo production run, and was seen by some as a clever ploy by the USA to remove a potential competitor from the market.

Although planned production totals have been cut by approximately 50 per cent, the AIDC Ching-Kuo IDF (Indigenous Defensive Fighter) continues to be regarded as being of vital importance. Minor teething troubles have now been overcome, though some aspects of its performance have proved disappointing. Under present plans the aircraft will equip two fighter wings (the 3rd TFW at Chin Chuan Kang and the 1st at Tainan). The 3rd TFW has completed its re-equipment with the aircraft, with No. 28 Squadron being declared operational on 22 November 1995.

With re-equipment of the 3rd TFW complete, the next unit to transition to the IDF was the 1st TFW at Tainan. The first of the wing's three units (No. 1 Squadron) commissioned in March 1997. When the wing completes its re-equipment, production of the Ching-Kuo will almost certainly end (at 130 aircraft, including 28 two-seaters). This is well short of the 256 (or even 420) once envisaged, though the total may be increased if current AIDC proposals to produce a dedicated advanced flying training and lead-in fighter training variant are accepted. This aircraft would lack gun, radar and ECM. The Ching-Kuo does have some unique capabilities, though, since it is the only fighter in the RoCAF inventory with an active radar homing missile, in the shape of the Taiwanese-designed and -built Tien Chien (Sky Sword) 2. The aircraft will also have a significant air-to-ground commitment, using a wide range of weapons.

F-16 acquisition

Planned IDF production was cut back when Taiwan gained a one-off opportunity to conclude a $5.8 billion deal to procure 150 F100-PW-220-engined F-16s. Taiwan had long sought F-16s, and a deal had first been put together by the Reagan administration. It was not finally approved until 1992 under President Bush, reportedly after Taiwan was offered 50 MiG-29s by Russia, including some aircraft ordered by Iraq before the Gulf War, and available at between $5 million and $7 million each. The decision to allow the export of F-16s came less than a year after the USA had finally relented sufficiently to clear the export of J79 engines. This had revived the prospects of an Israeli export of 40 IAI Kfirs to Taiwan, though this arrangement (which took 10 years to clear) was abandoned when it became clear that F-16s would be delivered.

The Taiwanese Fighting Falcons comprise 130 single-seat F-16As and 30 two-seat F-16Bs, with a number of AIM-7 missiles and Raytheon AN/ALQ-183 ECM pods. Although nominally F-16As, the Taiwanese aircraft are more capable than their designation might suggest, and are in some respects the most advanced Fighting Falcons ever exported. They are Block 20 F-16As, fitted with the APG-66(V)3 radar (even more advanced than the (V)2A radar of NATO MLU Block 20 F-16s), and have a wide-angle HUD, a digital TRNS, GPS, an NVG-compatible cockpit and a new modular mission computer. Their weakness lies in the armament with which they were supplied, and repeated Taiwanese attempts to procure AIM-120 AMRAAMs have so far been unsuccessful. The 1992 deal included a $600 million offset agreement which included the establishment of an F-16 maintenance and over-haul facility. A $40 million offset production

contract included local production of F-16 air inlets, engine access doors, ventral fins, centreline and underwing fuel tank pylons, and AIM-9 launcher rails (LAUs).

By the end of 1997 the first F-16s had virtually replaced the F-5Es hitherto serving with the three squadrons of the 4th TFW at Chiayi (Nos 21, 22 and 23 Squadrons) – initial deliveries were made to the base in April 1997. The next batch of new aircraft will re-equip the 8th TFW at Hualien. This unit currently includes one squadron equipped with a mix of F-5Es, F-5Bs and F-5Fs (No. 16 Squadron, the F-5 OCU) and two squadrons equipped (since 1994) with 40 T-38s leased from the USAF to cover a shortage of F-5Es, pending the delivery of the F-16s.

Mirages from France

Shortly after signing the F-16 contract, Taiwan also signed a $3.8 billion deal for the supply of Mirage 2000 fighters on 17 November 1992, although the deal was not announced until after the US election, in order to avoid embarrassing President Bush. Taiwanese interest in the Mirage 2000 had begun some time before, but had been interpreted by many as a clever ploy to nudge the USA into agreeing to F-16 exports. Whereas most air arms fight hard to standardise on a single aircraft type for a single role, the possible impact of sanctions makes the RoCAF keen to diversify. The Taiwanese sale was a welcome one for Dassault, since it followed a dry period of four years without an export order for a military aircraft, and immediately followed the selection of the F/A-18 in both Finland and Switzerland – both of whom Dassault had seen as likely customers.

This sales hiatus allowed Taiwan to extract favourable terms from Dassault, including a 20 per cent cut in the originally quoted unit price ($54 million per aircraft) and a guarantee of spares support for 25 years. The contract specified the delivery of 48 Mirage 2000-5Ei single-seaters and 12 Mirage 2000-5Di two-seat trainers, and included the supply of 400 Magic 2 and (more importantly) 960 MICA missiles. Taiwan actually received its first MICAs before the Armée de l'Air did. The aircraft themselves were of the advanced Mirage 2000-5 version, with RDY radar, a new onboard CPU and an integrated ECM suite. Each aircraft is powered by an uprated 97.8-kN (22,000-lb) M53 P20 turbofan. An Armée de l'Air Mirage 2000 squadron reportedly deployed to Taiwan during 1992 for ground and aircrew familiarisation; this marked the high point of Franco-Taiwanese co-operation, and, although the Mirage 2000 contract was honoured, Chinese opposition and retaliation ensured that it remained a one-off (potential orders by Chinese airlines for large fleets of Airbus airliners were enough to turn French attention away from Taiwan, though the same can equally be said of the USA and Boeing). Pending delivery of the RDY radar-equipped aircraft, Taiwan pressed for the lease or purchase of 20 second-hand Mirage 2000s as interim equipment, but even this request was eventually denied, despite support from France's Defence Minister, François Leotard.

In 1996 Taiwan finally concluded a $700 million offset agreement with Dassault (set at one-third of the purchase price). Under this agreement Dassault will transfer technology to AIDC, buy Taiwanese components and invest in Taiwan's semiconductor industry.

In Taiwanese service, the Mirage 2000 is replacing the fighter-tasked F-104s of the 2nd TFW at Hsinchu. For some years, the 2nd TFW has been operating at reduced strength, with two of the three squadrons inactive, and with many of the F-104s maintained as a war reserve. By 1996, only No. 42 Squadron was operational, with Nos 41 and 48 apparently non-operational. Ten Mirage 2000s had been delivered by mid-1997, but by the end of that year all three squadrons were operational (to some degree) with the Mirage 2000.

The almost simultaneous introduction of three front-line fighter types has not been easy, and has imposed some training and logistics challenges. It has also allowed the air force to deploy the aircraft to suit their optimum role, so the Mirage 2000s are primarily responsible for high-altitude long-range air defence, the AIDC Ching-Kuos for low- and medium-level air defence, and the F-16s for medium-level air defence and other tactical fighter missions. All three fighter types are equipped with modern BVR missiles, and all are superior to the PLA Air Force's current fighters, including its first generation 'Flankers'. All three types also have a very real air-to-ground capability, and the air force has an effective anti-ship capability using indigenously developed weapons and perhaps US-supplied AGM-84 Harpoons.

Taiwan's ASMs

In addition to the air-to-air missiles it has developed for the RoCAF (Tien Chien/Sky Sword 1 and 2), Taiwan's Chung Shan Institute of Science and Technology has developed a family of air-launched anti-ship missiles. Named Hsiung Feng (Male Bee) the latest version of this weapon is the Hsiung Feng 2, a turbofan-powered, inertial-/active radar-/IIR-guided missile, with a 225-kg (496-lb) HE armour-piercing warhead and a range of 80 km (50 miles). Hsiung Feng 2 closely resembles the US-built AGM-84 Harpoon, but it has a prominent IIR sensor fairing mounted above the missile, behind the warhead. The missile is believed to be operational, since 1996, with the Ching-Kuo, and perhaps also on the AT-3B. A ship-launched version has been in service since 1993 and an extended range Hsiung Feng 2 is believed to be under development.

The status of deliveries of air-launched Harpoons is uncertain. The US is known to have supplied only ship-launched RGM-84A missiles, for the Navy's 'Knox'-class frigates. However, some photographic evidence exists for Harpoon missiles marked as AGM-84s, on show alongside aircraft.

The last Starfighters

By the end of 1997, single squadrons of Mirage 2000s and F-16s were in full service, and it is expected that deliveries will be completed during 1999. This will leave all five of the air force's front-line fighter/composite wings equipped with modern fourth-generation fighters, with F-16s at Chia Yi and Hualien, Mirage 2000s at Hsinchu, and IDFs at Chin Chuan Kang and Tainan. F-5Es and RF-5Es will be based at Tao Yuan and Taitung. For many years, Taiwan's principal reconnaissance platform has been the RF-104G 'Stargazer', an extremely unusual conversion of the Starfighter which carried a Loral K-72 LOROP camera in an extended nose, with the covered aperture for the periscopic lens facing to

Above, below and right: Block 20 F-16A/Bs are now entering service with Nos 21, 22 and 23 TFSs, 4th FG, 4th TFW, based at Hsinchu AB. Deliveries to Taiwan began in April 1997.

Right and below: As the F-16 rapidly enters service with the 4th TFW at Chia Yi, that unit's remaining F-5E/Fs are being withdrawn. This process should be completed in early 1998.

Above and right: Three squadrons of upgraded 'Tiger 4'-standard F-5E/Fs (the 17th, 26th and 27th TFSs) will remain in service with the 5th FG, 5th TFW, at Taoyuan AB.

Above: Taiwan took delivery of 20 C-130Hs in 1986 and has an urgent need for a similar number of additional aircraft. At least one C-130H serves on Elint/Sigint duties, with No. 78 Sqn.

Above and right: The RoCAF's main transport assets are based at Pingtung, with the 6th Troop Carrier and Anti-Submarine Combined Wing. The 101st and 102nd TCSs operate the C-130H. A handful of C-119Ls soldiered on until December 1997.

port immediately ahead of the cockpit. The camera nose could be replaced by a shorter standard radar nose for training. It is believed that six F-104s and three TF-104s were 'Stargazer-capable'.

Taiwan finally began retiring its ageing Starfighters from late 1997 (a process to be completed in 1998), and is replacing these aircraft with seven surplus F-5Es converted to RF-5E Tigereye configuration by Singapore Aerospace. The programme was delayed for 18 months by AIDC's objections that the work was not being conducted in-country, but Singapore's bid was both cheap and credible, as a result of that company's previous experience producing RF-5Es for the Republic of Singapore Air Force. The new RF-5Es may only be an interim replacement for the RF-104s, and some sources suggest that a number of the F-16s may be delivered with a reconnaissance capability. Although nominally part of the 5th Composite Wing at Tao Yuan, No. 12 Squadron was actually based at Hsinchu, alongside the air defence Starfighters of the 2nd TFW, though it may move back to one of the F-5 wings when RF-5E conversion is complete.

Upgraded F-5 force

Re-equipment of the RoCAF proceeded apace during the 1990s. Those F-5Es not being replaced by AIDC Ching-Kuos, Lockheed Martin F-16s and Mirage 2000s (about 90 of the 284 built by AIDC) will be upgraded by AIDC. A previous upgrade undertaken by AIDC dramatically improved the F-5E's ground attack capability, with provision for AGM-65 Maverick ASMs and GBU-12 LGBs, and other operational improvements. The new upgrade will give the F-5s a new GEC HUD, APG-66 radar and HOTAS controls, with an avionics upgrade which will give maximum commonality with the air force's new F-16 fighters. This will allow the type to assume a useful role as a lead-in trainer for the F-16, while also fulfilling a front-line air defence and ground attack role. The type will also continue to operate in the adversary training role. The prototype 'Tiger 4' is due to fly for the first time by the end of 1998. Units continuing to operate the F-5E will be the 5th TFW at Tao Yuan (with Nos 17, 26 and 27 Squadrons) and the 7th TFW/TT&DC (Tactical Training and Development Centre) at Taitung. Other F-5E-equipped units are already converting to other aircraft types: the 1st TFW to the Ching-Kuo, and the 4th and 8th TFWs to the F-16. Plans for a more ambitious upgrade, with a new engine, appear to have been dropped.

China's sabre-rattling in 1995 and 1996 appears to have partially strengthened the resolve of Taiwan's few friends. The French had been deterred from supplying further Mirage 2000s by Chinese threats about trade and economic retaliation, and Jacques Chirac and the French government gave China reassurances that it would sell no more arms to Taiwan. The ban has not been lifted by the new Socialist government of Lionel Jospin, although Dassault clearly feels that further sales are again possible in the long term, and is understood to be actively marketing the Rafale to the Taiwanese.

Any new fifth-generation fighter (which will be a follow-on to the Ching-Kuo, F-16 and Mirage 2000) will almost certainly be imported, since it is thought that AIDC lacks the resources or the capability to produce an indigenous aircraft

of sufficient performance and capability. Difficulties with the Ching-Kuo have been overstated, but the fact remains that the aircraft represents a very expensive way of obtaining an F-16 level of capability. Taiwan had little alternative at the time, but foreign combat aircraft can now be obtained more easily on the open market.

Taiwan's interest is believed to be focused on the Rafale, Eurofighter and a possible FMS version of the F-22, though any foreign supplier of combat aircraft to Taiwan must face the real threat of objections and economic retaliation from mainland China. This may force Taiwan to acquire a less-than-ideal foreign aircraft from a supplier with less to lose, or to design another indigenous aircraft.

Tranport requirements

Arguably the most pressing requirement facing the RoCAF is the need for a new tactical transport aircraft. At least 18 are required to replace the last survivors of Taiwan's fleet of Fairchild C-119Ls, whose serviceability had become severely constrained by the poor availability of spares. The RoCAF finally withdrew the last of its C-119s in December 1997. Only one C-119 squadron (No. 103) remained, with No. 101 having converted to the C-130 in 1986, and No. 102 in 1993. Taiwan requires an aircraft that has a rear loading ramp (for paradrops and low-level cargo dropping), and a degree of rough-field/STOL capability. Front-runners to meet the requirement are the CN.235-300 and the AE2100-engined C-27J, with the ATR 52C being viewed as an outside contender. Interestingly, these three types have been shortlisted by Australia to meet the RAAF requirement for a Caribou replacement. The small number of aircraft required by Taiwan precludes local assembly, but a degree of local industrial participation is expected, perhaps including the manufacture of components or even of sub-assemblies (e.g., the empennage). Funding is expected in FY99, delayed by a year because of fighter procurement and the need to acquire a long-range VIP aircraft. The shortage of funding may eventually lead to the acquisition of second-hand C-130s, giving the RoCAF tactical transport force a single operational type. More Hercules are required in any case, since the 20 aircraft delivered (19 of which are used in the transport role) are insufficient even for the two existing C-130 units to operate at full strength. It is more likely, though, that the choice of tactical transport may be influenced by the resolution of the RoCAF's requirement for a new ASW and maritime patrol aircraft, described below.

AEW assets

The 6th Troop Carrier and Anti-Submarine Combined Wing also incorporates a single Electronic Warfare and Airborne Early Warfare Squadron (this unit has also been reported in some sources as No. 78 Squadron, but the EW&AEW title is still believed to be accurate). It is equipped with a single EW/Elint-configured Lockheed C-130H (delivered 'green' and equipped by AIDC) and four Grumman E-2T Hawkeyes. Although the E-2Ts began life as E-2Bs recovered from the USAF's 'boneyard' in Arizona, they were comprehensively refurbished before delivery and brought up to the same standard as the US Navy's current E-2Cs. They

were delivered by September 1995 and fulfil a vital airborne early warning and sea surveillance role. It was said that the arrival of the E-2T raised the 'warning of hostile air attack' time available to Taiwan from five to 25 minutes. Some sources suggest that Taiwan ordered eight E-2s, and that a second batch of four will soon be delivered.

The RoCAF did operate at least eight Elint/EW training/calibration-configured C-47s, and two Elint/Sigint C-54s. The last two C-47s in service have now been replaced by two Beech 1900Cs in the airfield/navaid calibration role.

The RoCAF's remaining transport aircraft are based at Sungshan, close to the island's capital of Taipei. The VIP Squadron of the Sungshan Air Base Command is currently undergoing major changes: its long-serving Presidential Boeing 720 and VIP C-47s have been retired and partially replaced by three Fokker 50s. Only one (of two) Boeing 727s remain in use, primarily used for resupplying the garrison on the island of Quemoy. A long-range Presidential aircraft is urgently required, with a new-generation Boeing 737 or 757 apparently being the most favoured option.

SAR helicopters

As an island nation, Taiwan has always placed heavy emphasis on SAR capabilities. In days gone by, the nation operated Grumman HU-16 Albatross amphibians, and was an early recipient of Sikorsky S-51s, S-55s (H-19s) and locally built HH-1Hs. These types were eventually replaced by Sikorsky S-70C-1A Blue Hawks. The Blue Hawk was basically a UH-60A, equipped with a rescue winch, similar to the USAF's HH-60As but without folding stabilators or an inflight-refuelling capability. Two of the 14 Blue Hawks delivered are maintained on detachment at Sungshan, where they operate in the SAR role while maintaining a VIP transport capability. This helps to explain the type's very smart (but relatively inconspicuous) colour scheme.

Another pressing requirement facing Taiwan is the need for a modern defensive missile system able to defeat the threat posed by Chinese M-9 and M-11 tactical ballistic missiles and newer systems. The Republic of China Army has taken delivery of Raytheon Patriot PAC-2 missiles, but they can only detect incoming missiles when they re-enter the atmosphere, leaving too little time to guarantee interception if incoming missiles are launched in very large numbers. The Patriots supplement army-operated Hawk SAMs and short-range MATRA Mistrals. Taiwan's indigenous Sky Bow missile is optimised as an anti-aircraft weapon, rather than for use against missiles. A further worry for Taiwan is the reported development of a precision attack version of the C-802 SSM, using GPS-based navigation systems accurate enough to attack targets like the Taiwanese Presidential Palace. This might well be air launched by China's new Xian B-7 fighter-bombers. At the moment, China's missile capabilities provide it with an excellent tool for low-level harassment of its neighbour, against which Taiwan can do little.

Taiwan is similarly powerless to prevent Chinese naval (and particularly submarine) operations in the area. Despite the conversion of Taiwan's S-2 Trackers to turboprop power during 1991, the aircraft has proved largely (and increasingly) inadequate, and a replacement is urgently sought. For the time being, though, the

Above and right: The 33rd and 34th Anti-Submarine Squadrons of the 6th TC&ASCW operate the S-2T from Pingtung AB. A replacement for the elderly Trackers is urgently needed.

Above, below and right: Taiwan's secretive E-2Ts are operated by No. 78 Sqn, which is attached to the Maritime Group of the 6th TC&ASCW. An Elint-configured C-130H is also operated by No. 78 Sqn, and one squadron shoulder badge shows outlines of the E-2 and C-130 superimposed.

Below and right: The three F-5 squadrons of the 7th TFW, based at Taitung, will be upgraded and will continue to provide a fighter weapons school and a dedicated aggressor unit.

Above and right: The 8th TFW, based at Hualien AB, is scheduled to be the next wing to transition to the F-16. It is currently equipped with T-38s and F-5E/Fs (as seen here).

1,645-shp (2205-kW) Garrett TPE331-1-5AW-powered S-2T TurboTracker remains in front-line use. Some 32 S-2Fs and S-2Gs (S-2As and S-2E having already been retired) were ear-marked for upgrade to the new standard by Grumman under a $260 million limited FMS contract. However, only 22 conversions are believed to have been undertaken as the programme became mired in a procurement scandal. Some reports have suggested that the anti-submarine and maritime patrol role will soon be entirely handed over to the navy, but this is not yet the case. Rotary-winged ASW capability is in the hands of the navy; the S-2Ts serve with the air force's 6th TC&ASCW at Pingtung, alongside that service's transports, AEW aircraft and Elint platform. It is felt that a larger platform, with longer-range sensors, more payload, longer range

and more operators is essential to cope with the threat posed by China's large and sophisticated navy. The Taiwanese have repeatedly requested the supply of P-3C Orions (having used P-3As for clandestine reconnaissance missions during the 1960s), but these requests have habitually been rebuffed. If P-3Cs continue to be denied, alternative maritime reconnaissance platforms could include the CN235MPA or the proposed maritime derivative of the C-27J.

Training programme

The Taiwanese aircrew training centre has undergone dramatic changes since the US disengagement, although, ironically, these changes have seen the wholesale withdrawal of two indigenous aircraft types and the introduction of (mainly US-built) new aircraft types. Five surviving

Pazmany PL-1s of the Flying Cadet School were sold to a US dealer in 1982, and have been replaced by a number of microlight aircraft to maintain that portion of the flying training syllabus. Under this, aircrew trainees transfer to basic flying training only after elementary training and screening on the new microlights. From 1984 the indigenous T-CH-1 trainer began to be replaced by 40 Beech T-34C Turbo Mentors. Reversing the trend away from indigenous aircraft types was the replacement of the T-33 by the AIDC AT-3 from 1985.

Taiwan's national aerobatic team, the 'Thunder Tigers' Air Demonstration Team, had always been provided by the 1st TFW (443rd TFW) with F-86Fs and F-5s, but, with the introduction of the indigenous AT-3, responsibility for the team passed to the Air Academy. All Academy AT-3s are now painted in the team's spectacular red, white and blue livery.

The AT-3 was always intended to have a front-line capability, and was designed as a potential replacement for the F-5E in the ground attack role. In fact, production of the type was limited, and only the last 18 aircraft were delivered in camouflage colours to No. 35 Squadron, for use in the ground attack and night attack training roles. There is some confusion as to the exact status of these aircraft, which are sometimes referred to as AT-3Bs and occasionally credited with having AN/APG-66 radar installed. Other sources suggest that the AT-3B designation refers only to a single prototype aircraft which incorporates the avionics developed for the single-seat A-3 Lui Meng, and that No. 35 Squadron's aircraft differ only in minor detail to the training aircraft. The A-3 Lui Meng was a single-seat attack derivative of the AT-3 (at times referred to as the AT-3A) with built-in cannon and a nose-mounted radar. Two prototypes were produced (from new) but the programme appears to have been suspended. Fuelling the controversy, some pilots at No. 35 Squadron wear a badge with an AT-3 silhouette and the legend 'AT-3B', which would indicate a distinct version/capability.

Pilots not destined for front-line fast jets transition from the T-34C or AT-3 to the Transport Training Group. This unit finally replaced its last five ageing DC-3/C-47s in January 1996, using the Raytheon Beech 1900Cs which had replaced the DC-3/C-47 in the light transport role. The surviving Beech 1900s (11 of 12 delivered) all belong to the VIP transport unit but one is flown each day to the Air Academy for multi-engine training tasks, returning to Sunshan each evening.

The Taiwanese training requirement is significant, since the air force has to at least maintain its present strength of 1,000 pilots, while retention (in the face of a booming civil sector) is not easy. Accordingly, the RoCAF recruits all officers as potential fast-jet pilots, and all officers undergo a four-year academic course at the Academy, with flying aptitude tests in the first year, and flying training beginning in the fourth year. The basic phase lasts six months and includes some 80 flying hours, with advanced flying training taking another six months and including 120 flying hours. Those not selected for aircrew complete further specialised training to become engineers, fighter controllers, intelligence officers and logisticians. Taiwan does recruit a limited number of female aircrew, but they are limited to second-line duties, including instruction.

Republic of China Air Force (Chung Kuo Kung Chuan)

Air Force Academy, Kangshan

Basic Training Group	Beech T-34C (40)	
Fighter Training Group	AIDC AT-3 (40)	
Transport Training Group	Beech 1900C (1, detached from Sungshan)	

No. 35 Squadron	AIDC AT-3 (12)

No. 35 Squadron is not formally part of the Academy but is now used for advanced training tasks, and is based at Kangshan to allow centralised servicing of its AT-3s with those of the Academy. It was previously based at Hsinchu and briefly Chin Chuan Kang.

Sungshan Air Base Command, Sungshan

VIP Transport Squadron	Boeing 727 (1+1 wfu)	VIP/resupply
	Fokker 50 (3)	VIP
	Beech 1900 (?)	VIP
SAR detachment	Sikorsky S-70C-1A (2)	SAR

1st Tactical Fighter Wing (443rd TFW), Tainan

1st Fighter Group

1st TFS	AIDC Ching-Kuo (converting)	
3rd TFS	F-5E/Ching-Kuo (converting)	tactical fighter
9th TFS	F-5E/Ching-Kuo (converting)	tactical fighter

No. 71 Squadron, equipped with approximately 15 AIDC A-CH-1s for FAC/patrol duties, has been disbanded and the aircraft withdrawn from use. The 1st TFW is undergoing conversion to the Ching-Kuo. When complete, the FAC role may transfer to an F-5E/F-16 wing, as these types will have a heavier ground attack commitment.

2nd Tactical Fighter Wing (499th TFW), Hsinchu

11th Fighter Group

12th Squadron	Lockheed TF/F-104G/J (c. 18)	fighter/OCU
41st TFS	Dassault Mirage 2000-5	
42nd TFS	Dassault Mirage 2000-5 (converting)	
48th TFS	Dassault Mirage 2000-5 (converting)	

The 2nd TFW is undergoing conversion to the Mirage 2000, and will build up to a strength of 20 aircraft per squadron, including in-use reserves. Large numbers of F-104s remain in storage as a war reserve, but will almost certainly be entirely withdrawn when Mirage conversion is complete.

3rd Tactical Fighter Wing (427th TFW, 30th TFW), Chin Chuan Kang

3rd Fighter Group

7th 'Wolf' TFS	AIDC Ching-Kuo (18)	fighter (OCU)
8th 'Dragon' TFS	AIDC Ching-Kuo (18)	tactical fighter
28th TFS	AIDC Ching-Kuo (18)	tactical fighter

4th Tactical Fighter Wing (455th TFW), Chia Yi

4th Fighter Group

21st TFS	Lockheed F-16A/B (converting)	
22nd TFS	F-5E/F-16A/B (converting)	tactical fighter
23rd TFS	F-5E/F-16A/B (converting)	tactical fighter
Rescue Squadron	Sikorsky S-70C-1A (12)	SAR

The rescue squadron maintains a two-aircraft detachment at Sungshan.

5th Tactical Fighter Wing (401st TFW), Taoyuan

5th Fighter Group

17th TFS	Northrop F-5E (18)	tactical fighter
26th 'Witch' TFS	Northrop F-5E (18)	tactical fighter
27th 'Go-Dragon' TFS	Northrop F-5E (18)	tactical fighter

No. 12 Squadron (det)	AIDC R-CH-1 (c. 6)	recce, coastal patrol

Taoyuan is the military enclave of Taipei's Chiang Kai-shek airport, but is set apart with its own runway and facilities. This wing may gain the newly-converted RF-5Es.

6th Troop Carrier and Anti-Submarine Combined Wing (439th TC&ASCW), Pingtung

10th Transport Group

101st TCS	Lockheed C-130H (10)	transport
102nd TCS	Lockheed C-130H (9)	transport
103rd TCS	Fairchild C-119L (4)	WFU December 1997

Maritime Group

33rd ASS	Grumman S-2T Tracker (11)	ASW/patrol
34th ASS	Grumman S-2T Tracker (11)	ASW/patrol

No. 78 Squadron	Lockheed C-130H (1)	Elint
	Grumman E-2T (4)	AEW

7th Tactical Fighter Wing (737th TFW), Taitung

7th Fighter Group/RoCAF Fighter Weapons School

44th TFS	Northrop F-5E (18)	tactical fighter
45th TFS	Northrop F-5E (18)	tactical fighter
46th 'Red Flag' TFTS	Northrop F-5E (18)	aggressor

The 44th and 45th TFS are both operational conversion units.

8th Tactical Fighter Wing (828th TFW), Hualien

8th Fighter Group

No. 14 Squadron	Northrop T-38 (20)	fighter pool
14th TFS (designate)	F-16A/B	(converting)
No. 15 Squadron	Northrop T-38 (20)	fighter pool
16th TFTS	Northrop F-5E/F (12, 12)	OCU

The T-38-equipped squadrons have been used for maintaining a pool of trained fast-jet pilots, prior to the introduction of the F-16. The wing is undergoing conversion to the F-16. When complete, the F-5 OCU role will pass to the 7th TFW. The last (six) F-5Bs in service with the 16th TFTS have been withdrawn.

US-style squadron and wing role designators are used occasionally, and are given in the table above, though use of simple numerical titles is equally common. Each wing has had an alternative identity, intended to mask its actual designation and thereby complicate the task of assessing air force strength. These three-digit numbers all added up to the 'real' numerical designation, or to 10 more than the real designation. Such designations are believed to have fallen into disuse and in recent times were only routinely used by non-operational arms of the RoCAF, such as the museum. Each wing has at least one constituent group concerned with aircraft operations. It is believed that those wings with more than one role may have more than one such group, but this cannot be confirmed.

In 1989/1990 the RoCAF roundel changed to take account of the revised political situation in Taiwan. Prior to that time, the star in the roundel reached to the edge of the blue circle, signifying the extent of the ruling party's power. When Taiwan permitted the establishment of opposition political parties, the armed forces decided to reduce the extent of the star.

Left and above: Forty T-38s serve with two squadrons of the 8th TFW, but they will soon be replaced by F-16s.

One of the last units to operate the A-CH-1 was No. 71 Sqn, based at Tainan, which recently disbanded. Note the unidentified underwing pods on this aircraft.

Above: Following the withdrawal of the Pazmany PL-1 from the Air Academy, all basic pilot selection training and screening is now undertaken on microlights.

This DC-3 was one of the very last active RoCAF examples. It was withdrawn from use at the Air Academy in 1996.

Right: This preserved F-86F wears the badge of the 2nd Fighter Wing. Taiwan retired the F-86 in the early 1980s.

Taiwan has a panoply of preserved historic airframes, including this F-84G at Chia Yi (above), T-33A at Hsinchu (below) and F-100D (left), also at Hsinchu.

Republic of China Navy (RoCN)

Taiwanese S-2E Trackers and HU-16 Albatrosses had long been operated by the RoCAF on the navy's behalf. A 'wholly-owned' naval air arm did not become a reality until 1979, with the delivery of the first of 12 Hughes 500MD/ASWs, 11 of which remain in service. The Hughes 500s can operate from most of the Navy's 13 1940s-vintage 'Wu Chin'/'Fram'-class destroyers (ex-USN 'Gearing'-class). The aircraft are equipped with a small search/targeting radar and a towed Texas Instruments MAD. Some reports suggest that six of these aircraft (or another six), perhaps without radar and MAD gear, are used by a subordinate marine aviation element.

Negotiations with IPTN for the supply of NAS 332 Super Pumas came to nothing, while Eurocopter's ongoing efforts to sell AS 532 Cougars to Taiwan seem likely to be frustrated by Chinese objections.

Taiwan took delivery of 10 S-70C(M)-1 Thunderhawks in 1993 to serve aboard its seven locally built 'Cheung Hung'-class frigates ('Oliver Hazard Perry'-class). The Thunderhawk is based on the airframe of the SH-60F Ocean Hawk, with a similar dipping sonar (actually a Bendix AN-ASQ-18(V) rather than the ASQ-13F) and with similar extended pylons to allow for greater payload. Unlike the USN's SH-60F, though, the Thunderhawk has an undernose Telephonics AN/APS-128 pulse-compression radar and Litton AN/ALR-606(V)2 ESM equipment. The initial Taiwanese Thunderhawks were equipped with an Indal RAST deck restraint harpoon. Eleven more Thunderhawks (one an attrition replacement) were ordered in the 1990s, to equip the six 'Kang Ding'-class frigates ('La Fayette'-class) built in France. At least some of these aircraft had French Samahe deck restraints. In late 1997 *Janes Defence Weekly* reported that some RoCN S-70Cs have been converted to a possible AEW/Elint standard, through the addition of a large radome/antenna above the rotor mast. No details are known.

Long-standing interest in the Kaman SH-2 Seasprite (to equip nine 'Knox'-class frigates leased from the US Navy) was revived in 1997, with a request being made for funding in that year. An earlier deal was scuppered in 1993 after an unrelated corruption scandal. Taiwan needs 12 T700-engined SH-2G Super Seasprites, unless the frigates have their decks strengthened (at about $1 million per ship) which would then allow them to operate S-70s. The adoption of additional S-70s would represent a more expensive solution, but would bring major logistics advantages and savings. The Super Seasprite's trump card currently lies in its ability to carry the Magic Lantern mine detection system.

It has been suggested that the navy will soon gain the entire ASW/maritime patrol role, and that the RoCAF's S-2Ts will be transferred to the navy. At the moment the aircraft come under naval command, but are operated by the air force. The navy would also take whatever aircraft is selected to replace the ageing Trackers. Taiwan would undeniably prefer to acquire P-3 Orions, but US willingness to supply P-3s is by no means assured, and a more modest aircraft (such as the CN.235MPA or C-27) might be more likely.

The exact order of battle of the navy's aviation arm remains unknown and the details provided below are speculative, to a degree.

Republic of China Navy air arm

501 Squadron, Hualien

Hughes 500MD/ASW

701 Squadron, Kao-hsiung

Sikorsky S-70C(M)-1

Republic of China Army (RoCA)

The Chinese Nationalist Army gained its own aviation element during the 1960s – small, and based on US Army practice and organisation. This new element took the majority of the Bell UH-1Hs built by AIDC, adding them to a handful of Cessna O-1 Bird Dogs (about 12 of the 20 delivered), together with a pair of Kawasaki KH-4 (Japanese licence-built Bell 47) trainers (later 10). These aircraft formed six small squadrons. Other published reports of ex-US Army Sikorsky CH-34s in RoCA service are false.

The army aviation element gained three Boeing Vertol 234MLR (CH-47) Chinooks in 1985, which ostensibly were civilian variants of the Chinook in order to allay Chinese objections.

The army issued a requirement for 48 anti-tank helicopters in 1984, evaluating the Hughes 500 and MBB BO 105. The army eventually overcame the many export problems associated with such an acquisition and ordered 42 Bell AH-1Ws, deliveries of which began in March 1993 and were due to be completed in 1997 (34 had been handed over by August 1996). Some sources suggest that the army may actually receive 50 (or even 53) AH-1W Supercobras. Taiwan's AH-1Ws are equivalent to the US Marine Corps' Integrated Weapons Systems (Phase 1) Supercobras. They are fitted with the Tamam/Kollsman Night Targeting System (NTSF-65) which incorporates a FLIR, TV sensors, day/night video and laser rangefinder/designator. This makes these AH-1Ws compatible with the AGM-114 Hellfire missile. Little has been reported about Hellfire deliveries to Taiwan but the missile is certainly in use (and incorporated into the badge of at least one army aviation squadron). The long-range, highly-lethal AGM-114 represents a major step forward in capability over the TOW missiles with which the RoCA's AH-1Ws are ostensibly equipped.

The Bell OH-58D is also Hellfire-capable. In February 1992 Taiwan ordered 12 of these aircraft, with 14 options which were subsequently converted into firm orders. Deliveries began in July 1993 and all examples are now believed to be in service. Equipped with a mast-mounted sight and designating system, the OH-58D is an effective combat scout helicopter, particularly when coupled with the 8-km (5-mile) plus stand-off range of the AGM-114.

In August 1997 the US Army awarded Bell Helicopter Textron a $40.3 million contract to produce 30 TH-67 Creek training helicopters for Taiwan. These aircraft will finally allow the army to train all of its own pilots.

Taiwan's UH-1s are now becoming somewhat long in the tooth, and a requirement for a replacement is expected to be issued soon. Sikorsky hopes to sell an S-70 variant, building on the company's success in selling S-70C-1As to the air force for SAR duties, and S-70C(M)-1s to the navy. A decision on a new transport helicopter type to replace the (approximately) 100 UH-1Hs in service is expected in 1998. Apart from the S-70, types under serious consideration include the Bell 412EP, Eurocopter AS 532L2 Cougar and the Kazan (Mil) Mi-17.

The army is also responsible for operating Taiwan's SAMs. They included a peak strength of 48 MIM-14B Nike Hercules launchers in two battalions, and three battalions with the Hawk SAM. Initial deliveries comprised 122 MIM-23A Hawk SAMs (72 launchers), converted to Improved Hawk standards in a 1976 $34 million contract. In 1980, Taiwan signed up for 280 more rounds (at $167.1 million) and then, later the same year, 90 more rounds with 24 extra launchers. The indigenous Tien Kung (Sky Bow) SAM has subsequently started to replace both Hawk and Hercules. The army also operates 646 MIM-72 Chaparral short-range SAM systems, with 40 launchers, delivered from 1983. SAM defences are continuing to be improved. In 1996, the army took delivery of six Raytheon Patriot PAC-2 launchers, as part of a $380 million plus contract for three fire units (each of up to eight launchers) with 200 rounds.

The exact order of battle of the army's aviation arm remains unknown, and the details provided below are speculative, to a degree.

Republic of China Army air arm

Headquarters of Army Aviation, Kueijen

Training Centre   TH-55, UH-1H, B.V. 234

1st Army Helicopter Group

10th Assault Helicopter Squadron
UH-1H   Lungtan-Taoyuan
11th Assault Helicopter Squadron
UH-1H   Lungtan-Taoyuan
20th Assault Helicopter Squadron
UH-1H   Singsher
21st Assault Helicopter Squadron
UH-1H   Singsher

1st Helicopter Reconnaissance Squadron (1st Army Avn Batt.)
OH-58D   Lungtan-Taoyuan
This unit maintains a detachment at Singsher

1st Attack Helicopter Squadron
AH-1W   Lungtan-Taoyuan
This unit maintains a detachment at Singsher

Above and right: The Navy's 11 Hughes 500MD/ASWs can each carry a single Mk 46 torpedo, or two depth charges or machine-gun pods.

Left and above left: The nine S-70C(M)1 Thunderhawks are a far more sophisticated ASW asset, and are equivalent to US Navy SH-60Bs.

Above and right: Taiwan's MMS-equipped OH-58Ds are highly advanced scout/attack helicopters. The aircraft above carries rocket pods. The aircraft seen right is fitted with Hellfire rails.

Above and below: AIDC-built UH-1Hs are the sole transport helicopters available to the Army. The search is now on to find a replacement for these elderly 'Hueys'.

Right: Taiwan is known to have only a single attack helicopter squadron equipped with Hellfire-capable AH-1W Supercobras, but at least 40 aircraft have been delivered.

INDEX

Picture acknowledgments

Front cover: Sergei Skrynnikov via Yefim Gordon. **4:** Dirk Geerts, Dave Bowers, Dipl. Ing. A. Fischer. **5-6:** Chris Schmidt. **7:** Marinus A. Tabak (three). **8:** Yefim Gordon, Mark Schenk (two). **9:** Mark Schenk, Neil Dunridge, Derek Bower. **10:** Lindsay Peacock. **11:** Richard H. Vandervard (two), Robert Sant. **12:** Louis Vosloo (two). **13:** Peter R. Foster, Yaso Niwa, Iván Siminic (two). **14:** Iván Siminic, Roger Westerhuis, Dylan Eklund, Lindsay Peacock. **15:** Alan Bayliss (two), Carl L. Richards. **16:** John W. Binford/Top Flight Photo, Robert Sant. **17:** Alan Bayliss (two). **22:** Jorge F. Nuñez Padin (two). **23-24:** NASA via T. Panopalis. **25:** R. Westerhuis (two), Chris Knott/API (two), Iván Siminic. **26:** Simon Watson (five), Cees van der Ende and Roland van Maarseveen. **27:** Simon Watson (six), Cees van der Ende and Roland van Maarseveen (six). **28:** Gulfstream. **29:** Anders Nylén/FlygvapenNytt. **30:** Andrew H. Cline, Saudia, Gulfstream, Ted Carlson/Fotodynamics, Bill Crimmins. **31:** Gulfstream (three). **32:** Jan Jørgensen (two). **33:** Jan Jørgensen (two). **34:** Gulfstream (three), Malcolm Nason. **35:** Gulfstream (three). **36:** Gulfstream (three), Gösta Bolander/FlygvapenNytt. **37:** Peter Liander, Gulfstream. **38:** Gulfstream (three). **39:** Ted Carlson/Fotodynamics, Dirk Geerts (two). **40:** Graham Robson, Sunil Gupta, Andrew H. Cline, Malcolm Nason. **41:** Jonathan Chuck, Bill Crimmins, Robert E. Kling, Carey Mavor (two). **42:** Matt Olafsen, Charles E. Taylor via Robert F. Dorr, Sunil Gupta. **43:** Jim Lee, Malcolm Nason, Sunil Gupta. **45:** Ted Carlson/Fotodynamics, Gulfstream, R. L. Uithoven, Andrew H. Cline, Robbie Shaw. **47:** Gulfstream (two). **48-55:** Ted Carlson/Fotodynamics. **56-57:** Hugo Mambour, Flygvapnet, Eric Bannwarth. **58:** Aerospace. **59:** Hugo Mambour, Yefim Gordon Archive. **60:** Yefim Gordon Archive (five). **61:** Nigel Eastaway/RART, Yefim Gordon, Steven Zaloga. **62:** Yefim Gordon, Steven Zaloga (three), Yefim Gordon Archive (four). **63:** Yefim Gordon (two), Steven Zaloga. **64:** Yefim Gordon (three). **65:** Yefim Gordon Archive (three), Steven Zaloga (three), Nigel Eastaway/RART. **66:** Yefim Gordon, Aerospace, Frank Rozendaal. **67:** Frank Rozendaal, Yefim Gordon. **68:** Yefim Gordon (six), Steven Zaloga, Yefim Gordon Archive. **77:** Yefim Gordon (five), Nigel Eastaway/RART. **78:** Steven Zaloga, Aerospace. **79:** Frank Rozendaal, Yefim Gordon Archive (three), Steven Zaloga (three), Nigel Eastaway/RART. **80:** Frank Rozendaal, Yefim Gordon. **81:** Frank Rozendaal, Yefim Gordon. **82:** Yefim Gordon Archive (four), Steven Zaloga. **83:** Yefim Gordon (five), Yefim Gordon Archive (two). **84:** Yefim

Gordon, Eric Bannwarth. **85:** G. Lewis. **86:** Yefim Gordon Archive (five), Yefim Gordon, Robert Meerding, US DoD, Nigel Eastaway/RART. **87:** US Navy, Yefim Gordon Archive (four), Nigel Eastaway/RART (three). **88:** Steven Zaloga, Yefim Gordon. **89:** Flygvapnet (two), Yefim Gordon. **90:** Yefim Gordon Archive (six), Yefim Gordon (two). **91:** Flygvapnet (two), Yefim Gordon. **92:** Steven Zaloga (four), Nigel Eastaway/RART (four), Hugo Mambour. **93:** Gordon Upton, Yefim Gordon. **94:** Sergei Skrynnikov via Yefim Gordon, M.J. Gerards. **95:** Yefim Gordon (two), William Turner. **96:** Sergei Skrynnikov via Yefim Gordon, Yefim Gordon Archive (three), Dennis Thomsen. **97:** Dennis Thomsen, Yefim Gordon. **98:** Yefim Gordon Archive. **100:** Yefim Gordon (two). **101:** Martin Baumann, Robert Hewson. **102:** Yefim Gordon, Frank Rozendaal (two), US Navy. **103:** Yefim Gordon (three). **104:** David Donald, Sgt Rick Brewell/DPR. **105:** British Aerospace, Sgt Rick Brewell/DPR, David Donald. **106:** David Donald, Sgt Rick Brewell/DPR. **107:** Sgt Rick Brewell/DPR, David Donald (two). **108:** David Donald, Sgt Rick Brewell/DPR. **109:** David Donald, Sgt Rick Brewell/DPR. **110:** MATRA/BAe, David Donald (two). **111-113:** David Donald. **114:** Rick Llinares/Dash 2, Ian Black, MO ANG. **116:** McDonnell Douglas (three), Harry Gann Collection. **117:** Larry Davis Collection, McDonnell Douglas , Ian Black. **118:** Aerospace, Ian Black. **119:** Aerospace/Jim Winchester, Mitsubishi. **120:** McDonnell Douglas (two), NASA via T. Panopalis. **121:** A.B. Ward, T. Panopalis, A. Roels/VSRP. **122:** NASA via Robert L. Burns (two), NASA via T. Panopalis (two), McDonnell Douglas (two). **123:** McDonnell Douglas (four), Larry Davis Collection, Mick Roth via Larry Davis. **124:** McDonnell Douglas (two), Larry Davis Collection, Mick Roth via Larry Davis (two). **125:** McDonnell Douglas (two), Larry Davis Collection, Mick Roth via Larry Davis (two). **126:** Ted W. van Geffen, Larry Davis Collection (two), Paul van Oers. **127:** US Air Force, B. Redfern, Larry Davis, McDonnell Douglas (two), Pratt & Whitney. **128:** McDonnell Douglas , NASA via T. Panopalis, T. Panopalis, NASA via Robert L. Burns (two), Mick Roth via Larry Davis. **129:** McDonnell Douglas (two). **130:** Ian Black (three), McDonnell Douglas. **131:** McDonnell Douglas , Mitsubishi, Paul van Oers. **132:** Luigino Caliaro, McDonnell Douglas, BIAF. **133-134:** McDonnell Douglas. **135:** Rockwell, McDonnell Douglas. **136:** McDonnell Douglas (three). **137:** Boeing (two), Lindsay Peacock. **138-143:** Andrzej Rogucki. **145:** Peter Steinemann (nine), Defence International, Alec Moulton. **147:** Alec Moulton, Peter Steinemann (nine). **149:** Peter Steinemann (nine), Alec Moulton (two), Alec Moulton, Peter R. Foster. **153:** Robbie Shaw, Paul van Oers. **155:** A. P. Li, Peter Steinemann (five), Alec Moulton, Berry Vissers, Yves Debay. **155:** Peter Steinemann (four), Berry Vissers, Robbie Shaw, Alec Moulton (three). **157:** Alec Moulton (three), Peter R. Foster (six).